연령을 초월한 일본 독자들의 지지

처음에는 제목에 끌렸지만, 내용은 그보다 훨씬 좋았다. 문장 곳곳에 인생의 소중한 말이 있어 가슴에 와 닿았다. 나는 이 책을 읽고 내 인생을 맘껏 즐기기로 했다.　　　14세 학생(여성)

이 책을 만난 건 행운이었다. 책 제목에 끌려 나 자신에게 선물한 이 책이 내 안의 뭔가를 조금씩 바꿔 가게 했다.　　　25세 교사(여성)

목표 실현을 향한 행동력이 대단하다. 사람은 변할 수 있으며, 바라는 자신이 될 수 있다는 걸 새삼 느꼈다. 좌절하더라도 살아갈 용기를 얻을 수 있는 책이다.　　　26세 공무원(남성)

솔직히 재미있고 감동적이다. 사람은 말 그대로 '죽을힘'을 다하면 뭐든 할 수 있다. 나도 인생에 목숨을 걸어 보겠다.　　　32세 회사원(여성)

공감할 수 있는 부분이 많아 빠져들게 되는 스토리였다. 나도 주인공 아마리처럼 시간을 소중히 하고, 다양한 일에 적극적으로 도전해야겠다는 생각이 들었다.　　　35세 회사원(여성)

완전 감동했다. 좋았다. 한 해 한 해의 인생을 헤아려 보며 삶의 에너지를 얻을 수 있었다. 꼭 영화나 드라마로 만들어졌으면 한다.　　　55세 회사원(남성)

감동했다. '살아가는 힘'을 얻을 수 있었다. 살아 있는 인간이 '죽음'을 주시하며 살아간다는 것이 이렇게 큰 힘을 발휘하게 한다는 사실을 새삼 깨달았다.　　　83세 주지(남성)

스물아홉 생일,
1년 후
죽기로
결심했다

스물아홉 생일, 1년 후 죽기로 결심했다

하야마 아마리 지음 | 장은주 옮김

예담

나와 같이 힘든 상황에 놓인 한국의 젊은이들에게

스물아홉은 내 인생의 터닝포인트였다.

어렸을 때 꿈꿨던 미래는 그 어디에도 없었고, 나는 안정된 직장과 애인, 돈······ 뭐 하나 갖추지 못한 인생에 절망하고 있었다. 절망이 너무나 큰 나머지, 인생을 끝내고 싶은 마음뿐이었고, 스스로 '1년의 삶'이라는 시한부 인생을 선고하게 되었다.

그래서 인생의 끝을 결심하고 나서야, 나는 그 준비를 하기 위해 펼쳐 본 적 없는 날개를 펼치기 시작했던 것이다. 그러자 그때부터 다양한 만남과 구원의 말들을 얻었고, 새로운 나 자신을 찾을 수 있었다.

이 책은 그러한 경험을 바탕으로 한 '스물아홉 생일부터 1년간의 치열한 기록'이다.

절망에 빠져 있을 때는 나 혼자만 힘들다고 생각되어 그 괴로움이 영원할 것만 같지만, 사실은 그렇지 않다.

혹시 지금 인생에 절망하고 있다면, 아직 펼쳐 보지 않은 날개를 한번 찾아 보는 게 어떨까? 그리고 저돌적으로 그 다음을 향해 달려 나가다 보면, 반드시 뭔가 얻는 게 있으리라 믿는다.

한국에도 취업난이 심각해 많은 젊은이들이 힘들어하고 있다고 들었다. 내 이야기가 조금이라도 그들에게 힘이 된다면 행복하겠다.

D-12개월

어차피 죽을 거라면 서른이 되기 직전, 스물아홉의 마지막 날, '이보다 더 좋을 순 없다'고 생각되는 그 멋진 순간을 맛본 뒤에 죽는 거야. 카지노에서 전부를 잃어도 상관없다. 내 인생의 전부를 걸고 승부를 펼쳐 보는 거다. 그리고 땡, 서른이 되는 날 미련 없이 목숨을 끊는다.

'1년, 내게 주어진 날들은 앞으로 1년이야.'

그날부터 내 인생의 카운트다운이 시작되었다.

조용한 절망 속에
스물아홉은 온다

"Happy birthday to me."

스물아홉, 내 생일을 축하한다. 3평짜리 원룸에 혼자 덩그러
니 앉아 노래를 부른다. 서늘한 형광등 불빛이 낡은 장판 구석구
석을 비추고 있다. 사방을 둘러싼 하얀 벽에는 그 흔한 달력이나
사진 한 장조차 걸려 있지 않다.

"Happy birthday to me."

동네 편의점에서 사온 조각 케이크엔 달랑 촛불 하나. 원래라

면 큰 초 두 개, 작은 초 아홉 개를 꽂아야 하지만 그럴 자리가 없다. 어쩔 수 없이 한 개만 꽂고 노래를 부른다.

"Happy birthday to…… me."

이 노래가 이렇게 긴 줄 몰랐다. 간신히 다 부르고 나서 '후' 한숨으로 촛불을 끈다. 그래도 생일이니까 힘을 내어 중얼거려 본다.

"축하해!"

스물아홉 번째 생일, 이제 혼자만의 파티를 시작한다.

혼자인 건 괜찮다. 작년에도 재작년에도 혼자였으니까.

그래, 괜찮다.

일어서서 물끄러미 방을 둘러본다. 냉장고, 텔레비전, 나무선반이 한쪽 벽으로 줄지어 있고, 한가운데에는 하얀 접이식 테이블이 덩그러니 놓여 있다. 밋밋하고 살풍경한 방 옆으론 작은 주방이 칸막이에 가려 있다. 일체형 욕실이 딸린 비좁은 원룸이지만, 회사와 집만 오가는 싱글에게는 충분하다.

장마가 끝난 뒤 무더위 직전의 후덥지근한 공기가 방 안에 가득했다. 딱 허리 높이 창까지 무릎걸음으로 다가가 초록색 무지 커튼을 젖히고 창문을 활짝 열었다. 뜨거운 바람만 쏟아져 들어왔다. 구형 붙박이 에어컨이 있지만 전기요금이 무서워 켤 엄두도 못 낸다. 덥고 끈적끈적하지만 그래도 생일이니까 파티를 시작해 보자.

습관처럼 텔레비전을 켜자 예능 프로그램 속 등장인물들이 호들갑스럽게 떠들고 있다. 방 안이 시끌벅적해진 기분이다. 이렇다 할 취미도 없다 보니 회사에서 돌아오면 배경음악처럼 텔레비전을 켜두곤 한다. 안 그러면 이 방은 무서울 정도로 적막하다.

주방에서 접시와 포크를 가져와 테이블에 올려두고 조각 케이크 하나로 만찬을 준비한다. 멋진 장소에서 생일 파티를 한다 해도 축하해 줄 만한 친구 따윈 내게 없다. 뭐 그렇다고 회사에서 미운털이 박혔다거나 동료에게 따돌림 당하는 것도 아니다. 비록 파견사원이지만 그래도 함께 점심 먹을 동료 정도는 있다. 하지만 그건 회사에 있을 때뿐, 퇴근 후나 휴일에 따로 만나서 놀 만한 사이는 아니다.

외톨이는 아니지만 혼자인 사람, 파견사원은 원래 그렇다.

나는 3개월마다 직장이 바뀐다. "잘 부탁합니다" 인사하고 나면, 얼마 안 가 "안녕히 계세요" 하고 떠난다. '어차피 금방 헤어질 텐데' 하는 생각이 늘 그림자처럼 따라다닌다. 정사원들과 개인적으로 교류할 일도 없지만, 설령 함께 어울린들 그들처럼 즐길 여유는 없다. 정사원과 파견사원의 임금 격차는 그만큼 크다.

테이블 위에 내던져 둔 우편물이 눈에 들어온다. 언제 봐도 흉물스러운 공공요금 독촉장들이다. 혼자서 낯선 곳을 전전하며 죽어라 일해도 독촉장은 늘 쌓여만 간다. 애써 무시하고 포크를 들어 케이크로 가져간다. 좋아하는 것부터 먹는 버릇 때문에 맨 먼저 케이크 위에 얹힌 탐스러운 딸기를 찍었다. 지그시 눈을 감고 입에 넣으려는 순간, 딸기가 툭 하고 떨어지고 말았다.

"안 돼!"

너무 순식간이라 손 쓸 틈도 없이 딸기가 바닥에 뒹굴었다. 나는 반사적으로 손을 쑥 뻗었다.

'바로 주우면 먹을 수 있어.'

딸기를 집어 들고 입으로 후후 불다 보니 크림 범벅이 된 딸기에 긴 머리카락 한 올이 달라붙어 있다.

'괜찮아, 괜찮아. 씻으면 돼.'

나는 스스로 최면을 걸며 싱크대로 달려갔다. 허리를 구부리고 수도꼭지를 트는 순간, 갑자기 마음의 끈이 끊어졌다.

'뭐 하는 거니, 너……'

스테인리스 싱크대에 쌓인 설거지 더미에 내 얼굴이 비쳤다. 바닥에 떨어져 더러워진 딸기를 기어코 주워 먹으려는 나, 뒤룩뒤룩 살 찐 서른 즈음의 외톨박이 여자, 그것이 지금의 나였다.

적어도 오늘만큼은 안 울려고 했다. 하지만 내 의지와는 상관없이 뜨거운 눈물이 볼 위로 주르륵 타고 내리기 시작했다. '안 돼!'라고 생각했지만 이미 늦었다. 그 한 줄기를 시작으로 그동안 억누르고 있던 울음이 한꺼번에 터지기 시작했다. 눈물은 흐르고 또 흘러 도저히 멈출 수가 없었다.

텔레비전 속의 연예인들은 박수를 치며 웃고 있었다.

나는 스물아홉이다.

나는 뚱뚱하고 못생겼다.

나는 혼자다.

나는 취미도, 특기도 없다.

나는 매일 벌벌 떨면서 간신히 입에 풀칠할 만큼만 벌고 있다.

어쩌다가 이렇게 된 걸까?

내가 이렇게도 형편없는 인간이었나?

처음엔 물이 뜨겁지 않았다. 그래서 괜찮은 줄 알았다. 하지만 어느 순간, 내가 끓는 물에 들어온 개구리라는 사실을 깨닫게 됐다. 아무리 발버둥 쳐도 현재의 삶에서 벗어나기 어려워진 것이다.

사실 돌이켜보면 20대 초반까지는 그런대로 괜찮았다. 상위권 대학을 정확히 4년 만에 졸업했고, 얼어붙은 취업 한파 속에서도 한 금융회사 정사원으로 당당히 입사하기까지 했다. 하지만 거기까지였다. 나는 회사 분위기에 끝내 적응하지 못하고 1년도 채 못 돼 그만두고 말았다. 그때부터 나에게 '현실'이라는 이름의 창살이 둘러쳐지기 시작했다.

계약사원으로 재취업한 회사에서는 얼마 안 가 계약이 중단되는 바람에 이후 계속해서 파견사원으로 일해야 했다. 20대 후반이 되어서야 나는 정사원이라는 메리트가 얼마나 중요한지 알게 되었다. 그때부터 다시 정사원이 되기 위해 직종을 가리지 않고 되는대로 이력서를 수백 군데나 뿌리고 다녔다. 하지만 경기는 계속 나빠지고, 이렇다 할 경험도 자격도 없는 나에게 돌아오는 것은 불합격 통지서뿐이었다.

기업 측은 입을 모아 이렇게 말했다.

"우린 경력자를 원합니다."

대체 경력이란 건 어디서 어떻게 쌓아야 한단 말인가? 파견처의 기업명은 이력서에도 쓰지 못한다. 자격증을 따고 싶지만 그럴 만한 자금도 시간도 없었다.

나는 20대 초반에 저질렀던 그 안이하고 어리석었던 행동을 두고두고 후회했다. 돌아가고 싶다고 해서 쉽게 돌아갈 수 있는 곳이 아니란 걸 모르고, 정사원이라는 그 엄청난 자리를 그토록 쉽게 내팽개쳤던 지난날의 내가 미치도록 미웠다.

물론 파견사원에게도 메리트는 있다. 융통성 있게 시간을 조절하고 근무 조건을 선택할 수도 있다. 하지만 나는 원해서 파견사원을 하고 있는 게 아니다. '3개월 후에는 계약을 연장할 수 있을까?', '이것마저 잘리면 어떡하지?' 하고 마음 졸이며 사는 게 너무 힘들었다.

하긴 지금은 워낙 불황이라 정사원이라고 해서 해고되지 않는다는 보장도 없지만, 어쨌든 맨 먼저 잘리는 것은 파견사원이다. 게다가 파견사원은 수입이 너무 적다. 매월 17만 엔 정도에 보너스는 제로, 교통비 따윈 꿈도 못 꾼다.

황금연휴니 여름휴가니 세상 사람들 모두가 고대하는 휴가도 내게는 사활이 걸린 문제다. 어디론가 떠날 돈도 없을 뿐더러, 휴가 동안엔 급여도 나오지 않는다. 결국 온 세상이 여행이다 뭐다 들떠 있는 동안에도 나는 마냥 집에 틀어박혀 지낼 수밖에 없었다. 그런데도 휴가 기간이 끝날 때쯤엔 늘 생활비가 모자라 허덕였다.

최근 들어 '워킹 푸어'라는 말이 나돌고 있지만 그 기준은 보통 세금을 포함한 연수입이 200만 엔 이하라고 한다. 사실 난 그 수입에는 간신히 턱걸이를 할 정도지만, 그건 1년 내내 파견처가 끊이지 않을 때의 얘기다. 파견처가 끊기면 나도 연수입이 줄어들어 여지없이 그 범주에 속하게 된다.

이제 1년 뒤면 서른, 그러나 통장잔고는 마이너스에 저축은 언감생심이다. 하루하루가 불안하고 또 불안해서 견딜 수가 없다. 세상은 거대한 유리거울 안쪽에 있고, 나 혼자 거울 바깥에서 발버둥치는 것만 같다.

어쩌다가 이렇게 된 걸까? 20대 초반에 회사를 그만뒀기 때문에 이렇게 된 걸까? 정말 그때 그 한 번의 잘못된 선택만으로 이 지경까지 오게 된 걸까? 그건 너무 억울하지 않은가? 아니, 더 큰 원인이 있겠지.

그럼 대체 어디서부터 어떻게 잘못된 걸까.

'하고 싶은 게 없다'는 죄

있어도 그만, 없어도 그만인 그런 아이가 있었다. 뭔가를 아주 잘하는 것도, 그렇다고 아주 못하는 것도 아니면서 아무런 의욕도 없는 그런 아이. 그게 나였다. 평범해도 그렇게 평범할 수가 없었다.

나는 어릴 때 피아노도 치고 수영도 하고 주산도 배웠다. 하지만 하고 싶어서 한 게 아니라 남들이 다 하니까 그냥 따라했던 것뿐이다. 물론 그런 배움을 통해서 잠재되어 있던 재능을 발휘하게 되는 경우도 있다지만, 나에겐 그런 싹이 전혀 보이지 않았다. 재능이란 '잘하는 것'이 아니라 '하고 싶은 것'을 뜻하니까.

그러다 보니 차츰 배우는 데 싫증을 내다가 결국 죄다 그만두고 말았다. 그래도 부모님한테 혼났던 기억은 없다. 부모님은 언제나 그렇듯이 늘 자상하게 나를 지켜봐 주었다.

어느 것 하나라도 이렇다 할 흥미가 없으니 특별히 잘하는 것도 있을 리가 없었다. 단, 공부만은 예외였다. 타고난 몸치는 어쩔 수 없어도 공부라면 웬만큼 했다. 그래서 학원도 다니고 집에서도 꽤 열심히 공부했다. 성적이 올라갈 때마다 부모님은 기뻐했고 나 역시 덩달아 기뻤다. 하지만 그것도 중학교 때까지였다. 일류 고등학교에 입학하자마자 긴장이 확 풀린 탓인지 수업 진도를 따라가지 못했다. 성적은 뚝뚝 떨어지고 눈 깜짝할 사이에 나는 수업을 전혀 이해 못하는 열등생이 되어 버리고 말았다.

다른 건 몰라도 공부만큼은 웬만큼 한다던 믿음마저 잃게 된 후로 나는 공부와 담을 쌓기 시작했다. 여기엔 '공부를 하건 수업을 등한시하건 모든 것은 개인의 자유'라는 지극히 자율적인 학교의 방침도 한몫했다. 나는 요리조리 출석 일수를 채워 가며 '간섭받지 않는 자유로움'을 오히려 적극적으로 악용했다. 그런 식으로 고교 1, 2학년 시절을 보내고 3학년이 되어 '진로 희망' 용지와 마주했을 때 나는 눈앞이 깜깜했다.

'더 이상 공부는 싫다. 그렇다고 벌써부터 일하는 것도 싫다.'

그렇게 말도 안 되는 논리로 나는 진학을 희망했다. 진학을 하기로 했으니 희망 학교를 정해야만 했다. 하지만 꼭 가고 싶거나 끌리는 학교는 없었다.

'그래, 오빠가 나온 대학에 가자. 그럼 뭔가 설레고 신나는 일이 생길지도 몰라.'

나보다 여덟 살 많은 오빠는 이미 사회인이 되어 독립했지만, 워낙 사교적이라 많은 친구들과 어울리며 즐거운 대학시절을 보냈었다. 나도 막연히 그런 대학생활을 하고 싶었다.

그런 유치한 동기로 나는 오빠가 다녔던 그 어려운 사립대학에 뜻을 두었다. 학교 수업도 제대로 따라가지 못하던 내가 명문대를 목표로 삼았으니 대체 누가 진지하게 받아들였을까. 그래도 나는 그때부터 혼자서 고교 과정을 처음부터 다시 밟기 시작했다. 그리고 거짓말처럼 오빠와 같은 대학에 입학할 수 있었다.

가끔은 '아무런 열정도 설렘도 없는' 사람이 공부를 잘하는 경우가 있다. 친구들과 어울려 놀거나 음악, 미술, 춤, 게임 같은 것들에 그다지 흥미를 못 느끼다 보니 그저 책상 앞에 앉아 공부만 하는 그 지루한 시간을 비교적 덤덤히 이어갈 수 있는 것이다. 불러내는 친구도 없고 별다른 유혹거리도 없이 나는 그냥 입시를 위해 공부를 해나갈 수 있었다.

훗날 사회에 나가서야 알게 된 사실이지만, 세상에는 그런 식으로 '공부만' 잘했던 사람이 꽤 많다. 자기가 뭘 좋아하고 뭘 잘하는지도 모른 채 고속열차처럼 학창시절을 내달리다가 어느 날 '툭' 하고 세상에 내던져진 그런 사람들 말이다.

얼마나 황당한지 모른다. 학교에서야 정말 잘나갔지만 사회는 공부와는 전혀 다른 것들로 굴러가고 있지 않은가? 게다가 사회에서 필요한 것, 예컨대 '관계의 기술' 같은 것들은 책으로 공부한다고 해서 쉽게 배울 수 있는 게 아니다. 그건 어릴 때 친구들과 엎치락뒤치락하면서 자연스럽게 몸에 배게 되는 '몸의 습관'과도 같은 것들이다.

그것보다 더 당황스러운 것은 사회에 나가서야 비로소 학교 때는 보이지 않던 '의지의 인간'들이 보인다는 것이다. 그들은 정말로 자기가 좋아하는 것을 하기 위해 살아가는 사람들이다. 그들은 말버릇처럼 '난 기필코 이 일을 꼭 해내고야 말 테야!'라고 외치며 살아간다. 잘하고 못하고가 중요한 게 아니다. 그런 절실함이 놀라울 따름이다. 고교 3학년, 그저 오빠가 다녔던 대학에 진학하겠다는 막연한 생각만으로 공부를 했던 나에게 그런 '가슴 떨리는 꿈' 따위는 전혀 없었다. 그게 문제였다. 그것도 아주 큰 문제.

나에게 죄가 있다면 그건 아마 '하고 싶은 게 없다'는 죄일 것이다.

세상은 널
돌봐줄 의무가 없다

지방에서만 살았던 젊은이들이 대도시에 가면 무조건 재미난 일들이 가득할 거라 믿는 것처럼, 나 역시 어떻게든 대학만 가면 마냥 신나고 즐거울 줄 알았다. 웃기는 소리다.

그저 약간의 자유가 더 늘었을 뿐 대학도 고교 생활의 연장이나 다름없었다. 각자 좋아하는 강의를 자율적으로 선택해 이수하고, 학점만 따면 출석 일수는 크게 문제 삼지 않겠다는 대강당 수업도 있었다. 나처럼 개인주의 성향이 강한 사람은 같은 과 친구들이 모이는 전공 수업 이외에는 종일 한마디도 하지 않고 보내는 날이 허다했다. 게다가 목표도 없이 적당히 선택한 과라서 관심 가는 수업도 없었고, 자극을 찾아 들어간 동아리 역시 흥미를 갖지 못했다. 나는 도쿄 근교의 집에서 시내의 대학까지 그저 시계추처럼 왔다 갔다 하며 하루하루 맹물처럼 살았다.

그렇게 무미건조하던 대학생활이 180도 바뀌게 된 것은 남자친구가 생기면서부터였다. 같은 과 친구가 마련한 소개팅 자리에서 처음 그를 봤을 때 나는 '괜히 나왔구나' 하고 생각했다. 체구는 왜소했고 얼굴은 '기준치 미달'이었기 때문이다. 나는 아주 형식적으로 인사를 하고 앉았다. 그리고 얼른 일어날 핑계거리만 찾기 시작했다. 그런데 그가 도쿄대학 재학생이라는 사실을 알고 난 뒤부터 생각이 바뀌어 버렸다. 사람이 달라 보였던 것이다.

'그래, 비록 내 이상형은 아니지만 그래도 도쿄대생이잖아?'

나에게 '도쿄대생'이라는 브랜드는 그의 부족한 외모까지 엄청 빛나 보이게 할 만큼 매력적인 것이었다. 좀 더 솔직히 말하면, 앞으로 설령 경기가 바닥을 친다 해도 도쿄대생인 그와 함께라면 나의 미래도 안전하지 않을까 하는 착각에 빠져 있었던 것이다. 나는 그만큼 속물적이고 한심하며 단순 무지한 사고방식의 소유자였다.

나는 적극적으로 그와 사귀기 시작했다. 남들처럼 영화도 보고 점심도 같이 먹고 함께 여행도 떠났다. 누가 나에게 대학시절 동안 무엇을 했느냐고 묻는다면 별로 할 말이 없다. 공부를 한 것도 아니고 나의 꿈과 미래를 위해 구체적인 준비를 한 것도 아

니었다. 그저 시간만 나면 남자친구와 데이트를 하고 강의 시간
이 되면 '그래야 하니까' 그저 책상 앞에 앉아 있었다. 그러다 보
니 어느새 졸업할 때가 되었다. 친구들을 만나면 다들 졸업 후의
인생에 대해 수다를 떨었지만 난 잠자코 있기만 했다. 나의 미래
는 이미 다 그려 놨기 때문이었다.

'졸업하고 스물다섯쯤에 결혼한다. 그때쯤이면 그 사람도 어
느 위치까지 올라가 있겠지? 그럼 난 임시로 취업했던 회사에서
모두의 축복을 받으며 퇴사하고 전업주부가 되는 거야.'

그렇게 장밋빛 미래를 설계해 놨기에 나는 친구들처럼 불
안해할 필요가 없었다. 그래서 졸업한 뒤 운 좋게 취직한 회사를
'적응 안 된다'는 이유만으로 미련 없이 그만뒀을 때도 전혀 위기
의식이 느껴지지 않았다.

'어차피 결혼할 건데 뭐…….'

곧이어 정사원이 아닌 계약사원을 선택한 것도 같은 이유에
서였다. 나는 전혀 불안하지 않았고, 치열하게 살아야 할 이유도
없었다. 스물다섯 살이 되던 해 어느 화창한 봄날, 그가 나를 불
러냈다. 그 즈음 나는 이제 슬슬 결혼 준비를 해야겠다고 생각하
던 중이었다.

"할 말이 있어."

카페에 앉자마자 그가 나직한 목소리로 말했다. 평소와는 달

리 진지한 표정이었다.

'프러포즈를 할 모양이구나.'

나는 침을 꿀꺽 삼켰다. 그리고 어떤 표정으로 대답할지 머리를 굴렸다. 바로 그 순간, 세상이 와장창 깨지는 것 같은 한마디가 날아왔다.

"우리 헤어지자."

"응?"

나는 귀를 의심했다. 그가 왜 그런 말을 하는지 도무지 이해할 수가 없었다. 몇 년 동안 사귀면서 그 어떤 이상한 낌새도, 헤어질 만한 이유도 없었다. 심지어 우리 커플은 그 흔한 말다툼조차 거의 없었다. 그런데 왜?

"나, 만나는 사람 있어. 너한테도 그 사람한테도 몹쓸 짓 하고 싶지 않아서 지금 솔직하게 털어놓는 거야. 그러니까 이해해 줘."

너무 급작스럽고 생뚱맞은 상황이라 화조차 나지 않았다. 그는 계속해서 나와 헤어질 수밖에 없는 이유에 대해 중얼중얼 얘기하고 있었다. 그러는 동안 나는 차츰차츰 내가 처한 현실을 이해할 수 있게 되었다.

스물다섯, 결혼하려고 마음먹은 그해에 보기 좋게 차인 것이다. 내가 불같이 화를 내고 격한 말을 쏟아내기 시작한 것은 그때부터였다. 그는 내가 공격하는 동안 차분하게 듣기만 했다. 그러다 막판에 결정적인 한 방을 날렸다.

"너, 나를 사랑했던 거니, 아니면 내 간판을 사랑했던 거니? 솔직히 난 네가 나를 진심으로, 있는 그대로 대하는 것 같지가 않아. 늘 그런 생각이 들었고 그래서 괴로웠어. 그리고 나 말이야, 내 인생 하나만 짊어지기도 벅차. 그런데 넌 네 몫까지 내게 떠안기려 하잖아. 더 힘들어지기 전에 우리 이쯤에서 쿨하게 끝내자."

하늘이 무너지는 것 같다는 표현이 딱 맞다. 영화나 드라마에서만 봐왔던 일들이 이런 식으로 내게 닥칠 줄은 꿈에도 몰랐다. 믿을 수 없고 있을 수도 없는 일이었지만 인정할 수밖에 없는 현실이었다. 그는 냉정하게 떠났고 난 절망에 빠졌다.

그 뒤로는 하루하루가 상처투성이처럼 흘러갔다. 그 남자에 대한 미련보다는 그에게서 얻을 수 있었던 미래를 잃어버렸다는 상실감이 나를 더 힘들게 했다.

그리고 좀 더 시간이 지나서야 나는 그가 말한 것처럼 그동안 내 인생을 송두리째 남에게 맡기고 있었다는 사실을 깨달았다.

나쁜 일들은 이어달리기처럼 닥쳐왔다. 날벼락처럼 실연을 당하고 온 정신이 만신창이가 되어 버린 어느 날, 갑자기 아버지가 쓰러지고 말았다. 나는 소식을 듣자마자 정신없이 병원으로 달려갔다. 병원 복도에는 엄마와 오빠가 초조하게 앉아 있었다.

"엄마, 도대체 어떻게 된 거야? 아빠는?"

"지금 중환자실에 계셔. 뇌경색이래."

나는 넋을 잃은 채 굳게 닫혀 있는 중환자실을 바라보았다. 기가 막히고 어이가 없었다. 나에게는 그럴 일이 없을 거라 생각했던 비현실적인 일들이 며칠 사이로 연거푸 닥친 것이다. 나는 갑자기 모든 게 두려워졌다.

여느 가장들처럼 아버지도 평생 일벌레처럼 살아왔다. 그리고 얼마 전에 정년퇴직을 하고 이제 막 제2의 인생을 즐기려던 참이었다. 우리 같은 평범한 사람들은 모두 그런 수순을 밟지 않는가? 큰 욕심도 없고 별다른 일탈도 없이 그저 꾸준하고 묵묵하게 살아온 삶의 대가가 어째서 뇌경색이고 중환자실이어야 한단 말인가? 나는 이 불공평한 결과들이 무서웠다. 그리고 이때까지 나의 삶을 지탱해 주던 기반들이 사실은 그렇게 튼튼하지 않다는 것에 두려움을 느꼈다. 마치 거역할 수 없는 어떤 절대적인 힘이 내게 이렇게 말하는 것 같았다.

"세상은 널 돌봐줄 의무가 없다. 그리고 너에겐 어떤 일이든 생길 수 있다."

아버지는 중환자실에서 며칠간 치료를 받은 뒤에야 간신히 목숨을 건질 수 있었다. 하지만 좌반신불수라는 후유증 때문에 걸음도 제대로 걷지 못하게 되었다. 나는 또 한 번 충격을 받았다. 늘 건강하고 부지런했던 아버지의 초췌한 모습을 매일매일 바라봐야 하는 것도 괴로웠다. 게다가 나는 생애 최초로 실연을 당했고, 굳건하리라 여겨 왔던 미래마저 모래성처럼 허물어져 버린 뒤였다. 일을 마치고 집에 돌아오면 피로보다 더 무서운 절망과 슬픔이 기다리고 있었다. 나는 도저히 견딜 수가 없었다.

그 무렵 나는 계약사원으로 일하고 있던 IT관련 회사에서 날마다 격무에 시달리고 있었다. 대기업의 소프트웨어를 통째로 교체하는 프로젝트에 끼게 된 바람에 눈코 뜰 새 없이 바빴던 것이다. 나는 차라리 잘됐다고 생각했다.

'난 지금 너무 바빠…….'

회사 일은 나에게도 식구들에게도 집을 나올 수 있는 핑계거리가 되었다. 내 나이 스물다섯, 계획대로라면 집에서 얌전히 회사 다니다가 결혼과 동시에 출가하는 것이었다. 하지만 계획은 모두 틀어졌고, 나는 오로지 절망과 우울로부터 벗어나기 위해 독립을 결심했다. 그리고 며칠 뒤, 나는 엄마에게 아빠의 간병을 모두 떠넘기고 도망치듯 집을 뛰쳐나왔다. 못된 딸이라고 손가락질당해도 어쩔 수 없었다.

나는 집에서 멀리 떨어진 곳에 3평짜리 원룸을 구했다. 가격이 저렴한 만큼 시설은 엉망이었지만, 어차피 거기서 오래 살 생각은 없었기에 그냥 계약을 해버렸다. 그러고는 곧장 일 속에 파묻혔다.

아침부터 밤까지 일을 하고 피곤에 절은 몸을 질질 끌고 돌아와 샤워를 하고 잠이 들었다. 야근에 휴일 근무까지, 피곤했지만 그래도 충실한 날들이었다. 오로지 회사와 집만 왔다 갔다 하는 날들, 그렇게 정신없이 일하는 동안에는 딴 생각이 끼어들 틈이 없었다.

하지만 그렇게 도피처로 삼아 왔던 프로젝트마저 기어이 끝이 나고 말았다. 그리고 나에게는 "수고 많았습니다. 잠시 편히 쉬세요"라는 말과 함께 다시 평범한 잡무가 주어졌다. 여느 때 같았으면 느긋하게 몸과 마음을 충전할 수 있을 그 시간들이 내겐 너무나 고통스러웠다. 그나마 가까스로 나를 지탱해 주던 버팀목이 한순간에 사라진 듯한 느낌이었다.

잠시 밀쳐 뒀던 실연의 아픔, 아빠의 병치레 등이 다시 한꺼번에 닥쳐왔다. 기댈 곳을 잃어버린 나는 처참하게 무너져 내리기 시작했다. 아무런 의욕도 없이 매일매일 무력감에 몸서리쳤고, 회사에 나갈 기력마저 잃어 쉬는 날이 점점 많아졌다. 우울증은 거대한 먹구름처럼 내 인생 위에 드리워졌다. 숨 쉬는 것조차 스트레스였다.

그때부터 나는 먹어대기 시작했다. 스트레스 배출이 식욕으로 향한 것이다. 나는 공허함을 음식으로 메우듯 뭔가를 끊임없이 입에 넣었다. 살찌는 소리가 들릴 정도로 몸이 불기 시작했다. 대학 졸업 때 53킬로그램이었던 체중이 눈 깜박할 새 70킬로그램을 넘어섰다.

나쁜 일은 이어달리기를 좋아한다. 의욕 없고 결근도 잦은 데다가 몸까지 비대해진 계약사원을 어느 회사가 계속 쓰겠는가? 결국 나는 계약을 갱신하지 못하고 잘려 버렸다. 그래도 일을 해서 최저 생계비라도 벌어야 했기에 나는 기력을 쥐어짜 내며 새로운 일을 찾기 시작했다. 무슨 일이든 당장 할 수 있는 일이라면 뭐든지 오케이, 그리하여 나는 파견사원이 되었다.

그때까지만 해도 나는 이런 생활이 오래가지는 않을 거라 믿었다. 하지만 그 이후로 4년이 지나도록 나는 철새처럼 3개월마다 여기저기 옮겨 다니며 늘 마음 졸여야 하는 파견사원 신세를 면치 못했다. 퀴퀴한 3평짜리 원룸에서도 역시 벗어나지 못했다.

인생의 정점을 향한
죽음의 카운트다운

싱크대 앞에 멍하니 서서 살아온 날들을 생각하니 한숨만 나왔다. 그리운 추억도, 아련한 풍경도 없이 너무도 짧게 끝나 버린 회상이었다. 눈물도 다 말랐고 이제 나에겐 아무것도 없다. 친구나 취미는 원래 없었고, 애인도 미래도 모두 사라졌다.

집안은 병든 아빠의 퇴직금과 연금으로 빠듯하게 살고 있어 기댈 수도 없다. 더구나 나를 그렇게 사랑해 주던 가족의 곁을 스스로 박차고 나온 마당에 무슨 낯으로 다시 돌아갈 수 있을까.

'그나마 좋아하는 것이나 몰두할 수 있는 취미라도 있었더라면……'

아무리 가난해도 친구들과 함께 아마추어 극단이나 밴드 활동을 하며 살아가는 사람들이 너무도 부러웠다. 뭐라도 한 가지 몰두할 수 있는 게 있었더라면 내 인생도 조금은 달라지지 않았을까. 하지만 스물아홉 해가 지나는 동안 한 번도 갖지 못했던 흥밋거리를 이제 와 어디서 찾을 수 있을까?

'대체 난 뭘 위해 살고 있는 걸까?'

그 순간, 갑자기 소름이 쫙 끼쳤다. 무시무시한 생각을 하고만 것이다. 마치 절대로 열어서는 안 될 재앙의 상자를 열어 버린 느낌이었다. 다시 닫으려 해도 이미 뚜껑은 열리고 말았다.

'나란 인간, 과연 살 가치가 있는 걸까?'

순식간에 나라는 존재가 너무도 무의미하게 느껴졌다. 아무에게도 도움 되지 않고 누구한테도 필요하지 않은 '있어도 그만, 없어도 그만'인 존재.

어릴 적에 나는 가족의 사랑 속에서 컸다. 지금도 그 사랑을 의심하지는 않는다. 야무진 구석이라곤 하나도 없는 딸이 이렇게 밑바닥 생활을 하고 있다는 걸 부모님이나 오빠가 알게 된다면 분명 괴로워할 것이다. 그런 가족에게 나란 인간은 짐밖에 되지 않는다.

문득 방 한가운데 놓인 테이블에 눈이 멎었다. 딸기를 잃고 찌부러진 조각 케이크가 눈에 들어왔다. 보잘것없는 싸구려 케이크와 아무짝에도 쓸모없는 스물아홉 살 여자, 그래 잘 어울리는

구나.

내세울 것 하나 없고 공공요금 내기에도 빠듯한 생활이지만, 그래도 지금까지는 젊음 하나로 어떻게든 버텨 왔다. 그러나 이제 30대가 되면 취직은 더 힘들어질 것이다. 지금까지 수백 군데 이력서를 뿌려 봤자 오라는 곳은 한 군데도 없는데, 자격증 하나 없는 나를 앞으로 누가 뽑아 주기나 할까.

장래에 대해 함께 이야기 나눌 만한 친구도 내겐 없다. 남자? 그들의 시선은 나를 투명인간처럼 통과하여 피부 관리에 열을 올리고 패션 감각이 뛰어난 젊고 화려한 정규직 여사원들에게만 향한다. 그녀들은 미팅이다, 술자리다, 매일매일이 즐거워 보인다. 하지만 나는 그런 모임에 나가 본 적이 없다. 설령 누가 미친 척하고 나를 불러낸다 해도 입고 나갈 옷조차 없다.

신데렐라는 마법을 걸어 줄 마녀가 나타날 때만 신데렐라다. 마법이 없으면 그저 재투성이 하녀에 불과하다. 못생긴 얼굴에 70킬로그램이 넘는 서른 문턱의 패배자에게 남은 인생은 그저 내리막길뿐이다. 앞으로 한 살, 또 한 살 나이를 먹는다는 게 너무도 끔찍하고 두려워 견딜 수가 없다. 지금보다 더 밑바닥 생활이라면 그건 도저히 살아갈 수 없다는 것을 뜻한다.

나는 태어나서 처음으로 온몸을 부르르 떨며 친구를 그리워했다. "아냐, 열심히 하면 좋은 일이 생길 거야"라고, 거짓말로

라도 격려해 줄 그런 친구가 그리웠다. 하지만 나는 철저히 외톨이였다.

'앞으로 1년이면 나의 20대도 막을 내린다.'

그런 생각이 들자 지금껏 품어 왔던 작은 희망마저 사그라졌다. 내 앞에 있는 인생은 깜깜한 터널과도 같다. 지금부터 여든까지 산다고 치면 앞으로 약 50년, 그 숫자를 떠올리자 몸서리가 쳐졌다.

'앞으로 50년이라니, 집세는 제때 낼 수 있을까. 수도가 끊긴 좁고 어두운 방 안에서 냄새 나는 늙은이로 혼자 쓸쓸히 생을 마치게 되진 않을까.'

문득 '고독사孤獨死'라는 단어가 떠올랐다. 간호는커녕 죽음조차 혼자 쓸쓸히 맞아야 하는 미래의 내 모습을 떠올리자 몸서리칠 정도로 무서워졌다. 그때 부엌에 걸어 둔 칼이 어떤 빛에 반사되어 반짝거렸다. 왜 갑자기 그 섬뜩한 칼날이 눈에 들어왔을까.

'그래, 지금 죽으면 그래도 아직은 나를 위해 슬퍼해 줄 사람이 있을 거야. 내 죽음을 이해해 줄 사람이 있을지도 몰라……'

나는 천천히 칼 쪽으로 손을 뻗었다. 단순한 조리도구에 지나지 않던 칼이 돌연 무시무시한 흉기로 변했다. 칼을 쥐자 주위의 모든 소리가 사라졌다. 칼을 쥔 오른손이 미세하게 떨렸다. 나는 천천히 칼날을 손목에 갖다 댔다. 그렇게 차가운 느낌은 처음이었다. 그 상태로 길고 긴 시간이 흘렀다. 아니, 마치 시간의 바깥에 서 있는 기분이었다.

엄마, 아빠, 오빠의 얼굴이 스쳐 지나갔다. 헤어진 남자의 얼굴과 학창시절의 몇몇 얼굴도 떠올랐다. 온몸이 덜덜 떨리고 천장이 빙빙 돌기 시작했다. 내 안에서 유혹의 목소리가 들려왔다.

'괜찮아. 눈 질끈 감고 단번에 싹 그으면 돼. 아프지 않아. 그냥 피만 나올 뿐이야. 그럼 천천히 잠자듯이 세상을 떠나는 거야.'

곧이어 또 다른 목소리가 들려왔다.

'아깝고 억울하지 않니? 한 번도 폼 나게 살아 보지 못했잖아. 잘 생각해 봐. 혹시 알아? 뜻하지 않은 기적이 생길지?'

사방은 무섭도록 적막했지만 내 머릿속은 지옥의 한복판처럼 요란한 소리로 가득 찼다. 칼을 쥔 손과 칼날이 닿은 손 모두 감각을 느끼지 못할 만큼 저려 오기 시작했다. 그리고 다음 순간 나는 칼을 떨어뜨리고 말았다. 그리고 풀썩 주저앉아 힘없이 고개를 떨궜다.

'못 하겠어, 못 하겠어.'

무서웠다. 죽는 게 무서웠다. 죽는 것보다 사는 게 더 무섭다고, 더는 못 견디겠다며 도망치고 싶어 하면서도 나에겐 죽을 용기조차 없었다.

❖ ❖ ❖

나는 공기 빠진 풍선처럼 널브러져 있었다.

'살아갈 용기도, 죽을 용기도 없다. 나란 인간…… 끝끝내 이도 저도 아니구나.'

초점을 잃어버린 나의 시선은 텔레비전 브라운관만 향해 있었다. 화면에서는 형형색색의 외국 풍경이 번쩍번쩍 빛났다 사라지기를 반복하고 있었다. 내레이션은 '일상에 지친 그대, 어서 떠나세요!'라고 말하지만, 나와는 아무런 상관도 없는 풍경이었다. 경쾌한 배경음악이 나에게는 장송곡처럼 느껴졌다. 이젠 울 기력마저 없었다.

그때였다. 갑자기 화면이 확 바뀌더니 뭔가 반짝이는 빛이 내 안으로 확 빨려 들어왔다. 화면 속에는 너무도 아름다운 세계가 펼쳐지고 있었다. 화려하고 눈부신 빛의 축제, 웃음이 끊이지 않고 세상의 모든 행복이 다 들어 있는 듯한 세계, 그곳은 바로 라스베이거스였다. 언제나 볼 수 있는 흔해 빠진 여행 프로그램이었지만, 화면 속 라스베이거스는 이상하리만치 전율로 다가왔다. 나는 화면에서 시선을 뗄 수가 없었다.

화려하게 차려 입은 연예인들이 라스베이거스의 거리에서 우아하게 즐기고 있었다. 테마파크처럼 흥미진진한 호텔 레스토랑에서 호화로운 식사를 하고, 거대한 아울렛에서 쇼핑을 즐기는 사람들, 스릴 만점의 쇼가 펼쳐지고, 카지노에서는 슬롯머신을 즐기며 큰 소리로 '잭팟jackpot'을 외쳐대는 사람들⋯⋯. 그곳은 '호화로움의 극치'이며 완벽한 '양陽'의 세계, 어둠은 없고 오로지 빛과 화려함만 존재하는 세계였다.

'저 사람들⋯⋯ 참 좋겠다.'

너덜너덜한 바닥에 퍼질러 앉아 있는 나의 현실과 라스베이거스 사이에는 영겁의 간격이 있어 결코 닿을 수 없을 것이다. 내가 숨 쉬는 것과 똑같은 공기로 호흡할 수 있는 곳에 저런 세상이 있다는 게 새삼 신기했다. 암울한 현실과는 동떨어진 곳, 날마다 행복한 축제가 펼쳐지는 세계, 그곳은 지상낙원 그 자체였다.

텔레비전 화면이 바뀌고 한참이 지나도록 나는 그렇게 멍하니 앉아 있었다. 하지만 식칼을 들고 있을 때와는 전혀 다른 기분이 생겨나고 있었다. 너무도 낯선 느낌, 너무도 생뚱맞은 느낌⋯⋯ 그것은 난생처음 '뭔가를 해보고 싶다'는 간절한 느낌, 가슴 떨리는 설렘이었다. 갑자기 내 속에서 너무도 낯선 욕망이 꿈틀대기 시작했다.

'어차피 죽을 거라면 좋다, 단 한 번이라도 저 꿈같은 세상에서 손톱만큼의 미련도 남김없이 남은 생을 호화롭게 살아 보고 싶

다. 단 하루라도!'

정말 멋진 아이디어가 아닌가.

나는 특히 카지노에 끌렸다. 지금껏 만져 보지도 못한 엄청난 거금이 순식간에 사라지거나 혹은 수십 배로 부풀려지는 곳……. 나는 그곳에 가고 싶었다. 가서 화면 속의 선택받은 사람들처럼 파라다이스 한복판에 나를 내던지고 싶었다. 생활비를 쪼개고 또 쪼개도 항상 돈에 쪼들리는 나로서는 당연히 상상도 못 할 일이었다. 하지만 뭐 어떤가? 어차피 죽으려고 하지 않았나?

갑자기 이 나이가 되도록 푼돈에 연연하고 있는 나 자신이 바보처럼 느껴졌다. 뭐 그리 아까운 인생이라고 그렇게 바들바들 떨면서 살아왔던가? 그래, 모든 것을 버리자. 죽을 용기조차 내지 못하는 것은 분명 아직 뭔가에 미련이 있기 때문이다. 카지노에 전부를 걸고 다 잃어버리면 아마 미련 따윈 남지 않겠지. 그러면 산뜻한 기분으로 죽을 수 있지 않을까?

차츰차츰, 캄캄하고 끝이 없던 터널에 갑자기 한 줄기 빛이 보이기 시작했다.

'그래, 라스베이거스로 가자!'

어차피 죽을 거라면 서른이 되기 직전, 스물아홉의 마지막 날, '이보다 더 좋을 순 없다'고 생각되는 그 멋진 순간을 맛본 뒤에 죽는 거야. 카지노에서 전부를 잃어도 상관없다. 내 인생의 전부를 걸고 승부를 펼쳐 보는 거다. 그리고 땡, 서른이 되는 날 미련 없이 목숨을 끊는다.

'1년, 내게 주어진 날들은 앞으로 1년이야.'

지금 나에게는 '죽지 못한 탓에 맞이하게 된 시간'밖에 없다. 나는 지금부터의 시간을 '남아 있는 목숨'이라 부를 것이다.

그날부터 내 인생의 카운트다운이 시작되었다.

D-9개월

'그래, 나는 지금 변화하고 있는 중이야.'

이제 나에겐 '계획'이란 게 생겼고, 반드시 달성해야 할 목표가 생긴 것이다. 계획, 목표…… 그런 게 이토록 대단한 것이었나? 시야를 변화시키고 사람의 걸음걸이마저 확 바꿔 버릴 만큼 힘 있는 것이었나?

기적을 바란다면
발가락부터 움직여 보자

스스로 부여한 여명餘命은 앞으로 1년.

더 이상의 삶은 바라지도 않는다. 오직 인생의 마지막 날을 라스베이거스에서 아낌없이 불태우리라. 그리고 미련 없이 세상을 떠나자.

이 생각이 그저 한순간의 충동에 그치지 않을 거라는 사실은 날이 밝은 뒤에 더욱 확실해졌다. 창문으로 쏟아져 들어오는 햇살 속에서 나는 간밤에 품었던 그 막연한 계획을 다시 끄집어냈다. 그리고 본격적으로 자금 계획을 세우기 시작했다. 라스베이거스에 가기 위해서 내게 필요한 돈은 도대체 얼마쯤일까?

물론 수중엔 땡전 한 푼 없었다. 하지만 어차피 서른 이후의 삶을 위해 돈을 모을 필요는 없었다.

지금부터 내가 버는 돈은 오로지 라스베이거스에서의 마지막 하루를 위해 쓰이게 될 것이다.

일단 현재 상황에서 식비를 줄여 매일 조금씩 절약하면 아주 저렴한 비행기 티켓이나 싸구려 호텔쯤은 가능할지도 모른다. 하지만 그 정도로는 턱도 없다. 나의 목표는 라스베이거스 관광 따위가 아니다. 원 없이 사치를 즐기다가 마지막 날 카지노에서 말 그대로 목숨을 건 일생일대의 승부를 펼치는 것이다. 그러자면 큰돈이 필요하다. 자, 그렇다면 1년 동안 도대체 뭘 어떻게 해야 돈을 마련할 수 있을까.

나는 옷을 걸치고 곧장 근처 넷카페로 달려가 머릿속에 맴도는 단 하나의 키워드를 검색창에 입력했다.

'고수익.'

곧이어 검색 결과가 주르륵 뜨기 시작했다. '임상실험 아르바이트', '유흥업', '소자본 창업', '긴자 호스티스'……. 잠깐, 긴자 호스티스?

거기서 시선이 딱 멈췄다. 말로만 들어 봤지 긴자의 고급 클럽에는 가본 적도, 가볼 생각조차 해본 적이 없었다. 거긴 마치 다른 우주처럼 나하고는 아무런 상관이 없는 세계였다. 하지만 나는 다시 검색창에 '긴자 호스티스'라고 입력한 뒤 검색결과를 꼼꼼히 읽기 시작했다. 그러다 문득 '내가 이런 직업을 놓고 이렇게까지 진지하게 생각할 줄이야' 하는 생각이 들었다. 어제까지만 해도 도저히 상상할 수 없는 일이었다.

아무래도 인생에는 돌이킬 수 없는 결정적 순간이 있는 것 같다. 서른 살이 되는 날 이 세상을 떠날 거라는 결심, 그리고 생의 마지막 날을 라스베이거스에서 맞이할 거라는 다짐은 이제 더이상 취소할 수 없는 운명처럼 여겨졌다. 주사위는 던져졌고 나는 한 번 건너면 다시 돌아올 수 없는 스틱스 강을 건너 버린 것이다.

만일 내 주변에 어설프게나마 조언을 해줄 수 있는 단 한 사람이라도 있었다면 아마 그런 결심을 하지 못했을 것이다. 하지만 나는 철저히 혼자였고, 나의 밑바닥 현실을 홀로 감당해야 하는 만큼 주어진 나만의 삶을 충동적으로 살아 버릴 자유도 있었다. 1년 뒤에 죽기로 결심한 여자에게 그런 자유조차 없다면 정말 너무한 것 아닌가?

검색 결과를 읽어 가는 동안, 긴자라는 그 이질적인 세계가 점점 익숙하게 느껴졌다. 라스베이거스처럼 거기도 역시 텔레비전 드라마에서나 만날 수 있는 세계였지만, 내 머릿속에서는 이미 긴자의 고급 클럽과 라스베이거스의 화려한 밤이 자연스럽게 연결되고 있었다.

'긴자, 그런 호화로운 세계에 몸을 담그면 라스베이거스와 좀 더 가까워지겠지.'

게다가 호스티스라는 직종은 밤일일 테니, 어쩌면 파견사원과 병행할 수 있는 최적의 아르바이트가 될 수도 있을 것이다. 아니, 무엇보다 아무런 자격증도, 재능도 없는 내가 최단기간 내에 라스베이거스 행 자금을 벌기 위해서는 어떻게든 이 일을 해야 한다.

긴자의 클럽은 지인의 소개 등 알음알음으로 들어가는 경우가 대부분이었다. 하지만 인터넷 상으로 호스티스를 모집하는 곳도 몇 군데 있었다. 나는 닥치는 대로 전화번호를 메모한 뒤 넷카페를 나섰다.

이상하다. 갑자기 세상이 달라진 느낌이다. 겉으로는 평소와 다를 게 하나도 없었지만, 거리의 자동차와 건물들, 오가는 행인들, 그리고 가로수와 하늘 모두가 좀 더 선명하게 보였다. 늘 나하고는 아무런 상관없이 저만치 거리를 두고 있던 세상이 어딘가 구체적인 윤곽을 드러내며 내게 다가오는 느낌이랄까.

무엇보다 내 안에서 벌어지고 있는 조용한 음모로 인해 몸과 마음이 바짝 조여지는 기분이었다.

'그래, 나는 지금 변화하고 있는 중이야.'

이제 나에겐 '계획'이란 게 생겼고, 반드시 달성해야 할 목표가 생긴 것이다. 계획, 목표…… 그런 게 이토록 대단한 것이었나? 시야를 변화시키고 사람의 걸음걸이마저 확 바꿔 버릴 만큼 힘 있는 것이었나?

아니, 어쩌면 나의 계획이란 게 앞으로 10년, 혹은 20년, 30년 정도의 시한을 두고 있었다면 이렇게 생생한 느낌을 주진 못했을 것이다. 하지만 1년이라면 해볼 만하지 않은가? 1년 동안 죽기 살기로 돈을 벌어 보는 거다. 죽을 각오로 말이다.

"어떻게 오셨나요?"

문을 열고 들어서자 카운터의 직원이 친절하게 맞아주었다.

"호스티스 모집 광고를 보고 왔어요."

그러자 직원은 약간 놀라는 눈치였다. 잠시 후 직원은 나를 어느 화려한 응접실로 안내했다. 거기엔 마담인 듯한 여주인이 앉아 있었다. 나는 그녀의 시선에 완전히 주눅 들고 말았다. 마담은 단 1초 만에 모든 판단을 끝내 버린 눈치였다. 나머지는 그저 예의상 던지는 질문일 뿐이었다. '몇 살이죠?', '이런 일 해본 적 있나요?', '호스티스가 어떤 직업인 것 같아요?' 그런 질문들에는 이미 대답할 말을 준비하고 있었다. 나는 마치 대기업 입사 면접을 치르듯 또박또박 대답했다. 그게 다였다. 마담은 미소를 지으며 내게 다가와 어깨를 톡톡 두드려 주었다.

"좀 더 생각해 보세요. 세상은 정말 만만치 않답니다. 가서 다니던 직장에서 열심히 일하면서 곰곰이 생각해 보세요. 찾아보면 할 만한 일들이 아주 많으니까."

퇴짜였다.

물론 처음부터 단박에 채용되리라 기대한 건 아니었지만, 다리에 힘이 풀리는 느낌은 어쩔 수 없었다. 그래도 여긴 정말 친절한 클럽이었다. 이후 다섯 군데를 더 경험하면서 나는 내가 얼마나 무지하고 순진했었는지 뼈저리게 느낄 수 있었다. 못생긴 외모는 제쳐 두고라도 서른 가까운 나이에다 체중은 70킬로그램이 넘는 여자를 어느 클럽에서 써주겠는가?

'뭐야, 지금 장난하는 거야?'라는 듯 기막히다는 표정을 짓는 것은 그나마 점잖은 편이었다. 대부분의 클럽에서는 면전에 대고 "거울도 안 보고 삽니까?"라는 말을 내뱉기 일쑤였다.

"누가 당신 같은 여자랑 술 마시자고 몇 만 엔씩 지불하겠어?"

그런 말들 하나하나가 유리 파편처럼 날아와 가슴을 후벼 팠다. 태어나서 이렇게 노골적으로 자존심을 짓밟혀 보긴 처음이었다.

사실 나이나 외모보다 더 어처구니없는 것은 내가 술을 한 방울도 못 마신다는 사실이었다. 그러고도 긴자에서 호스티스로 일하겠다니 욕을 얻어먹어도 싸다.

퇴짜를 맞을 때마다 나는 세상물정 모르고 살아온 지난날을 후회했고, 모집광고 하나만 보고 긴자 거리에 들어선 나 자신을 향해 저주를 퍼부었다.

메모에 적힌 마지막 클럽에서도 실패한 뒤, 나는 쫓겨나듯 긴자 거리 한복판으로 내몰렸다. 거리는 휘황찬란한 네온사인과 행인들로 한창 달아오르고 있었지만, 내 마음은 차갑게 얼어붙고 있었다. 그 누구도 나 따윈 안중에 없었다. 술 취한 사람들 사이에서 이리 채이고 저리 채이면서 나는 버려진 휴지조각처럼 아무렇게나 휩쓸려 갔다.

"어이, 아가씨!"

누군가 뒤에서 나를 불렀다. 깜짝 놀라 돌아보니 두 번짼가 세 번째 클럽에서 잠깐 봤던 검은 옷의 중년 남자였다.

'무슨 일이지? 뭘 두고 왔나……?'

나는 눈만 깜빡거리며 멍하니 서 있었다.

"클럽 말이야, 아직 못 구했나?"

나는 말없이 고개를 끄덕였다.

"내가 한 군데 소개시켜 줄까?"

나는 속으로 쾌재를 불렀다.

'그래, 아직 기회가 남아 있어.'

"아니, 정식은 아니고 다음 호스티스가 올 때까지 임시직일지도 몰라."

"괜찮아요. 일만 할 수 있다면 아무래도 좋아요."

나는 무턱대고 남자의 뒤를 따랐다. 걷는 동안 혹시 이상한 데로 끌고 가는 건 아닌가 겁도 났지만, 그래도 불안보다는 기회 쪽으로 마음이 기울었다. 정서적으로 완전히 만신창이가 되어 버려 사고 능력이 떨어진 탓도 있었지만, 무엇보다 1년이라는 데드라인이 남다른 각오를 갖게 만든 것이다.

'그래, 앞으로 딱 1년뿐이야. 망설이거나 고민할 시간이 없어. 아무리 극한상황이 닥치더라도 1년 뒤면 해방이다.'

'죽기 아니면 살기', '될 대로 되라'는 식의 체념으로 나는 검은 정장의 사나이를 계속 따라갔다. 남자는 몇 미터 떨어진 어느 빌딩으로 들어가더니 엘리베이터에 올라탔다. 엘리베이터는 3층에서 멈췄다. 복도 양쪽으로 육중한 문들이 줄지어 있고 네온으로 장식된 간판과 큰 화병이 놓여 있었다. 남자는 어둑하면서도 은은한 조명 사이로 계속 걸었다. 그리고 마침내 '클럽 사와'라고 적힌 곳에서 걸음을 멈춘 그는 익숙한 동작으로 문을 열었다.

"마담, 일하고 싶다는 아가씨가 있어서요."

남자가 말하자 기모노 차림의 요염한 여성이 나타났다. 중년쯤 되어 보이는 어딘가 기품이 느껴지는 여인이었다.

'아름답다.'

나는 감탄했다. 사람들은 흔히 20~30대의 늘씬한 여자들을 보며 꽃처럼 아름답다고 함부로 떠들어 대지만 나이와 상관없이, 아니 오직 그 연륜만이 간직할 수 있는 그런 아름다움이야말로 진짜가 아닐까.

나는 그 마담에게 호감을 가득 담은 표정으로 인사했다. 하지만 마담의 표정은 굉장히 복잡했다.

"……꽤 재미있는 아가씨를 데려왔군."

그렇게 에둘러 표현했지만 아무래도 내 외모를 보고 곤란해하는 게 분명했다. 게다가 이런 일도 처음인 데다 술마저 전혀 못 마신다는 말을 듣고는 한숨을 내뱉었다.

'역시 안 되나 보다……'

이젠 낙담하는 데에도 이골이 나 있었다. 그때 남자가 다시 한

번 밀어붙였다.

"호스티스들이 연거푸 그만두는 바람에 일손이 많이 달린다면서요?"

"응, 그건 그래. 하지만……."

"이 아가씨, 지금은 이래도 금세 바뀔 겁니다. 믿고 한번 시켜보시죠."

나는 남자를 힐끗 쳐다봤다.

'이렇게 고마울 데가, 생전 처음 보는 나를…….'

물론 그때는 클럽마다 소개료란 것이 발생한다는 것을 알 리가 없었다. 나중에 안 사실이지만, 이렇게 소개받아 일하게 되면 중개인에게 수만 엔에서 때로 수십 만 엔씩 지급해야 한다. 결국 남자가 그렇게 열심히 밀어붙인 데에도 다 이유가 있었던 것이다.

"어쨌거나 머릿수는 채워야 하잖습니까."

남자가 강하게 밀어붙이자 마담은 한숨을 길게 토해 내고는, "그래, 그러자. 다음 호스티스를 찾을 때까지만 대타로……" 하며 마지못해 승낙했다.

'해냈어!'

나는 덩실덩실 춤이라도 추고 싶었다.

'세상에, 내가 긴자에서 일을 할 수 있다니!'

하지만 마담은 단호하게 말했다.

"아가씨한테 일급 1만 엔을 다 줄 수는 없어. 8,000엔부터 시작해도 괜찮겠지?"

긴자의 호스티스는 일급이 기본 1만 엔이며, 그 밑으로 받는 호스티스는 없는 것 같았다. 하지만 나의 파견 시급은 1,350엔, 매일 8시간 정도 일해도 한 달에 쥐는 돈은 약 21만 엔이었다. 그런데 여기서는 단 4시간만 일해도 8,000엔. 주 4일 출근에 월 12만 8,000엔을 받을 수 있다는 계산이 나온다. 낮일과 겸하면 월 34만 엔 정도까지도 벌 수 있다!

나는 연신 고개를 끄덕였다. 그러자 마담은 곁눈질로 내 몸을 슬쩍 훑어보며 물었다.

"지금 몇 킬로그램이야?"

갑자기 가슴이 덜컥 내려앉았다.

"……73킬로그램인데요."

"거기서 20킬로그램만 빼면 1만 엔으로 올려 줄게. 열심히 해."

"네!"

살면서 그렇게 크고 명랑한 목소리로 대답해 보긴 처음이었다. 온종일 긴자의 클럽을 돌아다니며 받았던 마음의 상처들을 한순간에 보상받는 것 같았다.

"가명은 뭐로 할래?"

"가명이요?"

마담은 어이없어했다.

"가게에서 쓰는 이름 말이야. 별명 같은 거."

나는 골똘히 생각에 잠겼다.

'연예인들처럼 내게도 또 하나의 이름이 필요하게 될 줄이야.'

"아마리…… 아마리로 할게요."

"아마리?"

"예. 나머지, 여분이란 뜻의 아마리余リ."

그러자 마담은 또 한숨을 내쉬더니 마지못해 고개를 끄덕였다.

"그래, 그것도 괜찮은 아이디어네."

다른 호스티스들은 '린', '유리카', '아키호' 같은 귀여운 이름을 사용하지만 나는 덤으로 들어오게 된 '나머지' 같은 존재가 아닌가. 그런 생각에서 반은 자학적으로 붙인 이름이었다.

어떻게 보면 그 이름은 지금 내가 살고 있는 시간이 어떤 의미를 품고 있는지를 가장 명확히 말해 주는 것 같았다. 나머지 삶, 내가 나에게 부여한 1년 치 여분의 삶…….

그래도 막상 또 하나의 이름이 생기자 왠지 기분이 좋았다. 예전의 내가 아닌, 전혀 다른 사람이 된 것 같았기 때문이다. 그렇게 나는 긴자의 호스티스가 되었다.

그날 밤 불을 끄고 잠자리에 누운 뒤에야 나는 내게 닥친, 아니 내가 선택한 변화를 비로소 생생하게 느낄 수 있었다.

줄곧 패배자로 살아오던 내가 태어나서 처음으로 도전자가 되었다. 그리고 나와는 아무 상관없던 라스베이거스를 인생의 마지막 도달점으로 삼았다. 생각 속에 어떤 씨앗이 있었기에 이런 변화가 생겼을까? 목표가 생기자 계획이 만들어지고, 계획을 현실화시키려다 보니 전에 없던 용기가 나오기 시작했다.

인터넷에서 긴자의 호스티스 클럽을 검색하고, 전화를 걸어 직접 찾아간 사람이 정말 나란 말인가? 거듭되는 퇴짜에도 불구하고 결국 이런 외모, 이런 몸매로 클럽에 채용됐다는 것이 얼마나 기적 같은 일인지 그제야 피부로 와 닿았다.

정말이지 인생의 구석구석에서 언제 어떤 일이 일어날지는 아무도 모른다. 아무리 무모하더라도 일단 작정을 하고 나면 무슨 일이든 생길 수 있다. 정말 신기한 것은 내가 '움직였다'는 것이다. 원래의 나라면 좁은 방바닥에 드러누워 꼼짝도 하지 않았을 것이다. 그저 머릿속에서만 수십 채의 집을 짓고 허물며 게으른 몽상에서 한 발짝도 움직이지 않는 것이 나였다.

생각은 생각일 뿐이고 몽상은 그저 몽상일 뿐이었는데, 그런 내가 최초로 몸을 움직였다. 발가락부터 조금씩 움직여 본 것이다. 그러자 기적 같은 일들이 벌어지기 시작한 것이다. 나는 다시 불을 켜고 수첩을 펼쳤다. 그리고 앞으로 1년 뒤, 인생의 정점까지 가는 동안 나의 신조처럼 지키고 싶은 한마디를 적었다.

'기적을 바란다면 발가락부터 움직여 보자.'

가진 게 없다고 할 수 있는 것까지 없는 건 아니다

낮엔 평범한 회사원, 밤엔 긴자의 호스티스, 나는 마치 영화에 나 나올 법한 이중생활의 주인공이 되었다. 그 무렵 회사에서는 가끔 야근 명령이 떨어질 때도 있었다. 그래서 나는 퇴근 후 곧바로 긴자에서 일할 수 있게끔 집에서 가깝고 야근이 없는 회사로 파견지를 변경했다. 일하는 기간이나 시간, 근무지 등을 직접 선택할 수 있는 파견사원의 메리트를 처음으로 맘껏 활용한 것이다.

이제 매일 아침 9시부터 오후 5시까지는 회사에서 일을 하고, 오후 7시 30분부터 밤 11시 30분까지는 긴자의 클럽에서 호스티스로 일하게 된다.

"첫 근무까지 며칠 시간을 줄 테니 그동안 꼼꼼히 준비해 둬."

그러면서 마담은 준비해야 할 목록을 일러주었다.

호스티스는 갖춰야 할 것들이 산더미 같았다. 먼저 의상부터 장난이 아니다. 나이 든 마담은 기모노를 입지만 그 밑의 호스티스들은 형형색색의 화려한 드레스로 몸을 휘감아야 하고, 그 비용은 모두 개인 부담이다. 매일 똑같은 옷을 입을 수도 없는 노릇이라 최소한 두세 벌 이상 필요했다. 그래도 클럽 사와는 나은 편이었다. 다른 클럽에는 반드시 새 드레스를 입고 와야만 하는 '뉴 드레스 데이New Dress Day'라는 것도 있다고 한다. 물론 그만큼 버는 돈도 많겠지만, 수입이 많을수록 지출도 많아지는 것이 이곳 긴자의 방정식일지도 모른다.

여하튼 나로서는 어떻게든 초기 비용을 줄여야 했다. 하지만 아무리 싼 드레스를 찾으려 해도 도대체 어디서 파는지, 한 벌에 얼마나 하는지 통 알 길이 없었다. 긴자의 유명 백화점에 있는 파티 드레스 코너에 갔더니 그저 그런 드레스인데도 입이 딱 벌어질 만큼 비쌌다. 더 큰 문제는 가격보다 사이즈였다. 당최 내 몸에 맞는 빅 사이즈 따윈 눈을 씻고 봐도 없었다. 또 한 번 나의 '빌어먹을 외모'가 슬퍼지는 순간이었다. 하지만 기죽어 있을 시간이 없다.

결국 나의 충실한 정보통 역할을 해주는 넷카페로 달려가 인터넷 쇼핑몰을 샅샅이 뒤졌다. 77, 88, 99, 100…… 유명 백화점에서는 결코 취급하지 않는 빅 사이즈가 '저요, 저요' 하며 올라왔다. 나는 저렴하면서도 싸구려처럼 보이지 않는 원단과 디자인을 찾아 두 벌을 주문했다.

다음은 드레스에 맞는 구두를 찾아야 했다. 선배 호스티스들(그래봤자 스물아홉 살인 나보다 대부분 어리지만)은 잘 보이지도 않을 만큼 가늘고 뾰족한 힐을 신고 아무렇지도 않은 듯 우아하게 걸어 다녔는데, 내 눈엔 곡예로밖에 보이지 않았다.

'저렇게 가느다란 힐이 내 몸무게를 감당할 수 있을까?'

물론 불가능하다. 나는 이번에도 인터넷 쇼핑몰을 뒤져 굵고 낮은 굽의 펌프스를 구입했다. 목걸이와 귀걸이 같은 액세서리도 값싼 제품으로 대충 갖췄다. 싸다고는 하지만 그래도 상당한 지출이다. 앞으로 더욱 더 허리띠를 졸라매야만 한다.

자, 드레스에 구두에 액세서리까지 장만했다. 또 뭐가 필요하지? 참, 화장 도구도 한 세트 구해야 한다. 지금까지는 파운데이션과 아이브로펜슬만 쓰면서 거의 민낯에 가까운 화장을 해왔지만 긴자에서는 어림도 없다. 이젠 뷰티 잡지를 펼쳐 놓고 거울 앞에서 화장 연습을 해야 한다. 완전 생고생이다. 특히 속눈썹은 난생처음이라 엉뚱한 부위에 붙이는 바람에, 뗐다 붙였다를 반복해 가며 진땀을 흘렸다.

그러는 사이 호스티스로 데뷔하는 날이 점점 다가왔다. 그동안 나는 퇴근하자마자 곧장 집으로 달려와 밤늦도록 드레스를 입고 거울 앞에서 화장 연습을 했다. 처음엔 색조 화장이 서툴러 빨강, 파랑 등 원색으로만 화려하게 범벅을 하는 바람에 영락없는 피에로가 되어 버리곤 했는데, 그것도 시간이 흐르면서 점점 능숙해져 갔다. 밋밋했던 얼굴이 차츰차츰 '그래도 봐줄 만'해지자 왠지 기분이 좋아졌다. 오랜 세월 동안 의식 맨 밑바닥에 내팽개쳐 두었던 '여성성'을 오랜만에 만나는 느낌이었다.

머리 손질도 맹연습을 거듭했다. 고급 클럽들 중에는 매일 출근 전에 의무적으로 미용실에 들러야 하는 곳도 많다. 머리 손질에만 매일매일 3,000엔 정도를 들인다. 클럽 사와에서도 물론 미용실을 장려하고 있지만 강제 조항은 아니었다. 더러는 능숙한 솜씨로 직접 손질을 하기도 했다. 물론 나도 마땅히 그래야만 한다. 나는 밤마다 헤어 카탈로그를 손에 쥐고 구슬땀을 흘려 가며 세팅 방법을 익히고 또 익혔다.

드디어 호스티스 데뷔 첫날.

오후 다섯 시, 땡 하자마자 나는 회사에서 나와 번개같이 집으로 달려갔다. 샤워하고 화장하고 머리 손질까지 한 시간, 그리고 전철에 뛰어올라 개점 30분 전까지 클럽에 도착! 빈방에서 화장을 고치고 머리를 묶어 올린 뒤 하늘색 롱드레스를 걸쳤다. 그리고 거울 앞에 섰다.

거울 안에는 처음 보는 내가 서 있었다. 비록 다른 호스티스들이 입고 있는 고급 드레스에는 발끝에도 못 미칠 만큼 싸구려일지라도, 그렇게 치장을 하고 나니 왠지 마음이 들뜨기 시작했다. 20대 중반 이후로 몇 년 동안 '멋'과는 아주 동떨어진 생활을 해왔던 나로서는 참으로 설렐 수밖에 없는 순간이었다.

클럽 사와에 종사하는 호스티스는 모두 25명이며 상주 호스티스는 15명 남짓이다. 최고급 클럽이라기보다는 마담의 인맥을 중심으로 돌아가는 아늑한 분위기의 중급 클럽이라고 할 수 있다. 이제 나도 이 클럽의 멤버로서 생애 최초의 '손님'을 맞이하게 될 것이다.

소파에 앉아 시계만 바라보며 영업 개시를 기다리고 있자니 갑자기 불안감이 밀려오기 시작했다. 평소에도 낯가림이 심한 내가 과연 이 일을 감당해 낼 수 있을까? 완전히 망쳐 버리지나 않을까? 초침이 한 바퀴, 두 바퀴 돌아갈수록 긴장 때문에 현기증까지 느껴졌다. 그것을 눈치 챈 마담이 나를 밖으로 불러냈다.

"아마리, 어깨 쫙 펴! 어려울 거 하나도 없어. 그냥 사근사근

웃으면서 상대방 이야기만 잘 들어 주면 돼. 괜찮아."

나는 멍한 표정으로 고개를 끄덕였다. 그래도 불안했던지 마담은 세 가지 규칙을 설명해 주었다.

"첫째, 손님이 잔을 비우면 곧바로 술을 따른다. 둘째, 담뱃불은 호스티스가 켜고 재떨이에 꽁초 네 개비가 쌓이면 교체한다. 셋째, 대화의 포인트에서는 약간 과장되게 손님을 치켜세운다. 이것만 명심해, 알았지?"

나는 속으로 그 세 가지를 몇 번이나 반복했다. 그러는 동안 손님을 동반한 호스티스들이 차례차례 룸으로 들어오기 시작했다.

"어머, 사장님! 어서 오세요."

마담은 활짝 웃으면서 익숙하고 자연스러운 솜씨로 손님을 앉힌 뒤 나에게 시선을 돌리며 "아마리, 야마사키 씨 자리에 보조로 붙어" 하고 말했다. 내 이름이 불리자 몸에 전율이 흘렀다.

자리에는 고급스러운 슈트에 품위 있는 초로의 남자와 그 접대 상대로 보이는 두 명의 중년 남자가 앉아 있었다. 나는 그 옆자리로 가서 인사했다.

"실례합니다. 아마리예요. 잘 부탁드립니다."

목소리가 살짝 떨렸는데 눈치 채지는 않았을까, 초짜라고 비웃지는 않을까?

호스티스는 각각 자신을 '지명'해 주거나, '동반'이라 하여 미리 약속을 정해서 함께 가게까지 동행하곤 하는 스폰서가 있다. 가장 구석진 자리에 우두커니 앉아 있으니, 그 손님의 담당 호스티스가 오늘 막 들어온 나를 손님에게 소개했다. 하지만 손님은 누가 봐도 아름다운 호스티스들 틈에 생뚱맞게 끼어 있는 나를 그저 한번 힐끗 쳐다볼 뿐이었다. 그 눈빛은 마치 '뭐야, 애는?' 하고 툴툴거리는 듯한 느낌이었다. 나는 무심코 속으로 '죄송합니다'라고 중얼거렸다.

물론 손님들은 다들 신사적이라 대놓고 불만을 드러내지는 않았고, 시종일관 분위기는 온화했다. 나는 무조건 생글생글 웃으며 좌중의 이야기를 열심히 듣기만 했다. 지금 내가 할 수 있는 건 마담이 일러준 세 가지 규칙뿐이다.

'빈 잔을 집어 들어 표면의 물방울을 손수건으로 닦고 술을 따른다. 손님이 담배를 꺼내면 재빨리 라이터로 불을 붙인다. 대화의 포인트에서 약간 과장되게 액션을 취한다.'

잔, 재떨이, 리액션, 잔, 재떨이, 리액션…… 머릿속에서 끝없이 반복했지만 여전히 초조했다. 손님의 이야기에 신경 쓰다 보면 잔이 빈 것을 눈치 채지 못하고, 설령 눈치 챘더라도 손을 뻗으려 하면 이미 선배 호스티스가 잔을 채우고 있었다. 평소에도 행동이 굼뜬 터라 담뱃불을 붙이는 타이밍에서도, 재떨이를 교체하는 속도에서도 경험이 풍부한 선배 호스티스를 당해낼 재간이 없었다.

그녀들은 사방에 눈이 달려 있는 것 같았다. 모든 것을 꿰뚫어 보는 배려는 물론이거니와 겉으로는 조금도 티가 나지 않을 만큼 자연스러웠다. 나는 선배들에게 진심으로 존경심이 일었다. 그렇다면 이제 내게 남은 것은 리액션뿐이다.

'대화에 쓸데없이 끼어들지 말고 분위기를 파악하는 데 집중하자.'

단지 이 시간 자체를 즐기기 위한 대화, 조크와 유머가 끼어드는 그 포인트에서 웃거나 어울리는 액션을 취하는 것이다. 그러자 차츰차츰 손님의 반응이 느껴졌다.

시간이 얼마나 흘렀을까? 문득 시계를 보니 밤 11시 30분이 넘어가고 있었다. 호스티스 데뷔 첫날, 정신없이 네 시간이 훌쩍 흘러간 것이다. 그사이 대체 몇 테이블을 돌았던가? 머리가 어지럽고 천장이 빙빙 도는 것 같았다.

첫 번째 날이 이렇게 끝났다. 나는 빈방에서 혼자 옷을 갈아입고 마담과 다른 호스티스들에게 꾸벅 인사를 했다.

"먼저 가 보겠습니다!"

그러고는 곧장 가게를 나와 전철에 올랐다. 늦은 시간인데도 전철은 북적북적했다. 승객들의 시선이 일제히 내게로 와서 꽂혔다. 옷차림은 평범하고 수수한데, 머리 모양이며 화장은 너무도 튀었던 것이다.

'제발, 아는 사람한테 들키지만 마라.'

나는 간절히 기도하면서 구석진 출입문에 몸을 잔뜩 기댔다. 창에 비친 내 모습이 그렇게 낯설 수가 없었다. 나는 오늘 하루 동안 있었던 일들을 차근차근 되새김질하기 시작했다. 모든 것이 처음이었던 하루였다.

D-11개월.

눈 깜짝할 사이에 한 달이 훌쩍 지났다. 나만의 카운트다운으로는 앞으로 11개월이 남은 셈이다. 이제 가게 분위기도 조금씩 파악할 수 있게 되었다. 동료들의 수다를 엿들으며 긴자, 클럽, 호스티스의 세계, 그리고 마담에 대해서도 여러 가지 사실들을 알게 되었다.

클럽 사와를 수십 년째 운영해 오고 있는 마담은 언제나 세상사에 통달한 것처럼 보였지만, 어딘가 살짝 푼수기가 있는 귀여운 캐릭터였다. 그녀의 정확한 나이를 아는 사람은 아무도 없지만 대략 예순쯤은 된 것 같다고 한다. 그 연배치고는 등을 항상 꼿꼿이 펴고, 언제나 쇼트커트에 기모노 차림 등 흐트러짐이 전

혀 없다. 그중에서도 흰 기모노 차림은 마담의 트레이드 마크가
되어 있었다.

젊은 시절 다른 클럽에서 호스티스로 일할 때 알았던 손님들
은 여전히 그녀를 찾아온다. 이제는 다들 사회 원로급이 되어
"연금 할인으로 잘 부탁한다!", "내년엔 못 올지도 모른다!" 하며
짓궂은 농담을 던지곤 한다.

마담이 긴자에 자기 가게를 낸 것은 20대 초반, 당시 긴자의
마담 중에서는 최연소였기에 가히 전설적인 인물로 불렸다고 한
다. 물론 근거 없는 소문도 무성했다. 주로 아이가 있다거나, 젊
은 시절 유부남과 불같은 연애를 했다거나, 혹은 여배우 지망생
이었다는 얘기들이다.

마담을 중심으로 하는 클럽 사와는 화기애애하고 아늑한 분위
기를 지닌 중급 클럽이지만, 그래도 역시 긴자 클럽이라서 자리
에 앉기만 해도 기본이 3만 엔이다. 하지만 손님들은 그런 것엔
전혀 개의치 않고 기세 좋게 비싼 술을 주문한다. 어지럽게 날아
다니는 돈뭉치를 보며 나는 그저 어안이 벙벙했다.

여러 손님들을 대하면서 나는 차츰 세 가지 규칙에 익숙해져
가기 시작했다. 하지만 여전히 다른 호스티스들의 눈치나 배려,
씀씀이에는 따라갈 수 없었다.

그러던 어느 날, 마담이 나를 따로 불렀다.

"어때? 해볼 만해?"

"솔직히, 아직은 선배들 따라가기도 버거워요. 제가 워낙 둔하고 재능도 없어서⋯⋯."

"가진 게 없다고 할 수 있는 것까지 없는 건 아니지."

"예?"

"아마리, 손님들이 왜 클럽에 와서 술을 마시는 것 같아?"

"⋯⋯그건 아무래도 고급스러운 분위기, 서비스⋯⋯."

내가 더듬거리자 마담이 미소를 지으며 말했다.

"평생 이 일을 하면서 확실히 알게 된 게 있다면 그건 '사람은 결국 혼자'라는 거야. 낮 동안에는 그걸 인식할 겨를이 없지만, 밤이 되면 절실히 와 닿게 마련이지. 미녀들의 웃음이나 고급스러운 분위기, 값비싼 양주는 소품에 불과해. 능숙한 서비스도 역시 소품이야. 정말 중요한 건 마음의 메아리인 것 같아."

솔직히 너무 평범하고 일반적인 얘기들이었다. 사람은 누구나 외롭다는 것, 그리고 마음에서 우러나오는 서비스가 필요하다는 건 나도 안다. 그런 얘기를 구태여 따로 불러서 할 필요가 있을까?

하지만 마담이 왜 그런 얘기를 했는지, 그리고 그게 어떤 의미인지는 좀 더 시간이 흐른 뒤에야 알 수 있었다. 다른 호스티스들을 보면 정말 말솜씨가 뛰어난 사람도 있다. 그들은 이야기의 미세한 리듬을 능숙하게 이끌 수 있고, 교섭을 필요로 하는 대화의 테크닉도 놀랍다. 말주변이 없는 나로서는 그들을 따라간다는 사실 자체가 불가능했다.

하지만 자리가 거듭될수록 손님들과의 대화 사이에서 어떤 빈 공간이 느껴졌다. 말하는 사람의 이야기가 듣는 사람의 마음에 채 들어가지 못하고 겉돌 때일수록 그 빈 공간에서 느껴지는 허전함은 더욱 커졌다.

나는 그 느낌을 잘 알고 있었다. 무리 속에서 철저히 혼자가 되어 본 사람이라면 그 느낌을 이해할 수 있다. 회사의 회식자리나 회의 때, 혹은 휴게실에서 잡담을 나눌 때마다 나는 아무도 나와 '연결'되어 있지 않다는 느낌을 받곤 했었다.

그래서 나는 손님들과의 대화에서도 '연결'이 필요하다고 느꼈다. 마음이 접속에 성공하면 마담이 했던 말처럼 메아리가 울리지 않을까? 그때부터 나는 '경청'에 전념하기로 했다. 입을 열기보다는 귀를 잔뜩 기울이고 전체적인 맥락만 파악하면 적어도 '분위기 깨는 신세'는 면할 수 있을 거라고 생각한 것이다. 더 나아가 마담이 가르쳐 준 대로 대화의 포인트에서는 약간 과장되게 손님을 치켜세우는 것이다. 그러던 중에 요령을 터득하기 시작했다.

대화의 포인트란 한 문장이 끝나는 지점, 즉 마침표를 찍는 곳이다. 그런 부분에서는 고개를 끄덕이거나 가볍게 맞장구를 친다. 그리고 약간 과장되면서도 티 나지 않게 칭찬하거나 치켜세운다. 물론 처음에는 모든 게 두려워 머뭇거리기 일쑤였지만 요령을 터득한 뒤로는 점점 즐거워졌다.

치켜세울 때는 철저히 치켜세워야 한다. 평소라면 전혀 하지 않을 법한 과장된 리액션으로 "멋져요", "끝내줘요", "어머나, 세상에!"라는 극찬을 아끼지 않는다. 간혹 '조금 오버했나?'라는 생각이 들긴 했지만, 손님이 즐거워했기 때문에 오히려 내가 놀랄 정도였다. 인간관계에 있어서는 완전 숙맥인 데다가 낯가림도 심한 내가 이런 리액션을 취할 수 있다는 게 도무지 믿어지지 않았다.

어쩌면 그동안 살아오면서 나 스스로도 전혀 눈치 채지 못한 재능을 이제야 발견한 건 아닐까? '칭찬을 잘하는' 재능도 재능이라면 말이다.

사실 미인도 아니고, 스타일도 엉망인 데다가 말주변도 없고 도무지 내세울 게 하나도 없는 내가 여기서 잘리지 않고 계속 일하려면 없는 재능이라도 만들어 내야 할 판이었다. 그런 각오로 발버둥 치다 보니 '잘 들어 주고, 성의껏 칭찬하는' 재능 아닌 재능이 발굴된 것이다. 물론 그런 재능이 제대로 기능하려면 최우선적으로 진심 어린 경청이 우선되어야 하지만.

덕분에 내가 앉은 자리는 '썰렁' 단계를 지나 점점 흥겨운 분위기로 바뀌어 갔다. 술을 잘 마시지 못한다는 약점도 의외로 쉽게 극복되었다. 손님들은 내게 술을 권하기보다는 이야기를 들어주는 것을 원했다. 그러면서 언제부터인가 클럽 사와에서도 아마리를 찾는 손님이 생겨나기 시작했다. 나는 마담이 했던 이야기를 새삼 떠올렸다.

'가진 게 없다고 할 수 있는 것까지 없는 건 아니지.'

지속적인 당당함은
자기 무대에서 나온다

D-10개월.

불볕더위도 한풀 꺾이고 서서히 가을로 접어들고 있다. 낮과 밤을 달리하고 회사 생활과 호스티스 생활을 병행하는 이중생활도 이젠 제법 익숙해졌다. 다만 클럽 동료들과의 관계만큼은 아직 엇박자였다. 특히 레이나와의 관계가 가장 껄끄러웠다.

클럽 사와에서 일하는 25명의 호스티스들은 나이도 근무 형태도 제각각이었고 각자 복잡한 사정을 품고 있었다. 나는 이곳의 아늑한 분위기가 맘에 들지만, 호스티스 중에는 가게 분위기에 녹아들지 못하거나 '여기서는 원하는 손님을 절대 잡을 수 없다'며 다른 가게로 옮겨 가는 이들도 있었다. 그래서 한 달도 채 안 돼 그만두는 사람도 꽤 있다. 반면에 10년 넘게 일하고 있는 사람도 있는데, 레이나가 바로 그런 경우다.

레이나는 나보다 세 살 위인 선배였다. 마담에 버금갈 만큼 존재감이 있고, 호스티스 일에도 능숙해서 처음 온 손님들은 종종 새끼 마담으로 착각하곤 했다. 하지만 그녀는 내가 클럽에 처음 들어왔을 때 누구보다 못마땅하게 여겼다. 언제나 마주치면 '볼품도 없고 경험도 없는 애가 여긴 왜 와?' 하는 눈빛으로 나를 보곤 했다. 하긴 클럽의 모든 호스티스들이 똑같은 생각이었을 것이다. 레이나는 그런 마음을 솔직히 겉으로 드러냈을 뿐이다.

기분은 나빴지만 사실 나로서는 아무런 변명거리도, 스스로 변호할 만한 최소한의 무기도 없었다. 내가 할 수 있는 거라곤 그저 묵묵히 열심히 일하는 것뿐이었다.

그런 어느 날, 나는 평소처럼 선배 호스티스의 보조로 붙어 손님을 맞았다. 인사를 하자마자 성깔 있게 생긴 젊은 손님이 미간을 잔뜩 찌푸리며 호통을 쳤다.

"얜 뭐야? 마담! 당장 다른 애로 바꿔!"

나는 가슴 속에서 뭔가 쿵 내려앉는 것처럼 충격을 받았다. 아무리 발버둥을 쳐도 나란 인간은 이 세계에서 삼류 이하밖에 안 된다는 것쯤이야 나도 잘 안다. 하지만 빤히 얼굴을 보며 직접 그런 말을 하다니…… 엄청난 충격이었다.

나는 어깨를 축 늘어뜨린 채 터덜터덜 대기실로 돌아갔다. 그때 뒤에서 누군가 살며시 어깨를 두드려 주었다.

"괜찮아, 그냥 흘려들어. 어딜 가나 저런 손님은 있기 마련이야. 힘내!"

깜짝 놀랐다. 다름 아닌 레이나였기 때문이다.

"아, 네에……."

어떤 표정을 지어야 할지 난감해하는 사이, 레이나는 별일 아니라는 듯이 한쪽 눈을 찡긋하고는 다시 자기 자리로 돌아갔다.

그 일은 내게 아주 중요한 사건이었다. 왜냐하면 그날 이후로 나도 '친구'란 걸 얻었기 때문이다. 레이나는 내 주변을 소리 없이 맴돌면서 알게 모르게 나를 걱정하고 신경을 써주었다. 내가 손님에게 싫은 소리를 듣거나 마담에게 혼난 날이면 집에 돌아가서도 "오늘 괜찮았니?"라고 꼭 전화나 문자를 보내곤 했다. 짓궂은 손님이 무리한 요구라도 할 때면 어느새 내 곁으로 다가와 유연한 솜씨로 방어벽을 쳐주기도 했다.

그런 레이나의 행동에 처음엔 적잖이 당황했다. 지금껏 내게 그렇게 신경 써준 사람이 없기도 했거니와, 누구보다 나를 못마땅해 하던 사람이었으니까.

'왜 나에게 이렇게 친절할까?'

레이나의 마음씀씀이가 정말 고마웠지만 한편으론 너무 궁금했다. 나중에야 나는 그 이유를 레이나에게 직접 들을 수 있었다.

"처음엔 기가 막히고, 다음엔 안쓰럽고, 또 그 다음엔 너무 열심이라 그냥 친구가 돼주기로 했지 뭐."

그게 다였다.

솔직히 나는 남들과 엮이는 것도 싫어하거니와 괜히 남 일에 참견하는 사람과는 아예 거리를 두는 성격이었다. 하지만 지금은 '레이나가 없었다면 어떡할 뻔했지?' 하는 생각마저 든다. 진심이 느껴지는 그녀의 따뜻한 위로와 격려가 눈물 날 만큼 기뻤고, 그 힘으로 긴자의 호스티스 생활을 이겨 나갈 수 있게 된 것이다.

마음을 열고 보니 레이나는 아주 시원시원한 여장부 스타일이었다. 게다가 의리도 있어 한 번 마음에 든 사람은 철저히 챙기고 소중한 가족처럼 보살펴 준다. 가끔 휴식 시간이 생기면 난 어김없이 그녀 곁에 앉아 수다를 떨었다.

"있잖아, 이건 비밀인데 난 두 아이를 키우고 있어."

레이나가 말했다. 그녀는 두 살, 세 살 난 아이를 가진 싱글맘이었다. 레이나 본인도 그런 엄마에게서 자랐다고 한다. 술집을 하던 엄마는 남자에게 쉽게 의지하는 타입이라 돈과 먹을 것만 챙겨 두고 나가서는 몇 주 동안 돌아오지 않는 일도 종종 있었다고 한다. 남자와의 분쟁도 끊이지 않아 한번은 흉기를 든 남자가 집으로 쳐들어온 적도 있었단다. 그런 이야기를 레이나는 마치 드라마 줄거리 이야기하듯 천연덕스럽게 들려주었다.

"가족이란 건 말이야, 보이지는 않지만 어떤 질긴 끈 같은 걸로 단단히 연결돼 있어야 해. 안 그러면 엉망이 돼 버리거든. 가족이든 친구든 자기 주변 사람들을 소홀히 여기면 결국 인생이란 게 비극으로 치닫게 돼."

레이나 주변에 사람이 많은 것도, 그들 모두 마치 가족처럼 결속력이 강한 것도 이해할 수 있을 것 같다. 그녀 스스로 남보다 절실히 가족이라는 끈을 찾고 있기 때문이다.

"아마리, 돈 벌어서 뭐 할 거야?"

어느 날 레이나가 불쑥 물었다. 나는 약간 난감해 하다가 '비밀'이라는 단서를 붙이고 '라스베이거스'라고 말했다. 그러자 레이나는 충분히 이해한다는 표정으로 이렇게 말했다.

"난 고향 바닷가에다 음악 카페 차리는 게 꿈이야. 카페 겸 레스토랑 말이야. 주방은 아주 커야 해. 왜냐하면 대식구가 함께해야 하니까."

"대식구?"

"내 아이들, 그리고 그 아이들의 친구들, 그리고 내 친구들까지 죄다 모일 수 있는 공간이니까. 멋지지? 아마리, 너도 초대할게."

아픈 과거를 갖고 있으면서도 누구보다 쾌활하고 명랑하게 살아가는 그녀를 보면 '사람의 운명이란 스스로 만들어 나가는 것'이라는 흔해 빠진 이야기가 새삼 와 닿는다.

레이나 덕분에 서먹서먹했던 동료들과도 조금씩 가까워졌다. 그중에는 '치카' 같은 별종도 있다. 그녀는 여자인 내가 봐도 반할 만큼 몸매도 늘씬하고 얼굴도 예쁘다. 게다가 '이런 데'서 일하는 여자들에게서는 좀처럼 찾아보기 어려운 요조숙녀 같은 분위기마저 풍겼다. 알고 보니 그녀는 실제로 고베 출신의 '대단한 집' 딸이었다.

치카는 손님이 권하는 술을 절대로 거절하는 법이 없다. 정말 잘 마신다. 게다가 엄청난 독서가였다. 나도 책은 꽤 읽는 편이라 생각했지만, 치카의 풍부한 지식에는 비할 바가 못 되었다. 치카가 인기 있는 건 당연한 일이다. 그래서 그녀는 누구보다 개인 손님을 많이 확보하고 있었고 마담도 그런 치카를 아주 마음에 들어 했다. 정말이지 치카를 싫어하는 사람은 한 명도 없었다.

나는 언제부터인가 치카의 손님이 방문하면 그 옆에 보조로 붙거나, 레이나의 손님 옆자리에 치카와 나란히 함께하곤 했다. 그렇게 셋이 손님을 맞는 날은 모두가 파티처럼 시간을 보낼 수 있었다.

치카는 분위기도 잘 읽고 지식도 풍부해서 어떤 화제든 자연스럽게 이어 나갈 수 있었다. 그래서 나는 곤란할 때면 "그렇지? 치카" 하며 말을 넘기곤 했다. 그러면 치카는 절대 아는 척하지 않고, 지식을 과시하는 일도 없이 대화를 이끌어 갔다. 때론 아는 것도 모르는 척해 가며 손님에게 공을 돌릴 줄도 알았다. 나는 가끔 그녀가 어떻게 사람의 마음을 사로잡는지 감탄스럽게 지켜보곤 했다.

어느 날, 단골손님이 쌍둥이 남자 손님 두 명을 데려온 적이 있었다. 우리는 입을 모아 "정말 똑같아, 똑같아!"를 연발했다. 하지만 치카만은 "전혀 닮지 않았는데요?" 하고 말했다. 우리는 놀랐지만 쌍둥이 손님들은 기뻐하며 이렇게 말했다.

"우린 어딜 가나 똑같다는 말을 귀가 닳도록 들었지. 그런데 닮지 않았다는 말을 들으니 새삼 개성을 인정받은 것 같아 기분이 좋군 그래."

치카는 그런 사람이었다. 그런 요조숙녀가 어쩌다가 긴자의 호스티스가 되었는지 나는 늘 의아했다. 어느 날 호기심을 참지 못하고 레이나에게 물었더니 "아마 연극에 빠지는 바람에 가족들과 소원해진 모양이야"라고 했다. 치카는 지금도 버는 족족 연극 활동에 쏟아붓고 있는 모양이었다. 집안의 도움 없이 혼자 힘으로 극단을 꾸려 나가다 보니, 정작 본인은 아주 작은 원룸에서 소박하게 살고 있다는 것이다. 긴자에서 잘나가는 호스티스라면 월세가 10만 엔이나 되는 호화로운 고급 맨션에 사는 사람도 적지 않다. 하지만 치카는 그런 데에 전혀 관심이 없었다. 마치 연극만을 위해 사는 사람 같았다.

그런 치카가 어느 날 나를 초대했다.

"아마리, 내 무대 보러 오지 않을래?"

반가운 제안이기도 했지만, 그보다는 도대체 무엇이 그녀를 그토록 빠져들게 했는지 확인하고 싶었다. 그로부터 일주일이 지난 어느 휴일, 나는 나카노의 소극장 객석에 앉아 치카의 연기를 숨죽이고 지켜봤다. 그녀가 맡은 배역은 주인공의 상대역인 악역이었다. 늘 생글생글 웃기만 하는 그 선한 얼굴이 무대에서는 전혀 다른 얼굴로 변해 버렸다. 자기 역할에 완전히 몰입해 있는 치카에게서 나는 굉장한 감명을 받았다. 연기를 잘하고 못하고는 나랑 상관없었다. 그저 그토록 몰두할 수 있는 자기만의 인생을 살아가는 그녀가 나는 진심으로 부러웠다.

"어땠어?"

공연이 끝나자마자 치카는 재빨리 옷을 갈아입고 나왔다. 분장이 지워진 그녀의 얼굴은 다시 '내가 알던 치카'로 돌아와 있었다.

"응, 너무너무 재미있었어!"

"정말? 아, 기분 좋다!"

치카의 뺨이 붉게 상기되었다. 그러고는 "단원들하고 뒤풀이가 있으니까 나중에 가게에서 만나!" 하며 서둘러 분장실로 되돌아갔다. 나는 치카의 뒷모습을 바라보며 그 자리에 한참 서 있었다.

'치카한텐 자기 무대가 있구나.'

호스티스들은 저마다 화려하게 살기 위해, 아이를 키우기 위해, 해외 유학을 가기 위해, 혹은 자기 가게를 열기 위해 대부분 투잡으로 일을 한다. 나 역시 낮엔 파견사원, 밤엔 호스티스로 일하고 있지만, 치카처럼 목적과 수단을 동시에 수행하는 건 아니다. 나에게는 두 가지 일 모두 '라스베이거스에서의 화려한 마지막'을 위한 수단일 뿐이다. 솔직히 라스베이거스 행 역시 인생의 목적이라고 말하기엔 너무 한시적이다. 나에게 그 다음은 없다. 그러니까 지금 나를 살아가게 만드는 힘은 1년짜리 시한부 에너지인 셈이다.

하지만 치카는 그렇지 않다. 늘 활기차고 에너지 넘치는 그녀의 힘은 연극이라는 인생의 목적과 호스티스라는 수단을 동시에 추구하는 데에서 나오고 있다. 바닷가의 아름다운 음악 카페를 꿈꾸는 레이나의 힘 역시 마찬가지다. '자기 무대'를 가진 사람 특유의 자신감과 지속적인 당당함, 그런 것들이 나에게는 없다. 외톨이는 사람들로부터 소외됐기 때문이 아니라, 자기 무대를 만나지 못했기 때문에 외톨이인 것이다. 라스베이거스에 가겠다는 집념은 변함없지만, 솔직히 그들이 너무 부럽다.

사람들은 긴 학창시절 동안 참 많은 것을 배운다. 수없이 시험을 치르고 성적을 올리고 많은 공부를 한다. 그리고 사회에 나와 직장을 구하고 열심히 일을 한다. 하지만 그 모든 과정도 대부분 인생의 수단을 갖기 위한 것에 불과하다. '그 다음'은 가르쳐 주지 않고, 또 그럴 수도 없다. 그것은 자기 안에서 찾아야 하기 때문이다.

나는 그것을 찾지 못했다. 만일 텔레비전 화면에서 라스베이거스를 만나지 못했더라면 그나마 지금 같은 시간도 갖지 못했을 것이다.

단 한 걸음만 내디뎌도
두려움은 사라진다

D-9개월.

어느 날 마담이 내게 말했다.

"아마리, 그 드레스 너무 뚱뚱해 보여. 자긴 원래 뚱뚱하니까 좀 더 날씬해 보이는 옷으로 골라 봐. 그리고 그 구두 말이야, 약간 높은 걸로 바꾸는 게 어때?"

기가 팍 꺾였다.

뚱뚱한 여자가 면전에서 '뚱뚱하다'는 말을 직접 듣는 경우는 사실 거의 없다. 실례를 넘어 너무도 잔인한 말이기 때문이다. 하지만 여기서는 이런 말을 아무렇지도 않게 해댄다. 특히 마담은 더욱 그렇다. 이해한다. 왜냐하면 마담에게 호스티스는 일단

'상품'이기 때문이다. 가게를 지탱하는 호스티스들이 예쁜 옷을 입고 있으면 기뻐하고, 어울리지 않는 옷을 입고 있으면 고개를 젓는 게 당연하다. 마담은 내게 '볼에 뭐 묻었네?' 하는 식으로 '너무 뚱뚱해 보이잖아'라는 말을 스스럼없이 한다. 그것 말고도 마담은 시시콜콜한 부분까지 내게 직언을 해준다.

"파운데이션은 꼼꼼히 발라. 들뜨면 보기 싫어."

"립스틱은 좀 더 선명한 색을 골라 봐. 그렇게 칙칙한 색을 바르면 상대방 기분마저 칙칙해지잖아."

엄마한테서도 배운 적이 없는 것들을 여자의 시선으로 일일이 지적해 주는 마담이 가끔은 너무도 자상하게 느껴질 때도 있다.

"담뱃불 붙일 때는 손님이 눈부셔 하지 않게 한 손으론 불을 막고, 다른 손으로 불을 붙이도록 해."

"웃을 때는 입을 크게 벌리지 말고, 손을 입 근처에 대고 우아하게 웃어."

물론 그 모든 세심함이 가게를 유지하기 위한 방침의 일부인 건 사실이지만, 누군가 자신을 위해 매순간마다 꼼꼼히 지적해 준다는 건 고마운 일이다. 다른 곳에서라면 평생 자각하지 못할 것들을 나는 마담에게서 아주 많이 배우는 셈이다.

경력이 많은 호스티스들은 대부분 자기만의 스타일을 갖고 있기 때문에 마담의 충고를 귓전으로 흘려듣기도 한다. 하지만 나

같은 초짜는 뭐든지 "예예" 하고 진지하게 귀담아 들을 수밖에 없다. 그래서인지 마담은 용모도 처지고 술도 못 마시는, 전혀 긴자의 호스티스 같지 않은 나를 어떻게든 보듬어 주려고 애쓴다.

'그래, 새 드레스랑 구두를 장만해야겠어.'

날마다 눈부시게 예쁜 여자들의 패션과 화장을 가까이에서 봐온 터라 나도 점점 눈이 높아지고 있었다. 처음에 주머니를 탈탈 털어 샀던 드레스는 세련 따위와는 정말 거리가 먼 옷이다. 내가 봐도 확실히 뚱뚱해 보였고, 고급스러운 옷으로 휘감은 여러 호스티스들 틈에 서면 너무 생뚱맞아 보였다. 이래선 곤란하다. 마담도 언젠가는 정나미가 떨어져 "아마리, 내일부터 쉬어!"라는 말을 하게 될지 모른다. 실제로 마담 눈 밖에 나서 잘린 호스티스들도 여러 명 있었다. 마담의 말투는 온화하지만 토를 달 수 없는 카리스마가 있다.

그래, 마담은 자선사업을 하는 게 아니다. 경영자인 것이다.

그러니까 나도 앞으로 계속 긴자에서 일하며 돈을 모으려면 어쩔 수 없이 좋은 옷을 장만해 둬야만 한다. 그런데 문제는 앞으로 9개월 안에 많은 돈을 모아야 한다는 점이다.

나는 딜레마에 빠졌다. 계획했던 대로 돈을 모으려면 호스티스 일을 계속해야 하고, 그러자면 드레스며 구두며 자기 투자를 지속적으로 해야만 하는 것이다. 하지만 내가 계획한 라스베이거스 일정은 7일이며, 경비는 200만 엔이다. 거기서 원 없이 호화롭게 보내려면 조금이라도 빨리, 더 많이 자금을 불려야 한다.

밤낮으로 일하고 지출을 최소화해도 현재 통장 잔고는 아직 30만 엔을 못 넘고 있다. 나는 초조했다. 앞으로 9개월 안에 최소한 170만 엔을 더 모을 수 있을까? 이 상태론 불가능하다. 하루 세 끼와 원룸 유지비용은 극단적으로 줄여야 하고, 휴일과 주말을 이용해서 또 다른 일을 해야만 한다.

며칠 동안 남모르게 고민하고 있을 때, 마침 메구미가 말을 걸어 왔다. 치카의 극단 후배인 메구미 역시 배우의 길을 걷고 싶어 한다. 그녀는 언제 어떤 역할을 맡아도 능숙하게 해낼 수 있도록 날마다 다양한 캐릭터를 공부하고 있었다. 나보다 세 살 아래인 스물여섯이지만 레이나처럼 그녀 역시 싱글맘으로, 생활을 위해 밤에는 호스티스 일을, 낮에는 댄스 스쿨에서 댄스를 가르치고 있었다. 내가 돈 문제로 고민하고 있다는 사실을 어떻게 알았는지 메구미는 내게 '수지맞는 아르바이트'를 알려줬다. '수지맞다'는 대목에서 나는 잔뜩 구미가 당겼다.

"어떤 일인데? 설마 불법 같은 건 아니겠지?"

"누드모델이야."

"누드모델…… 옷 벗는 그 누드모델?"

"응, 미대생들 앞에서 나체로 포즈만 취하면 돼."

미술계에는 모델 전문 에이전시가 있는데, 메구미도 그곳 소속이라고 했다.

"꽤 짭짤한 아르바이트야. 두 시간에 1만 엔. 해볼래?"

나더러 사람들 앞에서 발가벗으라고?

"못 해! 죽어도 못 해!"

나는 딱 잘라 거절했다.

"왜?"

"왜라니?"

나는 그녀가 '왜?' 하고 천진한 눈빛으로 물어 오리라고는 상상도 못 했다.

"창피해……."

그러자 메구미는 타이르듯 말했다.

"거기 사람들은 여자 몸을 보러 오는 게 아니야. 나체를 모티브로 데생 기술을 연마하려는 것뿐이야."

물론 그렇겠지. 하지만 메구미처럼 몸매가 좋다면 모를까, 나조차도 쳐다보기 싫은 이런 몸을 사람들 앞에 죄다 드러내놓을 수는 없는 노릇 아닌가.

"너야 몸매도 늘씬하고 얼굴도 예쁘지만 난……."

"비너스가 S라인이디?"

"무슨 소리야?"

"누드모델은 의외로 통통한 사람이 인기가 좋아."

"정말?"

의외였다. 모델은 당연히 늘씬해야만 한다고 믿었는데.

"오히려 너 같은 체형이 더 수요가 많기도 해. 그리고 그게 말이야, 처음엔 죽기보다 싫겠지만 하다 보면 재미도 있거든."

그녀의 태평스러운 웃음을 보고 있자니 왠지 저항감이 사라지는 것 같았다. 마음 한 구석에서는 '정말 이런 체형도 필요로 할까?' 하는 호기심마저 생겨났다.

"한번, 해볼까……?"

"해볼래?"

머뭇머뭇, 쭈뼛쭈뼛, 한참 망설이다 나는 작심하고 고개를 끄덕였다. 메구미는 생긋 웃었다.

"그래, 알았어. 내가 사무실 가서 얘기해 놓을게."

메구미가 나간 뒤에도 내 가슴은 쉴 새 없이 콩닥거렸다.

❖ ❖ ❖

그 다음 주 토요일, 드디어 사람들 앞에서 옷을 벗는 날이다.

'아아, 말도 안 돼!'

긴자의 클럽에서 일하기 시작하면서부터 나는 거의 매일같이

'생전 처음'이라는 말을 달고 살 만큼 낯선 경험들을 많이 해왔다. 하지만 그 어떤 일도 누드모델만큼 두렵지는 않았다. 메구미한테 해보겠다고는 했지만, 나는 여전히 마음의 준비를 못 한 채 기어코 디데이를 맞았다.

'부모님은 뭐라고 하실까?'

생각이 거기에 미치자 가슴 한 구석이 저려 왔다. 좁은 집에서 아버지의 휠체어를 밀고 있는 엄마의 모습이 떠올랐다. 도망치듯 집을 뛰쳐나간 딸이 호스티스와 누드모델 일을 하고 있다는 사실을 안다면 두 분 모두 기절해 버리지 않을까. 물론 나쁜 일을 하는 건 결코 아니다. 그래도 왠지 스스로 완전히 떳떳해지기는 힘들다.

나는 우울한 심정으로 한 걸음, 두 걸음 문화센터로 향했다. 200미터도 채 안 되는 길인데 너무나도 멀고 아득하게 느껴졌다. 가다가 멈추고, 또 가다가 멈추고, 몇 번이나 다시 돌아갈까도 생각했다. 하지만 한 번 약속한 것을 깨뜨릴 수는 없었다. 메구미의 얼굴에 먹칠을 할 수는 없지 않은가.

'아냐, 아무래도 누드모델은 아닌 것 같아. 돌아가자, 가서 메구미한테 백배사죄하자.'

그러는 동안, 어느새 눈앞에 '크로키 교실'이라고 적힌 간판이 떡하니 나타났다.

'아, 기어코 와버렸구나!'

나는 잠시 꼼짝 않고 서 있었다.

한 걸음이 문제다. 여기서 앞으로 한 걸음 내딛는 것과 뒤로 한 걸음 물러나는 것은 엄청난 차이가 있다. 느닷없이 '한 인간에게는 작은 걸음이지만 인류에게는 커다란 도약'이라던 닐 암스트롱의 말이 떠올랐다.

'그런데 그게 이거하고 무슨 상관인데? 과연 지금 내가 디디게 될 한 걸음이 내 운명의 커다란 도약이 될 수 있을까?'

그때 마음속에서 또 다른 목소리가 들려왔다.

'어차피 죽을 거잖아. 쓸데없는 감상 따윈 집어치워!'

그래, 지금 나에게 필요한 것은 돈이다. 단지 옷을 벗고 서 있기만 해도 1만 엔을 받을 수 있다. 갑자기 머릿속에 휘황찬란한 라스베이거스의 풍경이 떠올랐다. 그곳에서 화려하게 돈을 뿌리는 내 모습을 그려 본다. 가슴이 설렌다. 뭐든 할 수 있을 것 같은 대담한 기운이 불끈불끈 솟기 시작한다.

나는 마음을 독하게 먹고 문을 열었다. 교실을 연상케 하는 30평 정도의 공간이 펼쳐져 있었다. 판자를 붙인 바닥에는 흰 캔버스를 올린 이젤이 줄지어 있었다. 그 앞에 앉아 대기 중이던 20명 남짓 되는 학생들의 시선이 일제히 내게로 집중되었다. 나는 피가 거꾸로 치솟는 것을 느끼며 교실 옆에 있는 작은 대기실로 허둥지둥 들어갔다.

아무도 없는 빈방에 나는 멍하니 서 있었다. 그리고 잠시 후 머릿속의 온갖 생각들을 외면한 채 '무념무상'의 상태가 되어 옷을 벗기 시작했다. 알몸뚱이가 되는 건 금방이었다. 사무실에서 일러준 대로 속옷을 느슨하게 입은 덕분에 몸에 속옷 자국은 나 있지 않았다. 나는 벌거벗은 채 문틈으로 교실을 엿보았다.

성별도 연령도 제각각인 학생들이 조용히 대기하고 있었다. 하나같이 진지한 얼굴이었고, 히죽대거나 장난기를 가진 사람은 한 명도 없었다. 내가 수줍어하면 오히려 그들에게 실례가 될 것 같은 진지한 분위기였다. 그 순간, 내가 쭈뼛쭈뼛하게 굴수록 나도 학생들도 민망해질 뿐이라는 생각이 스쳤다. 다이빙 선수가 겁을 먹으면 공포에 지배당해 절대로 뛰어내릴 수 없듯이, 이런 일은 순간적인 담력을 필요로 한다. 나는 심호흡을 하고 문을 열었다. 그리고 오직 나만을 위해 준비한 목욕탕으로 들어가듯이 사뿐사뿐 걸었다.

"잘 부탁합니다."

학생들 앞에서 꾸벅 인사를 한 뒤, 흰 천이 걸린 높은 단 위에 가서 앉았다. 그러고는 '이런 일, 아주 익숙해요'라는 듯 새침한 표정으로 두 손을 머리 뒤에 대고 허리를 꼬아 등줄기를 휘게끔 동작을 취했다.

'나한테 이런 배짱이 있었나?'

솔직히 나 스스로도 놀라웠다.

적막한 공간 속에 멈춘 듯 포즈를 취한 상태에서 나는 사각사각, 학생들의 연필 소리를 들으며 이런 생각을 했다.

'절박함, 인생의 막판에 이르면 정말 생각지도 못한 힘이 솟는 거구나.'

울퉁불퉁 지방 덩어리인 뱃살, 고스란히 드러난 치부…… 하지만 그런 나를 어느 누구도 비웃거나 조롱하지 않았다. 나체의 여성이 그곳에 있는 게 당연하다는 듯 모두들 캔버스에 머리를 박고 데생에 여념이 없다.

두려움이란 건 어쩌면 투명한 막에 가려진 일상인지도 모른다. 그 투명 막을 뚫고 들어가기 전까지는 미치도록 무섭지만, 정작 그 안으로 들어가면 여전히 아무렇지도 않은 또 하나의 평범한 세계가 펼쳐져 있기 때문이다. 불과 15분 전만 해도 내가 사람들 앞에서 옷을 벗는다는 건 공포 그 자체였다. 하지만 지금은 내가 생각해도 놀라우리만치 급속도로 익숙해져 가고 있다.

'하긴, 미술 교과서에서 봤던 서양 누드화 주인공들도 다들 나처럼 풍만했었지.'

사실 '풍만'과 '펑퍼짐'은 엄연한 차이가 있지만, 그 정도로 나는 뻔뻔스러워지고 있었다. 다시 몇 분이 흐르자 긴장이 풀리면서 '좋아, 나체에 익숙해지기만 하면 게임 오버다!' 하는 여유마 저 생겨났다.

하지만 나는 아직 누드모델의 진짜 고충을 모르고 있었다. 시간을 확인하려고 시계를 봤더니 겨우 10분이 지났을 뿐이었다. 어라, 벌써부터 몸의 곳곳이 점점 굳어지기 시작한다. 들어 올린 팔과 휘어진 등이 뻐근하게 아파 온다. 평소에 단련이 안 된 데다가 기초 체력마저 형편없다 보니 점점 고통이 심해졌다.

나는 같은 포즈를 계속 취하는 일이 얼마나 힘든 건지 비로소 깨달았다. 땀이 솟아나기 시작한다. 어깨라도 살짝 비틀고 싶지만, 모델은 한번 포즈를 정하면 절대로 바꿔서는 안 된다. 나는 눈싸움을 하듯 시계를 보며, 휴식시간까지 앞으로 몇 초인지 카운트다운을 하기 시작했다.

'애초에 이렇게 어려운 포즈를 취하는 게 아닌데……'

후회해 봤자 이미 엎질러진 물이다.

드디어 15분이 지나고 휴식 신호가 울렸다. 나는 곧바로 손을 내리고 편안한 자세를 취했다. 물에 푹 잠겨 있다가 겨우 숨을 쉴 수 있게 된 느낌이었다. 팔과 등이 욱신거려 참을 수가 없었다.

'이번엔 좀 더 쉬운 포즈를 취해야지.'

하지만 어떤 포즈든 15분 동안 같은 자세를 유지하기란 너무 괴로운 일이다. 휴식 시간이 끝나고 다시 포즈를 취했을 때도 여전히 몸이 부들부들 떨려 왔다. 하지만 아마추어 티가 날까 봐 애써 냉정을 유지했다. 그렇게 땀을 뻘뻘 흘리는 동안 고행 같았던 두 시간이 모두 끝났다. 대기실로 돌아와 옷을 입을 때까지 내 몸은 와들와들 떨리고 있었다. 팔이 뒤로 돌아가지 않아 속옷 후크를 잠글 수 없을 정도였다.

'세상에 만만한 일은 없구나.'

D-5개월

나는 스스로 목숨을 끊고 싶을 만큼 삶에 대한 의욕이 없었다. 그러다 라스베이거스라는 시한부 목표가 생겼고, 오로지 그 목표만을 향해 전력질주하고 있다. 그렇게 6개월이 지나는 동안 조금씩 변화가 생겼다. 모두가 스스로 정해 버린 시한부 목표가 있었기에 가능한 것들이었다.

변하고 싶다면
거울부터 보라

　나는 누드모델 아르바이트가 한 번으로 끝날 줄 알았다. 나 같은 사람을 처음이야 몰라서 썼겠지만, 이제 다시 부를 일은 절대 없을 거라 생각했다. 그런데 신기하게도 계속 모델 의뢰가 들어왔다. 통통한 모델이 의외로 인기 있다더니 정말 메구미 말이 맞다. 주말마다 규칙적으로 일이 잡혔고 때론 하루에만 서너 군데의 아틀리에를 거치기도 했다. 이렇게 잘나가는 모델이 되리라고는 정말 꿈에도 몰랐다. 몸은 고되지만 그래도 수입을 늘릴 수 있어 기뻤다.

　누드모델을 시작한 지 한 달이 되어 가던 어느 날, 사무실에서 알게 된 한 선배 모델과 이야기를 나누다가 어떤 중년 모델에 대한 이야기를 들었다.

"40대 후반의 주부인데 카리스마가 굉장하대."

벗는 순간 베테랑 화가조차 포로가 된다는 전설의 누드모델이란다. 과연 어느 정도이기에 '전설'이라고까지 불리는지 정말 궁금했다. 육체의 미가 절정을 이루는 20대 초반을 지나 40대 후반이라는 나이에 어떤 아름다움을 유지하고 있을까? 정말 만나보고 싶었다.

나는 결국 사무실에다가 '모델 일을 더 잘하기 위해' 그분을 뵙고 싶다고 간청했다. 그리하여 어느 토요일 오후, 그 전설적인 인물을 볼 수 있게 되었다.

나는 데생 교실에서 설레는 마음으로 그녀를 기다렸다. 잠시 후 문이 열리고 그녀가 들어섰다. '잘 부탁합니다!' 하며 쾌활하게 인사를 하는 순간, 나는 고개를 갸우뚱할 수밖에 없었다.

'저 사람이 전설의 모델?'

나이보다 젊고 아름다운 사람일 거라 생각했건만, 그녀는 그저 어디서나 만날 법한 평범한 주부에 불과해 보였다. 특별히 얼굴이 예쁜 것도 아니고(내가 이런 말을 할 주제는 아니지만), 스타일도 평범한 데다 눈에 띄게 섹시하지도 않았다.

그녀는 허리끈을 꽉 조여 맨 얇은 가운을 걸친 채 정해진 위치로 걸어가 물이 든 페트병과 타월을 내려놓았다. 그것도 참 이상

했다. 나는 항상 바로 벗을 수 있는 목욕 가운 같은 것을 걸치고 있다가, 일이 시작되기 직전 대기실에서 미리 가운을 벗고 등장한다. 나뿐만 아니라 대부분의 모델이 그렇게 하고, 사무실에서도 그렇게 가르친다. 전라로 포즈를 취하는 데에는 거부감이 없다손 쳐도, 남들 앞에서 옷을 벗는 과정까지 보인다는 건 아무래도 수치심이 따르기 때문이다. 하지만 그녀는 시간이 되자 허리끈을 풀고 그 자리에서 바로 전라가 되었다. 그리고 너무도 자연스럽게 그 장소에 녹아들었다. 나는 순식간에 교실의 분위기가 싹 달라졌다는 것을 느낄 수 있었다.

'아우라'라는 말은 이럴 때 쓰는 것일까? 몸이야 당연히 모델답게 관리되어 있다 해도 팽팽한 20대의 몸과 비교하면 역시 40대의 완만함이 눈에 띈다. 하지만 그것마저 좋았다. 그리는 사람의 감성에 따라 어떤 표현이라도 가능하게 만드는 폭넓은 관용 같은 것이 느껴지는 몸, 그런 포즈였기 때문이다. '나를 보라!'고 강하게 주장하기보다는 '나는 하나의 피사체이며 당신이 표현할 예술적 소재다!'라는 듯 통달한 모습, 그리하여 그리는 사람으로 하여금 '이 진귀한 재료를 어떻게 요리할까?' 하는 강한 동기를 불러일으키는 달인의 모습이었다.

실제로 학생들이 그린 작품을 보면 소녀에서 노파까지 아주 다양하게 표현되고 있었다. 그리는 사람이 어떤 느낌으로 무엇을 표현했건 그녀 자체와는 차이가 있었지만, 각각의 작품들을 만들어 내는 소재는 오로지 그녀가 아니면 안 되는 것이었다.

아름다운 곡선을 이루는 그녀의 자세는 굉장한 고난이도였다. 나중에 집에서 흉내를 내보기도 했지만, 겉보기에 아름다운 것과는 정반대로 근육의 모든 부분을 사용하는 가혹한 포즈였다. 더구나 그날은 장시간 똑같은 자세를 취해야 하는 고정 포즈였다. 하지만 그녀는 휴식 후에도 전과 다름없는 포즈로 되돌아왔다.

마침내 데생 시간이 모두 끝나자 그녀는 "고맙습니다!" 하며 들어올 때와 마찬가지로 쾌활하게 미소를 지었다. 학생들도 자연스럽게 웃으며 답례했다. 그녀의 발랄한 에너지가 주위로 전파되는 듯했다. 나는 그 행동에 매료되었다.

한 사람의 모델과 수십 명의 학생들이 예술적으로 깊이 동화된 상태에서 신명나는 퍼포먼스를 한 판 끝낸 것이다. 그리고 그 주인공은 바로 모델이었다. 불혹을 넘긴 나이에도 저토록 멋진 여성이 될 수 있다는 사실이 놀랍기만 했다.

마치 한 편의 공연을 감상한 기분으로 건물을 나오다가 다시 그녀를 보게 되었다. 교실에서 엄청난 아우라를 뿜어내던 그 모델은 온데간데없고, 그녀는 다시 40대 후반의 주부로 돌아와 있었다. 그녀는 학생들이 다 떠나고 조용해지자 혼자 벤치에 앉더니 먼 곳을 응시하다가 살며시 눈을 감았다. 잠시 쉬는 걸까, 아니면 명상에 잠긴 걸까?

나는 그녀에게서 오랫동안 시선을 뗄 수가 없었다. 그녀가 벤치에 앉는 순간부터 풍경이 완성된 느낌이었다. 저런 멋은 어디에서 나오는 걸까? 아마 40대 후반에 이르는 시간이 있어야만 가능하겠지.

그 40대 모델을 본 뒤로 나는 거울 앞에 서는 시간이 많아졌다. 모델 아르바이트를 계속할 생각은 없었지만, 그래도 하는 동안에는 조금이라도 나아지고 싶다는 생각이 들었기 때문이다. 나는 서거나 앉거나 누워서 다양한 포즈를 취해 보기도 하고, 장시간 멈춰 있어도 몸에 부담을 주지 않는 생생하고 아름다운 포즈를 연구하기도 했다. 그러면서 나 자신을 보는 시간이 점점 많아졌다.

아름답건 어떻건 사람이 자기 몸을 자주 본다는 건 좋은 일인 것 같다. 자주 보면 볼수록 정이 들기 때문이다. 살찐 몸이 보기 싫은 건 주인이 그 몸을 싫어하기 때문이다. 자기가 자기 몸을 싫어하는데 누군들 좋아해 줄까. 하지만 '통통하긴 해도 그런대로 봐줄 만한 걸?' 하는 마음으로 자기 몸을 대하면 변화가 생긴다. 아닌 게 아니라 거울 앞에서 내 몸을 자주 들여다볼수록 마담이나 동료들한테서 '요즘 보기 좋네? 몸에 신경 좀 쓰나 봐?' 하는 소릴 심심찮게 듣게 되었다.

나는 모델이 되어 포즈를 취하고 있는 동안 하얀 캔버스 위에 다양하게 그려지는 내 몸을 상상하곤 했다. 실제로 학생들에게 그림을 보여 달라고 부탁하기도 했다.

하나같이 뛰어난 작품들이었다. 그런데 신기한 건 어느 것 하나 똑같은 모습이 없다는 점이었다. 나는 내가 그토록 다양하게 표현될 수 있다는 사실에 놀랐다. 마리아 상처럼 온화한 표정의 나, 험악한 표정의 나, 삶의 고단함이 묻어나는 우울한 나, 뭔가를 간절하게 원하는 나…….

'같은 시간, 같은 포즈, 같은 표정의 나를 보고 있는데 그리는 사람에 따라 이렇게 달라질 수 있구나.'

내가 알고 있는 나는 하나뿐이지만, 남들이 보는 나는 천차만별이었다. 사실 그림 속의 나는 '나'이면서 또한 내가 아니었다. 내가 느끼는 나와 남이 느끼는 내가 같지 않기 때문이다.

나는 늘 내가 알고 있는 느낌과 나의 기준대로 이해받길 원했다. 그러다 보니 자연히 '왜 아무도 날 이해해 주지 않을까?' 하고 의기소침해질 때가 많았다. 하지만 그들의 작품을 보면서 생각과 느낌은 십인십색, 사람의 숫자만큼 다르다는 것을 알았다.

그러니 나와 똑같은 느낌을 요구하거나 이해해 달라는 것은 무리이고 어리광이며, 오만일지도 모른다.

사람은 진정한 의미에서 타인을 완전히 이해할 수는 없다. 다만 나에 대한 남들의 느낌을 긍정적으로, 혹은 부정적으로 바꿀 수 있을 뿐이다. 매일매일 거울 앞에서 나 스스로를 애정 어린 눈으로 바라보는 것만으로도 클럽 사와의 마담과 동료들로부터 긍정적인 반응을 끌어낸 것처럼.

그 뒤로 나는 데생 시간이 끝나고 나면 학생들의 그림을 꼬박꼬박 감상하는 습관이 생겼다. 현재의 나를 반영한 그림들을 통해서 역으로 나를 보는 것이다. 우울하고 음침한 모습보다 밝고 아름다운 모습이 많이 그려진 날은 은근히 기분이 좋아지곤 한다. 재미있는 것은 거울 앞에서 내가 만족스러운 기분을 많이 느낄수록 그림 역시 밝은 분위기가 더 많다는 사실이다.

D-8개월, 시간은 계속 전진하고 있었다.

뜻밖의 변화를 불러오는
데드라인

D-7개월.

계절은 어느새 겨울의 문턱으로 접어들고 있다. 낮에는 파견 사원, 밤에는 호스티스로 일하고 집에 돌아오면 새벽 1시, 그리고 주말 내내 누드모델로 아틀리에를 순회하느라 계절이 가는 것조차 느낄 겨를이 없었다.

단 하루의 휴일도 없이 평균 4시간의 수면으로 악전고투하고 있다. 하릴없이 어영부영 보냈던 지난날들이 꿈처럼 아득하기만 하다. 끈기도 없고 체력도 평균 이하였던 내가 이렇게 악바리처럼 버텨내고 있다는 게 믿어지지 않았다.

그저 바쁘기만 한 생활이었다면 일찌감치 나가떨어졌을지도 모른다. 하지만 내겐 너무도 선명하고 절대적인 목표가 있었다. 그 목표를 향해 전속력으로 질주하면 할수록 아드레날린이 분비되어 힘이 솟았다. 더 좋은 것은 이렇게 바쁘게 지내다 보면 고독이니 뭐니 하는 나약한 감상에 빠져들 겨를이 없다는 것이다. 게다가 나는 일 이외에도 개인적으로 해야 할 일이 많았다.

먼저 라스베이거스와 갬블에 대해 철저히 조사해야만 했다. 라스베이거스와 관련된 책이나 카지노에 관한 책은 닥치는 대로 읽고, 틈만 나면 저렴한 넷카페에 가서 최신 정보를 조사했다. 라스베이거스 여행을 위해 영어 회화도 시작했고, 트럼프를 갖고 다니며 카지노 게임을 연습하느라 날밤을 새기도 했다. 주중에 한 번 있는 호스티스 휴일은 물론 출퇴근 시간 등 자투리 시간도 최대한 이용했다.

조금이라도 돈을 아끼려고 도서관을 찾아가 여행 회화 책을 빌려 보거나, 듣기용 CD와 비디오 등을 활용하기도 했다. 평일에는 퇴근 후 회사에서 가장 가까운 도서관으로 달려갔고, 주말이나 휴일에 누드모델 일이 일찍 끝나면 집 근처 도서관으로 직행했다. 또 자격증이 있으면 시급이 올라간다는 말에 파견처에서 추천하는 간단한 자격증 시험까지 준비했다. 라스베이거스 행 자금을 가능한 한 더 많이 모으고 싶었기 때문이다.

이런 혹독한 일정으로 인해 당연히 몸이 상했지만, 결근은 물론 지각조차 한 번도 하지 않았다. 몸살을 앓더라도 회사 휴게실에서, 클럽 대기실에서 혼자 몰래 앓았다. 내가 그렇게까지 독해질 수 있었던 것은 밤과 낮을 구분하는 경계선을 철저히 지켜 내고 싶었기 때문이다.

평범한 회사원으로 일하는 낮의 세계, 그리고 화려한 호스티스로 살아가는 밤의 세계, 나는 비록 이 두 개의 세계를 넘나들고 있지만 어느 한쪽이라도 다른 쪽 업무로 인해 침해받게 하고 싶지 않았다. 밤의 세계로 인한 피로가 낮의 세계를 망쳐서도 안 되고, 낮의 세계로 인한 시간 부족이 밤의 세계에 영향을 끼쳐도 곤란하다.

특히 밤의 세계는 너무나 매력적이고 개성이 강해 인생의 모든 것을 빨아들일 것 같은 마력이 있었다. 실제로 투잡을 병행하다가 밤일 때문에 낮일을 완전히 저버리게 되는 호스티스들도 많았다. 그건 마치 '아직은 괜찮아, 괜찮아' 하며 노를 저어가다가 어느 한 순간 망망대해에 휩쓸려 두 번 다시 뭍으로 돌아올 수 없게 되어 버리는 조각배와도 같았다. 나는 그것을 피하고 싶었다.

남다른 미모도 재능도 없는 내가 앞으로 계속 밤의 세계에서 버틸 수 없다는 것은 잘 알고 있다. 어디까지나 호스티스 일은 1년 동안만 하는 시한부 아르바이트다. 그렇기 때문에 어떤 경우라도 낮일을 완벽하게 처리하는 것이 내가 밤의 세계로 말려들지 않게 하는 버팀목이라고 생각했다. 그 결과 나는 마치 지킬박사와 하이드처럼 낮과 밤이 완전히 다른 사람으로 변해 갔다.

밤이 되어 긴자의 네온사인이 불을 밝히면 한껏 멋을 부리지만, 회사에서는 주위의 시선 따윈 전혀 의식하지 않는다. 늘 잠이 부족하기 때문에 화장할 시간이 있으면 잠을 잤고, 막 깨어나 퉁퉁 부은 눈에는 렌즈도 들어가지 않아 민낯에 안경을 쓰고 부스스한 머리를 질끈 동여맨 채 출근하기도 했다. 하기야 내 업무란 게 종일 책상에서 데이터를 입력하는 일이라 애초에 멋 부릴 필요도 없었다.

점심시간에는 부리나케 밥을 먹고 동료들과 차 한 잔 마실 틈도 없이 여직원 휴게실에서 토막잠을 잤다. 이마에 눌린 자국이 선명하게 찍힌 내 얼굴을 보고 사람들은 흠칫했지만, 나는 아랑곳하지 않고 자리로 돌아와 묵묵히 일을 처리했다.

데이터를 입력하는 건 한눈만 팔지 않으면 정시에 끝나는 일이지만 월말에는 아주 바빴다. 입력하는 양도 평소의 배가 되기 때문에 나의 전임자는 항상 2시간 정도 야근을 했다고 한다. 하지만 나는 클럽에 지각할 수 없기 때문에 무슨 수를 써서라도 시간 내에 그 일을 마쳐야만 했다. 그럴 때면 이마에 자국이 찍힌 채 평소보다 맹렬한 기세로 홀린 듯 키보드를 두드린다. 그런 내 모습은 내가 봐도 섬뜩할 정도였다. 하지만 겉모습 따윈 아무래도 상관없다. 어쨌든 일을 빨리 마치고 싶다는 일념으로 나는 엄청난 속도로 일을 처리했다. 주위에서 말도 못 붙일 만큼 집중했기에 실수도 거의 없었다.

회사 사람들은 내가 야근을 한사코 용납하지 않는 속사정을 알 리가 없기에 나를 '아주 개성적(?)이지만 일은 똑 부러지게 하는' 파견사원으로 평가하고 있었다.

D-6개월.

어느덧 반 년이 훌쩍 지난 어느 날, 마담이 나를 보더니 깜빡 잊고 있었다는 듯 말했다.

"세상에, 아마리. 언제 이렇게 예뻐졌어?"

"에이, 농담하지 마세요."

"농담 아니야. 거울 좀 봐."

마담은 내 손을 잡아끌더니 전신 거울 앞에 세웠다.

"자, 봐! 정말 날씬하고 예쁘잖아!"

거울에 비친 내 모습은 확실히 몇 달 전과는 달라져 있었다. 하긴 매일매일 그렇게 지독한 강행군을 하는데 살이 안 빠질 수야 없겠지. 그건 나 자신도 느끼고 있었다. 옷 사이즈가 XL에서 M으로 두 사이즈나 줄었던 것이다. 몸무게도 20킬로그램이나 줄어 있었다. 아직 날씬한 정도는 아니지만 53킬로그램이면 그런대로 봐줄 만하지 않은가.

마담은 처음에 했던 약속을 잊지 않고 있었다.

"좋았어, 이제 일급을 1만 엔으로 올려 줄게. 잘했어!"

"감사합니다, 감사합니다!"

나는 뛸 듯이 기뻤다. 이제 한 달에 16만 엔 정도의 급여를 받을 수 있다. 라스베이거스로 성큼 더 다가간 느낌이었다.

살이 빠지면서 뜻하지 않던 일들이 뒤따랐다. 손님의 유혹이 눈에 띄게 늘기 시작한 것이다. 호스티스는 자신의 손님과 개점 전에 만나 식사를 하고 가게로 동행하는 '동반'이나, 폐점 후 함께 다른 클럽에 놀러가거나 하는 '애프터' 등의 데이트가 많다. 하지만 평일에 파견사원으로 일하는 처지로선 불가능한 일이다. 그렇다고 클럽 사와에 할당량이 있어 급여에 반영되는 것도 아니다. 그러니 필사적으로 돈을 모아야 하는 나에겐 전부 시간 낭비였다. 그래서 고맙기는 하지만 이런저런 이유를 대가며 손님의 요청을 간곡히 거절했다.

늘 잠이 모자라 낮에도 조각 잠을 자곤 했지만, 1년이라는 여명의 절반을 지나면서부터 새벽에 잠 못 드는 일이 많아졌다. 알수 없는 불안 때문에 가슴이 막막해질 때마다 나는 창문을 열어놓고 멍하니 하늘만 바라봤다.

나는 스스로 목숨을 끊고 싶을 만큼 삶에 대한 의욕이 없었다. 그러다 라스베이거스라는 시한부 목표가 생겼고, 오로지 그 목표만을 향해 전력질주하고 있다. 그렇게 6개월이 지나는 동안 조금씩 변화가 생겼다. 살이 빠지고 '예쁘다'라는 소리도 듣게 되었으며, 일과 돈에 대한 집착과 더불어 가까운 동료들까지 생겼다. 모두가 스스로 정해 버린 시한부 목표가 있었기에 가능한 것들이었다.

나는 새삼 '데드라인'의 가공할 만한 위력에 놀랐다. 하지만 또 그만큼 불안했다. 만일 그 목표가 사라지거나 6개월 뒤 기한이 만료된 이후에도 그것들을 계속 유지할 수 있을까? 자신이 없었다. 라스베이거스 이후의 삶을 아무리 생각해 보려 해도 극지방의 화이트아웃처럼 온통 하얗기만 했다.

나는 여전히 불안했고, '행복'이라는 느낌 역시 나와는 멀리 동떨어져 있는 것 같았다. 그런 생각이 들 때마다 나는 더욱 병적으로 라스베이거스에 매달렸다. 지출을 줄이고 돈을 더 모을 수 있는 방법을 연구하거나 카드를 펼쳐 놓고 블랙잭을 공부했다. 그러다 날이 밝으면 곧장 회사로 달려갔다.

자기 시선으로
살아간다는 것의 즐거움

"걔 말이야. 글쎄 남자 빚 때문에 결국 욕탕으로 간 것 같아."

레이나가 말했다. 동료들은 귀가 솔깃해져서 '정말, 정말?', '어머, 어떡하지?' 하며 호들갑을 떨었다. 하지만 나는 그 말이 무슨 뜻인지 통 알 수가 없었다.

"욕탕은 왜요? 아! 집세 아끼려고 사우나에서 자나 봐요?"

그러자 레이나는 길게 한숨을 내쉬었다.

"정말 모르는 거야, 아니면 내숭 떠는 거야?"

나는 그저 눈만 끔뻑거렸다.

"이 바닥에서 욕탕이란 건 그거야, 그거. 그래도 모르겠어?"

나는 그제야 욕탕이 '사창가'를 칭하는 말이란 걸 알았다.

클럽이란 호스티스와 손님이 서로 밀고 당기기를 즐긴다는 점에서 어디까지나 유사 연애의 장이다. 반드시 그 장소에 한해서만 '신사 숙녀'로 연애를 즐기는 것이다. 더 이상 깊이 들어가는 것은 금기다. 물론 클럽 사와도 그랬다. 하지만 알 수 없는 게 남녀 사이라 자기도 모르게 친밀한 관계가 만들어지기도 한다.

실제로 손님의 연인이 되어 버린 호스티스도 꽤 있다. 클럽 사와는 가족적이면서도 아늑한 분위기를 자랑하지만, 예전에는 조폭이나 건달 같은 남자와 엮여 돌연 가게에서 자취를 감춘 이들도 있었다고 한다.

나는 고개를 절레절레 흔들었다. 남자라면 질색이다. 스물다섯 살 때 겪었던 그 비참했던 연애의 말로를 더 이상 되풀이하고 싶지 않았다.

'조심하자. 더 이상 남자 때문에 인생이 꼬이고 싶진 않아.'

그런 어느 날, 클럽 사와에 한 남자가 나타났다. 내 심장은 반사적으로 격하게 요동쳤다.

'혹시나 했는데 역시나…… 이런 일이 벌어지고 마는구나.'

그는 바로 내가 파견사원으로 근무하고 있는 회사의 사장이었다. 이런 기막힌 우연이 또 있을까.

물론 그런 생각을 전혀 안 해본 건 아니었다. '혹시라도 회사 사람들이 클럽을 찾는 일은 없을까? 그러다 나를 알아보게 되는 일은 없을까?' 하는 상상을 왜 안 해봤겠는가? 그런데 눈앞에 사장이 떡하니 나타난 것이다.

40대 초반인 K사장은 회사에서도 늘 여직원들에게 선망의 대상이었다. 이른 나이에 혼자 힘으로 회사를 세워 성공적으로 경영해 나가고 있을 뿐만 아니라, 연예인 뺨칠 정도의 핸섬한 외모를 지녔기 때문이다. 게다가 학식은 물론 유머와 품위까지 갖췄으니 더할 나위가 없지 않은가? 나는 가끔 '저렇게 우월한 유전자를 타고난 사람도 있구나' 하며 그저 먼발치에서 외계인 보듯 바라볼 뿐이었다.

바로 그가 클럽 사와에 나타난 것이다.

"아마리, 저기 저분 쪽에 보조로 붙어."

마담의 말에 가슴이 철렁했다. 나는 가슴 졸이며 K사장 옆자리에 가서 앉았다. 하지만 행여 눈치 채지나 않을까 하는 내 생각은 순전히 기우에 불과했다. 나는 새도 떨어뜨릴 기세로 급성장하는 기업의 우두머리가 변변찮은 파견사원의 얼굴까지 일일이 기억하고 있을 리가 없었다. 만에 하나 내 얼굴을 기억한다고 한들, 부스스한 머리에 민낯인 사원과 화려한 긴자의 호스티스를 연결시키기란 쉽지 않을 것이다.

역시나 K사장은 나를 전혀 알아보지 못했다. 나는 속으로 휴우, 하고 마음을 놓았다. 그런데 이 씁쓸한 기분은 뭐지?

내 속에서 어떤 생각들이 소용돌이치고 있는지 죽었다 깨어도 알 리가 없는 K사장은, 그저 장난꾸러기 소년처럼 조크를 던지며 호스티스들을 즐겁게 하고 있었다. 단번에 좌중의 시선을 끌어오는 남자, 어느 틈엔가 더 알고 싶고 더 이야기하고 싶게 만드는, 그래서 호스티스마저 사로잡아 버리는 타입의 남자…….

K사장은 능력 있을 뿐만 아니라, 사적으로도 그만큼 매력적인 남자였다. 그런 K사장의 특별한 일면을 접한다는 사실에 나는 묘한 우월감마저 느꼈다.

즐겁던 시간은 금세 지나고 어느새 폐점 시간이 다가왔다. 모두들 이대로 헤어지기가 섭섭하다는 눈치였다. 그때 K사장이 내게 속삭였다.

"애프터 신청해도 될까?"

심장이 쿵쾅거렸다.

'혹시 내가 맘에 들었다는 건가? 아냐, 그냥 내가 옆에 앉아 있으니까 별 생각 없이 해본 말일 거야.'

오버하지 말자. 착각해서 상처 받는 쪽은 나다.

"죄송해요. 내일 일찍 나가 봐야 해서······."

"내일? 낮에도 일하나? 대단한데."

나는 속으로 '그래요, 당신 회사에서 일한단 말이에요' 하고 중얼거렸다. 그런데 K사장은 난처하게도, 아니 고맙게도 그냥 물러서지 않았다.

"그래, 그렇다면 별 수 없군. 사실은 말이야, 아마리가 워낙 잘 들어 줘서 좀 더 얘기를 나눴으면 했거든. 내가 생각해도 이런 말 꺼낸 게 신기하지만 역시 차였구먼."

그런 말까지 듣자 내 마음은 마구 흔들리기 시작했다.

"그럼, 올리비아····· 클럽 올리비아라면."

말을 내뱉고선 아차 싶었다. 클럽 올리비아라면 긴자에서도 최고급 클래스 아닌가. 저명인사들이 은밀히 이용한다는 소문에 호스티스들의 미모 또한 엄청나다고 들었다. 적어도 나 따윈 면접조차 안 받아줄 정도의 일류 클럽이라 은근히 동경하던 곳이었다. 기회가 된다면 그곳에 한 번쯤은 가보고 싶었던 차에 순간적으로 '올리비아'라는 말이 튀어나오고 만 것이다. K사장이 되물었다.

"올리비아?"

너무 뜻밖이었던 걸까, 아니면 놀란 걸까? 아니면····· 그저 기가 막혔던 걸까.

"죄송해요. 호스티스로서 다른 가게를 봐두는 것도 좋은 경험이 될 것 같아 저도 모르게 그만…… 신경 쓰지 마세요. 농담이에요."

나는 이 상황이 얼른 끝나기만을 바랐다. 하지만 K사장은 잠시 생각하더니 차분하게 말했다.

"전에 가끔 거래처 사람을 따라 가본 적이 있어. 어차피 내가 먼저 제안했으니까 어때, 올리비아에 한번 가볼까?"

그렇게 나의 첫 애프터 체험은 급작스럽게 진행되었다.

휘황찬란한 네온이 춤추는 긴자 거리는 매서운 겨울바람에도 불구하고 많은 사람들로 북적이고 있었다. 평소라면 전철역을 향해 날쌔게 달려가고 있을 테지만 오늘은 다른 목적지를 향해 걷고 있다. 그것도 '낮의 세계'에 속하는 회사의 사장과 함께.

클럽 올리비아는 클럽 사와 같은 조촐한 곳과는 비교가 안 될 만큼 넓었다. 흰 색을 바탕으로 한 산뜻한 내부는 호화로우면서도 세련된 느낌이었고, 곳곳에 큰 화병이, 벽에는 회화가 장식되어 있었으며, 실내 전체에 그랜드피아노의 라이브 연주가 은은하게 흐르고 있었다. 마담이 3명, 상주하는 호스티스는 40명쯤 돼 보였다. 나처럼 어설픈 솜씨로 머리를 직접 손질한 호스티스 따윈 없었다. 함께 자리에 앉은 두 명의 호스티스는 나란 존재 때문에 난처한 기색이었다. 긴자 클럽에 여자 손님이 등장하는 일은 좀처럼 없기 때문이다.

"귀여운 아가씨군요."

호스티스는 K사장의 속을 떠보려 하지만 사장도 만만치 않다.

"그렇지? 아무리 유혹해도 좀처럼 넘어오질 않네."

호스티스들은 K사장과 이야기를 나누면서도 시종일관 힐끔거리며 나의 정체를 읽으려는 눈치였다. 나는 나대로 긴자 최고 클럽의 호스티스들이 어떤 식으로 대화를 하는지 귀를 열고 집중했다. 긴자의 일류 호스티스들은 경제신문이나 시사 잡지를 읽는다는 소문을 익히 들어왔던 터라 얼마나 고상한 대화를 나누게 될지 내심 기대했던 것이다.

하지만 별 소득은 없었다. 적어도 내가 받은 인상은 그저 '비싼 고급 클럽'일 뿐이었다. 계산할 때 슬쩍 엿보았더니 클럽 사와의 세 배 정도는 되는 듯했다. 물론 K사장에게는 대수롭지 않은 돈이겠지만 난 너무 아까웠다.

'이렇게 비싼 돈을 지불하지 않아도 클럽 사와에서는 손님을 훨씬 즐겁게 해줄 수 있는데……. 하기야 고급 브랜드라는 이유만으로도 손님을 끌 순 있겠지. 그런데 '고급'이란 대체 뭘까?'

그런 생각을 눈치 챘는지 그는 가게를 나오자마자 내게 물었다.

"어땠어? 그렇게 보고 싶다던 일류 클럽은?"

나는 솔직하게 대답했다.

"일류라는 포장에 너무 기대를 너무 많이 했나 봐요. 기대만큼은 아니었어요. 인테리어에 굉장히 많은 돈을 들인 것 같고 호스티스도 미인들이지만, 그것만으로 일류라고 하기에는……."

"동감이야."

K사장은 나를 향해 씩 웃더니 마치 오랜 친구에게 하듯 진지하게 얘기하기 시작했다.

"뭐든 그렇겠지만 일류니 고급이니 하는 말은 늘 조심해야 해. 본질을 꿰뚫기가 어려워지거든. 출세니 성공이니 하는 것보다 중요한 것은 자기만의 잣대를 갖는 거라고 생각해. 세상은 온통 허울 좋은 포장지로 덮여 있지만, 그 속을 들여다볼 수 있는 자기만의 눈과 잣대만 갖고 있다면, 그 사람은 타인의 평가로부터 자신을 해방시키고 비로소 '자기 인생'을 살 수 있을 거야. 그게 살아가는 즐거움 아닐까?"

K사장은 시계를 보더니 '어이쿠, 늦었네' 하면서 내게 집이 어느 방향이냐고 물었다. 태워 줄 기세였다.

"아주 가까워요. 혼자 갈 수 있어요. 오늘 정말 고마웠습니다."

K사장과 헤어져 집까지 오는 동안 나는 줄곧 그가 했던 말을 되뇌었다.

'자기만의 잣대……'

아주 잠깐 동안이었지만, 라스베이거스에서 화려한 마지막을 장식하고 미련 없이 떠나려는 나의 계획이 처음으로 흔들리는 느낌이었다. 사장에게 나의 계획을 얘기하면 어떤 반응이 돌아올까? 그만, 그만! 나는 생각하지 않기로 했다. 무슨 일이 있어도 나의 계획은 확고부동하게 진행되어야 한다.

좁고 어둑어둑한 원룸으로 돌아와 옷을 갈아입고 누웠더니 새벽 3시였다. 몸은 축 늘어질 정도로 피곤했지만 잠은 쉽사리 오지 않았다.

'살아가는 즐거움이라……'

타인의 평가와 세간의 잣대와는 아무런 상관없는 자기만의 삶이란 과연 어떤 것일까?

그날 이후로 K사장은 클럽에 들를 때마다 내게 애프터를 신청했다.

"아마리, 오늘도 딱 한 잔만 말동무 해주면 안 될까?"

솔직히 나는 어안이 벙벙했다.

설마…… 이 인기 많은 꽃중년이 나를 마음에 들어 한 걸까?

K사장은 나를 올리비아 클럽 같은 '공공장소'가 아닌 자기만의

단골 바로 데려갔다. 거긴 뭔가 비밀스럽고 특별한 사연을 가진 남녀의 밀회에나 어울릴 법한 곳이었다. 사장은 어딘지 베일에 가려 있는 듯한 나의 본모습을 알고 싶어 했다.

"낮엔 회사원이라고? 어느 회사에 다녀?"

그때마다 대충 얼버무리느라 여간 고생이 아니었다. 하지만 내가 피하면 피할수록 사장의 호기심만 자극하는 꼴이었다.

"아마리는 꼭 신데렐라 같아."

"예?"

"낮엔 어디서 뭘 하는지 전혀 모르겠거든."

나는 (마담이 가르쳐 준 대로) 손으로 입을 가리고 웃었다. 그렇다면 나를 공주로 변신시켜 준 마녀는 사와의 마담이겠지? 그리고 밤이 지나고 해가 뜨면 나를 치장해 준 온갖 의상과 화장은 다 사라지고 다시 '별 볼 일 없는' 파견사원으로 돌아가 있겠지?

사장과 이야기를 나누는 동안, 나는 그가 왜 나를 말벗으로 선택했는지 어렴풋이 짐작할 수 있었다. 어느 조직이나 그렇듯이 최고결정권자 위치에 있는 사람들은 의외로 고독한 경우가 많다. 하루에도 수십 명을 상대해야 하고, 늘 냉정한 판단과 단호한 결단을 요구하는 치열한 시간을 견뎌야 하는 것이 그들의 숙명이다. 그리고 회사의 운명을 결정지을 수도 있는 최종 결정은 늘 혼자 해내야 한다. 얼마나 고독한 일인가? 사장이 만나는 거의 모든 사람들은 늘 무언가를 부탁하거나 의사를 묻는 등 일방통행 같은 대화만을 하게 마련이다.

"그런데 아마리는 내게 한 번도 질문을 하지 않더군. 그냥 잠자코 내 이야기를 듣기만 하지. 난 그게 참 편해."

그렇게 몇 번의 만남이 거듭되면서 나 역시 K사장에게 점점 끌리고 있다는 사실을 알았다. 회사에서는 눈길조차 받지 못할 만큼 먼 존재인 그에게서 나는 아무도 모르는 여리고 순진한 모습을 보았다. 그리고 산전수전 다 겪어 온 사업가의 생생한 인생론은 죽음까지 생각했던 나의 혼을 자극하기에 충분했다.

하지만 우리의 관계는 거기까지였을 뿐, 남녀의 애정관계로는 더 이상 발전하지 않았다. '딱 한 잔만'이라는 나의 조건을 존중하려는 듯 K사장은 약속했던 그 한 잔이 비면 "조심해서 들어가"하며 항상 택시비를 슬쩍 쥐어 주곤 했다.

혹시나 관계가 더 가까워질 만한 제안을 하면 어떡하나 하고 늘 조마조마했지만, 사람의 마음이란 게 참 이상해서 혼자 집으로 돌아올 때면 약간 허전한 기분도 느껴졌다. 그래도 난 그 상태가 좋았다. 아주 멀지도, 아주 가깝지도 않으면서 낮과 밤의 경계처럼 미묘한 거리를 유지하는 것이 내게도, 그에게도 가장 이상적이다.

스물다섯 살 때 남자친구와 헤어진 뒤로 쭉 여자인 것을 잊고

살았다. 살이 찌면서부터는 아예 여자로서도 끝났다는 생각을
했었다. 그래서 나를 배려하는 사람이 있다는 사실만으로도 가
슴이 벅찼다. 가끔은 '애인'이라는 말이 머릿속에 떠올랐다. 남자
한테 휘둘리는 인생은 딱 질색인데도 이따금 '그러면 뭐 어때!'라
는 생각을 하게 되는 나 자신이 두렵기도 했다.

길 위에 올라선 자는
계속 걸어야 한다

따지고 보면 K사장과 나의 관계는 정말 아무것도 아니다. 그저 손님과 종업원의 관계가 조금 연장된 것에 불과했다. 혼자 설레건 말건 그건 순전히 내 몫이며, 친구처럼 서로 말벗이 되어주는 것만으로 충분했다. 하지만 이런 소박하고 점잖은 관계마저도 결코 쉽지 않다는 것을 알게 되었다.

D-5개월.

여느 때처럼 K사장과 '딱 한 잔만' 함께 한 다음 날, 나는 늘 그렇듯 푸석푸석한 민낯으로 출근했다. 그런데 분위기가 이상했다. 여직원들이 나를 힐끗힐끗 쳐다보며 소곤대는 것이었다.

"에이, 설마 그럴 리가."

"그럼 본인한테 직접 물어볼까?"

아무리 모른 척해도 자꾸 귀가 근질근질했다. 불길한 예감과 동시에 섬뜩한 느낌이 몰려왔다. 예감은 적중했다. 화장실 앞 복도에서 나는 어느 여직원과 딱 마주쳤다.

"어제 긴자에 갔었죠?"

역시……. 나는 선 채로 얼어붙고 말았다. 하지만 마음의 동요를 억누르며 애써 시치미를 뗐다.

"거길 내가 왜 가요? 잘못 봤겠죠."

"사장이랑 같이 가지 않았어요? 코트도 똑같고, 분명히 봤는데……."

같은 여자지만 감각이 정말 예리하다. 머리를 세팅하고 짙은 화장을 하고 있어도 역시 날 알아본 것이다. 하지만 어떡하든 끝까지 시치미를 떼야 한다. 그녀의 기억을 가로막듯 나는 다급하게 말했다.

"흔한 옷이잖아요. 나도 똑같은 코트 입은 사람 많이 봤어요."

"…… 그런가? 그렇죠? 그럴 리가 없겠죠?"

그녀는 그제야 고개를 끄덕이며 "이상한 걸 물어서 미안해요" 하고는 자리로 되돌아갔다. 그녀 역시 반신반의한 게 틀림없다. 그도 그럴 것이 두꺼운 안경에 부스스한 머리, 게다가 거의 민낯으로 다니는 파견사원이 마치 동화 속 신데렐라처럼 밤에만 화려하게 꾸미고 다닌다는 걸 상상하기란 쉽지 않을 것이다. 게다가 모두가 흠모하는 꽃중년 사장과 단둘이 앉아 술을 마실 거라고는…….

아무튼 그녀의 의심은 풀렸지만 진짜 걱정은 그때부터였다.

'만약에 이 소문이 사장 귀에 들어간다면?'

오싹해졌다. 만일 소문이 K사장 귀에 들어가서 뒷조사라도 하게 된다면, 내가 긴자의 아마리라는 사실이 드러나는 건 시간문제일 것이다.

'그럼 분명히 해고당하겠지?'

물론 회사에서 파견사원의 겸업을 금하는 건 아니지만, 그래도 '호스티스'라는 이미지는 환영받을 일이 못 된다. 사장 역시 그런 소문에 휩싸이는 건 바라지 않을 게 틀림없다. 노골적으로 자르지는 않더라도 다음 계약을 갱신할 수 있다는 보장은 없다.

아니, 단지 그뿐만이 아니었다. 솔직히 말하면 나는 계속해서 사장의 '신데렐라'로 남고 싶었다. 하지만 나의 본모습을 안다면 분명 실망하겠지? 물론 퇴근 후 긴자에서 하고 있는 일에 대해 나는 떳떳하다. 그것은 나를 목표점까지 데려다 줄 신성한 직업이니까. 하지만 세상의 시선은 그렇지 않다. 아무리 부정해도 그건 엄연한 사실이지 않은가.

그날 하루, 내 머릿속은 엉킨 실타래처럼 복잡했다. 무거운 마음으로 퇴근한 뒤 다시 변신하여 긴자로 가는 동안, 나는 어느 정도 마음의 정리를 하고 있었다.

'그래, 분위기에 휩쓸려 너무 깊이 들어갔어.'

마음은 아프지만, 나는 앞으로 K사장의 애프터는 받아들이지 않는 것으로 결론을 내렸다. 그런 내막을 알 리가 없는 K사장은 여느 때처럼 나에게 애프터 신청을 해왔다. 나는 준비해 둔 핑계를 댔다.

"죄송해요. 오늘은 다른 애프터가 있어서……."

사실 다른 애프터가 없었던 건 아니지만, 이 말을 꺼내기가 얼마나 힘들었는지 모른다. 미련이 질긴 끈처럼 뒤통수를 계속 끌어당겼다. 더욱 가슴 아픈 건 K사장의 대답이었다.

"그래? 거 참 유감이네…… 뭐 어쩔 수 없지."

그것으로 끝이었다. 그는 약간 씁쓸한 표정을 짓더니 이내 호쾌하게 웃었다. 그 웃음이 내 가슴을 후벼 파는 것만 같았다.

❖ ❖ ❖

K사장의 애프터를 매번 거절하다 보니, 이젠 다른 손님의 애프터를 적극적으로 받아들일 수밖에 없게 되었다. 가능한 한 '아

무 일도 안 생길' 할아버지뻘 되는 손님을 선택하거나, 젊은 남자 손님일 때는 다른 호스티스와 바꾸는 식이었다.

그때부터 참 많은 사람들을 알게 되었다. 하지만 교양과 유머, 재치 같은 면에서 그 누구도 K사장을 대신할 수는 없었다. 이후로 K사장의 발길은 점점 뜸해졌고, 오더라도 주로 다른 호스티스들과 자리를 가졌다. 나는 상실감과 그리움으로 인해 의지가 약해지는 것이 두려웠다. 그래서 더욱 다른 손님들과의 애프터에 좀 더 충실해지려고 애썼다.

클럽을 찾는 손님들은 주로 마담과 오랜 친분관계를 유지해온 사람들이었고, 대부분 자기 분야에서 나름 성공을 거둔 이들이었다.

"혹시 라스베이거스에 가보셨어요?"

가끔 이렇게 물어보면 그들은 흥에 들떠 카지노 이야기를 늘어놓곤 했다. 그들은 비단 라스베이거스뿐만이 아니라, 내가 꿈도 꿔보지 못한 수많은 경험들을 갖고 있었다. 지금껏 너무도 단조로운 생활에 새로운 경험도, 특별한 만남도 없었던 나는 메마른 스펀지처럼 모든 것을 흡수하고 싶어졌다. 그런 어느 날, 단골손님 한 분이 내게 흥미로운 제안을 해왔다.

"아마리, 경마 좋아하나? 한번 같이 가볼래? 마주석에 앉게 해줄게."

그는 꽤 큰 회사의 창업주인 L회장이었다. 물론 나는 경마를 좋아하기는커녕 관심조차 없었다. 경마라면 그저 붉은 펜을 귀에 꽂은 채 한 손에는 경마신문을 들고 고함을 지르는 아저씨들만 떠올랐다.

"여자도 갈 수 있어요?"

그러자 L회장은 껄껄 웃었다.

"물론이지, 요즘은 여성 관중도 아주 많아. 게다가 마주석은 아주 특별하지."

갑자기 호기심이 발동했다. 명사들의 사교장이라는 마주석은 대체 어떤 곳일까? 일반인이 마주석에 앉으려면 마주에게 초대받아 가는 방법 외에는 없다고 했다. 경마에는 관심이 없었지만 특별한 사람들만 누리는 그 세계만큼은 궁금했다.

'나의 호스티스 생활은 딱 1년이다. 가고 싶다면 기회는 지금밖에 없다.'

휴일에 손님과 만난다는 게 조금 걸리긴 했지만, 그날은 마침 누드모델 일도 없었다. 결국 나는 제안을 받아들였다. L회장은 아주 흡족한 표정을 지었다. 아마 나의 어설픔과 순진함이 신선하게 느껴졌던 모양이다.

잘나가는 호스티스들은 다양한 경험을 쌓았기 때문에 웬만한 일에는 놀라지도 않고 마음을 움직이지도 않는다. 그래서 세상

물정 모르는 나의 어수룩함이 L회장의 '가르쳐 주고 싶다'는 욕구를 자극한 것일지도 모른다. 게다가 회장이 말할 때마다 "네? 정말요? 대단하세요!" 하며 가식 없이 감탄사를 연발했던 것도 회장의 마음에 전해지지 않았을까.

아마 클럽 사와의 마담도 그랬을 것이다. 내가 뭐든지 곧이곧대로 흡수할 수밖에 없는 신출내기였기에 일일이 호스티스의 마음가짐과 교양 있는 태도를 가르쳐 주고 또 귀엽게 봐주었겠지.

나는 사람들한테는 '가르쳐 주고 싶은 욕구'가 있다는 사실을 알았고, 그래서 '무지'가 의외로 유리하게 작용한다는 것을 어렴풋이 깨달았다.

생전 처음 경마장에 가던 날.

며칠 동안 '투자' 차원에서 새 옷을 살까 말까 고민하던 차에 이때다 싶어 큰맘 먹고 하늘색 원피스를 샀다. 어차피 라스베이거스에 가서도 제대로 된 옷 한두 벌쯤은 필요할 테니까 과감히 질러 버린 것이다.

L회장을 따라 접수대를 지나 엘리베이터를 타고 올라가자 마주 전용 입구가 나왔다. 수화물 보관소에 짐을 맡긴 뒤 우리는 호텔 라운지 같은 공간에서 잠시 쉬었다. 마주 플로어에는 드레스코드가 있어 남성은 재킷을 걸치거나 슈트 차림인 사람이 많

앉고, 여성 중에는 기모노나 드레스 등으로 한껏 치장한 사람들도 있었다.

"아마리, 직접 마권을 사보는 게 어때?"

L회장이 웃으며 어떤 마권을 사야 하는지 일러줬다. 나는 마권을 사들고 관람석으로 들어섰다. 커다란 유리로 격리되어 시끌벅적한 일반석과는 전혀 다른 고급스러움이 느껴지는 자리였다.

'굉장하다······.'

영화관처럼 넓고 쾌적한 관람석에는 2인용 좌석이 줄지어 있었다. 그리고 좌석마다 작은 모니터가 달려 있어, 다른 경마장에서 치러지는 레이스나 예상 배당 등 여러 정보를 한눈에 확인할 수 있었다. 물론 나 같은 초짜야 다른 레이스까지 볼 수 있는 여유는 없었지만, 회장과 주위 사람들은 한꺼번에 모든 레이스를 보고 즐기는 것 같았다.

드디어 우리를 초대한 마주의 말이 출발선에 모습을 드러냈다. 눈으로 직접 경주마를 보는 순간 나는 눈을 뗄 수가 없었다. 팽팽한 근육질의 다리, 바람에 반짝이는 갈기, 아름다우면서도 긴장감이 가득한 눈동자······ 말이란 동물이 그렇게 아름다운 줄은 미처 몰랐다.

탕!

드디어 레이스가 시작됐다. 두두두, 말발굽 소리와 장내의 함성이 일제히 터져 나왔다. 말들이 앞서거니 뒤서거니 할 때마다 환호와 탄식이 교차했다. 말들이 결승점 앞의 직선 고개를 뛰어 올라갈 때는 경마장 전체가 함성의 도가니로 변했다. 나도 관중들 틈에서 흥분에 들떠 정신없이 응원했다.

바로 그 순간 내 눈에는 아직 가보지 못한, 그러나 곧 가게 될 라스베이거스의 풍경이 오버랩 되었다. 7개월 전 혼자 맞은 스물아홉 번째 생일날, 손목까지 가져갔던 칼을 다시 내려놓고 망연자실 바라보던 텔레비전 속의 라스베이거스 풍경……. 그리고 1년 뒤 라스베이거스에서 인생의 최후를 맞이하기로 결심하던 그때의 그 흥분이 다시 떠오른 것이다. 그때 레이스가 끝났다.

안타깝게도 마주의 말은 패하고 말았다. 1번부터 3번까지 인기 있는 말이 전멸한 대 파란의 레이스였다. 하지만 결과가 나오자 L회장은 만세를 불렀다.

"이겼다! 아마리, 우리가 이겼어!"

이럴 수가! 회장이 일러준 것 말고 내가 감으로 적당히 샀던 마권이 적중한 것이다. 무려 100배 배당권이었다. 나는 어안이 벙벙했다. 단 1,000엔으로 구입한 마권이 순식간에 10만 엔으로 바뀐 것이다. 재미 삼아 나하고 똑같은 마권을 샀던 L회장은 '초보자의 행운'이라며 기뻐했다.

"아마리, 자네가 복덩이로군, 복덩이야!"

나는 또다시 라스베이거스를 생각했다.

그래, 이건 분명 라스베이거스에서의 예행연습이야. 앞으로 반년 뒤 실전에서는 과연 어떤 결과가 나올까?

그 후로도 L회장은 나를 '행운의 여신'이라 부르며 상류사회 사람들이나 드나드는 여러 장소를 구경시켜 주었다. 낮의 세계에서는 상상도 못 할 일들이 밤의 긴자에서는 현실이 된다. 하지만 밤늦게 돌아와 어두운 원룸에 불을 밝히면 '원래의 나'를 만나게 된다. 그리고 야무지게 마음먹은 나의 목표도 선명해진다.

'그래, 라스베이거스다. 지금 이 순간들은 단지 과정에 지나지 않아.'

밤의 호화로운 세계에 빠져 길을 잃어서는 안 된다. K사장과의 달콤한 애프터도, L회장이나 다른 손님들과의 특별한 '상류사회 체험'도 모두 샛길일 뿐이다. 여기에 머무는 순간 라스베이거스는 영원히 도달할 수 없는 곳이 되어 버릴 것이다.

길 위에 올라선 자는 계속 걸어야 할 것이다. 안주하는 순간 길을 잃을지도 모르니까.

D-1개월

나는 지금까지 서른을 코앞에 둔 대부분의 여자들은 결혼과 함께 안정된 생활만을 바라고 있을 거라 생각해 왔었다. 그래서 안정과는 도무지 거리가 먼 나 같은 사람은 세상에 뒤처져 있는 거라고 굳게 믿었다. 그런데 그렇지 않은 사람도 있었다. 세상이 뭐라 하건 자신의 길을 뚜벅뚜벅 나아가는 사람이 있는 것이다.

범선은 타륜과
돛으로 항해한다

D-4개월.

한 통의 엽서가 날아왔다. 고교 동창회 초대장이었다. 졸업하고 10년이 넘도록 매년 그랬듯이 나는 엽서를 테이블 위에 휙 내던졌다. 동창회 따윈 참석한 적도, 그럴 마음도 없었다. 친한 친구도 없고 만나고 싶은 선생님도 없다. 고교시절의 추억…… 그런 게 있었나? 게다가 살이 찐 뒤로는 더욱 주눅이 들어 '대인기피증' 비슷한 지경까지 갔었다. 그러니 동창회가 다 뭔가.

그런데 엽서를 휴지통에 넣으려다가 나도 모르게 멈칫했다.

'이번에 안 나가면 앞으로 영원히 못 볼지도…….'

미련 따윈 남기고 싶지 않았다. 살아 있는 동안 그래도 한 번

정도는 참석해 보는 것도 나쁘지 않을 것 같았다. 어쩌면 그런 생각을 하게 된 데에는 '더 이상 뚱뚱하지 않다'는 자신감도 한몫 했을 것이다.

동창회 날, 나는 라스베이거스에 갈 때 입으려고 사뒀던 새 옷을 꺼내 입고 모임 장소인 호텔로 향했다. 미리 만나기로 약속한 친구는 없었지만, 그래도 혹시 아는 얼굴이 있을까 하고 입구에서 잠시 두리번거렸다. 그때 낯익은 친구와 눈이 딱 마주쳤다.

"야, 정말 오랜만이야!"

3학년 때 같은 반 친구였다. 졸업하고 처음 만나는 건데도 예전 얼굴이 어렴풋이 기억났다.

"너 지금까지 한 번도 안 나왔었지? 어떻게 지내나 모두들 궁금해 했어."

나 말고는 다들 꼬박꼬박 참석하면서 지속적으로 교류를 해 온 모양이었다. 세상에는 나처럼 간단하게 연을 끊어 버리는 사람보다는 그것을 소중하게 이어가는 사람이 더 많은 것 같다. 또 그래야 세상이 굴러가겠지.

"얼른 들어가자 얘, 다들 반가워할 거야."

나는 친구에게 떠밀리듯 연회장으로 들어갔다. 꽤 많이 모여 있었다. 한 반에 약 40명 정도가 있었는데 대충 눈대중으로 봐도 30명은 족히 넘을 것 같았다. 나는 약간 떨어져서 그 얼굴들을 하나하나 바라봤다. 이름조차 생각나지 않는 친구들도 많았다. 모두가 십대 시절의 끄트머리를 함께 했던 학우들이지만, 지금은 누구에게서도 그때의 풋풋함은 찾을 수 없었다.

'가만, 내가 지금 뭘 하고 있지?'

매일 밤마다 화려하게 꾸민 긴자의 호스티스들만 봐온 탓에 나도 모르게 외모에 잔뜩 신경을 쓰고 있었다. 긴자의 호스티스들은 30대 후반, 40대 중후반이라도 이들보다 훨씬 예쁘고 상큼하다. 그건 어쩔 수 없는 사실이다. 연예인들처럼 사람의 눈을 즐겁게 해줘야 하는 직업 아닌가? 하지만 나야말로 몇 개월 전만해도 이 자리에 모인 동창들 중 그 누구보다 뚱뚱하고 볼품없지 않았던가? 그리고 사람을 외모로 평가하는 세상의 잣대를 미치도록 원망하지 않았던가?

그때 한 무리의 친구들이 내 주변으로 몰려들었다.

"우와, 이게 누구야? 딴 사람인 줄 알았네. 어쩜 이렇게 예뻐졌어?"

예뻐졌다는 말을 싫어할 여자가 어디 있을까? 어쨌거나 기분은 좋다. 하지만 그 다음 질문에서 금방 기분을 잡치고 말았다.

"그런데 요즘 뭐 해?"

"응, 파견사원이야."

난 솔직하게 대답했다. 그리고 상대방의 얼굴에 '쯧쯧' 하는 표정이 스쳐 지나가는 것을 나는 놓치지 않았다.

"그렇구나, 요즘 파견사원들 많이 힘들다더라. 남편 회사에서도 많이 잘렸대."

비참했다.

동창회에 참석한 친구들은 거의 다 안정적으로 자리를 잡은 것처럼 보였다(물론 그래서 더욱 기를 쓰고 동창회에 나오는 거겠지만). 그들에게 파견사원이란 한마디로 '가여운 존재'였다. 삼삼오오 모여서 나누는 이야기의 화제는 주로 자녀 양육비, 학비, 주택 대출금 같은 것들이었다. 내가 끼어들 틈은 전혀 없었다. 물론 그들 중에는 나처럼 싱글도 더러 있었지만, 물어볼 것도 없이 대부분 유명한 기업의 정사원들이었다.

'역시, 괜히 왔나 봐.'

나는 힘없이 고개를 떨어뜨린 채 요리 테이블로 향했다. 허겁지겁 로스트비프와 전채 요리 몇 점을 접시에 담았다. 그러고는 야경이 내려다보이는 창가로 다가갔다. 거기엔 이미 누가 먼저 와 있었다. 캔 맥주를 손에 쥔 채 당당하게 서 있는 여성…… 누구더라?

그래, 생각난다. 미나코!

❖ ❖ ❖

고교시절, 미나코는 무리에 휩쓸리지 않으면서 혼자 당당히 살아가는 타입이었다. 외톨이가 아니라 스스로 사람들과 적당한 거리를 유지해 가는 '독립적인 존재'였던 것이다.

그녀는 예전에도 항상 그랬듯이, 지금도 쇼트커트에 그레이 팬츠 슈트의 세련된 차림으로 서 있었다. 그리고 언제나처럼 무리에서 떨어져 혼자 창밖을 바라보고 있었다. 학생 때보다 더 길어진 팔과 다리, 그리고 곧게 뻗은 등…… 미나코는 여전히 당당했고, 변함없이 '나는 나'라는 자아로서의 에너지가 느껴졌다. 나와 눈이 마주치자 그녀는 생긋 미소를 지었다.

"오랜만이네."

"그래 오랜만이야, 미나코."

그녀는 내게서 시선을 떼지 않은 채 맥주를 한 모금 마시더니 말을 이었다.

"애들 대화에 낄 수가 없네. 내가 모르는 얘기들만 해서……."

"나도 그래, 넌 아이 없어?"

"아이? 아직 싱글인 걸?"

"나도 마찬가지야."

우리는 서로 마주보며 웃었다.

미나코는 현재 꽤 유명한 광고회사에 다니고 있지만, 언젠가는 일러스트레이터로 독립할 생각이라고 했다.

"다들 말리더라. 안정된 직장 놔두고 그 나이에 무슨 짓이냐고 말이야. 하지만 난 도저히 꿈을 포기할 수가 없어. 하고 싶은 걸 못 하면 죽을 때 엄청 후회하게 될 거야."

미나코는 나를 향해 말하면서 동시에 자기 자신에게도 말하고 있었다. 나는 그녀의 말이 놀라우면서도 반가웠다. 나는 지금까지 서른을 코앞에 둔 대부분의 여자들은 결혼과 함께 안정된 생활만을 바라고 있을 거라 생각해 왔었다. 그래서 안정과는 도무지 거리가 먼 나 같은 사람은 세상에 뒤처져 있는 거라고 굳게 믿었다. 그런데 그렇지 않은 사람도 있었다. 세상이 뭐라 하건 자신의 길을 뚜벅뚜벅 걸어가는 사람이 있는 것이다.

"멋지다, 미나코!"

"고마워."

미나코는 환하게 웃었다.

그녀의 열정이 내게 옮아온 것일까? 나는 단 한 번도 발설하지 않았던 '나의 계획'을 그녀에게 말해 주고 싶었다. 만약 그녀가 비웃거나 이상하게 생각한다 해도 상관없다. 앞으로 만나지 않으면 되니까. 하지만 왠지 미나코는 나를 이해해 줄 것 같았다. 결국 나는 미나코에게 호스티스 일을 한다는 것과 그렇게 모은 돈으로 라스베이거스에 가서 호화롭게 펑펑 써버리겠다는 얘기를 털어놓고 말았다. 말해 놓고 나니 얼마나 속이 후련한지 몰랐다. 어쩌면 나는 그동안 나의 은밀한 계획을 누군가와 절실히 공유하고 싶어 했었는지도 모른다.

미나코는 내 얘기가 끝날 때까지 너무도 진지하게 귀 기울여 주었다. 그리고 내 손을 꽉 쥐더니 "정말 대단해!" 하고 말했다.

"그건 아무나 할 수 있는 일이 아니잖아. 나도 응원할게!"

그 한마디에 오랫동안 혼자 짊어져 왔던 짐이 훨씬 가벼워진 느낌이 들었다.

"그럼 라스베이거스 다녀와서는 뭐 할 거야?"

갑작스러운 질문에 나는 적잖이 당황했다. '그냥 라스베이거스까지야. 거기서 다 끝나'라고 대답할 수는 없지 않은가.

"그냥, 내 미래를 점쳐 볼까 해서……."

"그래?"

미나코는 잠시 입을 다물고 나를 물끄러미 쳐다보았다. 그러더니 다시 시선을 창밖으로 던지며 이야기를 하기 시작했다.

"난 늘 혼자였지만 외롭다는 생각은 별로 안 해봤어. 혼자서 그림 그리고 생각에 잠기는 그 시간이 좋았거든. 늙어 죽을 때까지 내가 좋아하는 그림을 그리면서 살고 싶었어. 하지만 사람들 속에 파묻혀 있다 보면 오히려 내가 가고 싶어 하는 방향이 뿌옇

게 흐려지곤 했어. 그래서 자꾸 나도 모르게 무리에서 떨어져 지내게 되더라. 적어도 혼자서 나를 만나는 그 시간만큼은 내 믿음을 확신할 수 있었거든. 물론 서른 문턱까지 오도록 아직 내 꿈을 펼치진 못했지만 그래도 난 아직 내 길을 가고 있다고 확신해. 하지만 이제 좀 더 과감하게 달려가야겠어. 뭐랄까, 인생의 목적은 늘 분명했지만 지금 이 순간에 뭘 해야 할지, 그런 목표는 약간 희미했었다는 생각이 들어. 네가 라스베이거스라는 선명한 목표를 가진 것처럼 이제 나도 분명하고 확실한 목표를 정해야 할 것 같아."

나는 그녀의 이야기를 한마디도 빠짐없이 들었다. 삶의 목적을 알고 있는 미나코는 방향을 잃지는 않았지만 자신의 발걸음이 너무 더디다고 했다. 반대로 나는 눈앞의 목표는 너무도 선명하지만 삶의 목적을 모르기 때문에 라스베이거스 이후의 시간을 상상할 수가 없다. 아무래도 인생이란 바다는 목적이나 목표하나만으로는 불완전한 항해를 할 수밖에 없는 모양이다. 신대륙을 찾아가는 범선은 타륜으로써 방향을 잡지만, 돛과 노가 없으면 움직일 수 없다. 결국 미나코와 나는 각각 하나씩만 가지고 있는 셈이다.

난 미나코의 이야기를 듣는 동안 몇 번이고 전율을 느꼈다. 나는 '죽음의 의식儀式'으로서 라스베이거스를 생각하고 있었지만,

그녀는 '삶의 출발점'으로 이해하고 있었던 것이다. 게다가 나의
목표와 계획을 존중할 뿐만 아니라 부러워하기조차 했다. 물론
그녀는 나의 라스베이거스 행에 대해 정반대의 해석을 하고 있
지만, 왠지 전혀 의미가 다른 것 같지는 않았다. 무엇보다 그녀
는 '내가 생각해 왔던 나'를 훨씬 더 괜찮은 존재로 격상시켜 주
었다.

　나는 속으로 미나코를 만나게 해준 동창회 행사에 감사했다.
라스베이거스라는 꿈 덕분에 그때까지 외톨이였던 내게도 비밀
을 공유할 수 있는 친구가 생기게 된 것이다.

나를 망설이게 하는 것들 너머에
내가 찾는 것이 있다

그날 이후 나는 주말을 틈타 미나코를 종종 만났다. 둘 다 시간을 쪼개 가며 사는 처지라 만나는 시간은 늘 자정 무렵이었고, 약속 장소도 딱 중간지점인 롯폰기였다.

미나코는 나를 만날 때마다 "서둘러! 더 늦기 전에 한 잔이라도 더 마시려면!" 하고는 내 팔을 잡고 곧장 싸구려 술집으로 끌고 갔다. 그런 식으로 우리는 롯폰기에서 가장 싼 와인 바, 맥주바 등 다양한 바를 섭렵했다. 물론 술이 약한 나는 알코올 도수가 약한 술을 마셨지만 미나코는 독한 위스키를 쭉쭉 들이켰다.

"미나코, 술을 왜 그렇게 마셔대니?"

"스트레스는 이렇게 미리미리 싹을 잘라야 해."

미나코는 일이 너무 많아 밤샘 작업을 해야 할 때도 있었다. 주어진 일을 모두 완수하기 위해서는 무엇보다 '기분'을 잘 관리해야 한다는 게 그녀의 노동 철학이었다.

"마음 맞는 친구하고 술 퍼마시는 것보다 더 좋은 방법은 없잖아. 안 그래?"

미나코는 한쪽 눈을 찡긋하면서 또 스트레이트 잔을 확 들이켰다. 저돌적이면서도 낙천적인 그녀의 자세가 정말 멋져 보였다.

나는 미나코와 함께 보내는 시간이 즐거웠다. 클럽 사와의 동료들이나 손님들과의 애프터 자리에서 술을 마실 때와는 전혀 다른 기분이었다. 일의 연장인 술자리와 10여 년 공백 이후 비로소 제대로 만난 옛 친구와의 술자리는 차원이 다르지 않겠는가.

그렇게 둘이서 주말 아침까지 날밤을 새우고 거의 눈도 붙이지 못한 채 다시 누드모델 일을 하러 아틀리에로 향하곤 했다. 그래도 전혀 피곤하지 않았다. 미나코와 함께 있으면 왠지 힘이 솟고 에너지가 넘쳐났다. 전에는 '벌써 스물아홉 살'이라고 한숨을 내쉬었지만, 미나코와 같이 있으면 '아직도 스물아홉 살'이라며 웃을 수 있었다.

긴자의 상점들은 일찍 문을 닫는 편이다. 오후 7시부터 자정까지는 클럽과 바의 네온이 하늘의 별보다 환하게 빛나지만 그 시간이 지나면 거리는 금세 차분해진다. 하지만 롯폰기는 달랐다. 거리는 자정이 넘으면서부터 사람들이 늘기 시작해 날이 밝을 때까지 온통 활기로 넘쳐난다. 롯폰기는 잠들지 않는 거리였다.

늦바람이 무섭다는 말처럼 나는 미나코와 함께 밤새도록 거리를 쏘다녔다. 그리고 어디서건 값싼 음료만 골라 마셨다. 지출에 관한 한 미나코와 나는 똑같은 입장이었다. 나는 라스베이거스 행을 위한 자금을, 미나코는 프리랜서로 독립하기 위한 자금을 모으고 있는 중이라 쓸데없는 낭비는 피했다. 그래도 우리는 충분히 즐거웠다.

그런 어느 날, 주로 20대들이 모이는 작은 바에서 어떤 할머니를 만났다. 젊은이들로 왁자지껄 붐비는 그곳에서 할머니는 혼자 술을 마시고 있었다. 미나코와 나는 자연히 그 할머니에게서 시선을 뗄 수가 없었다. 롯폰기에서 놀 만큼 세련된 마담도 아니고, 보풀이 인 촌스러운 갈색 스웨터에 부스스한 백발까지, 도무지 그 장소와는 어울리지 않았기 때문이다.

차마 말하긴 뭣하지만 '정신 나간 노인네가 배회하는 건가?'라는 생각도 들 법했다. 하지만 가끔 바텐더와 또박또박 얘기하는 모습을 보면 이런 분위기에 아주 익숙해 보였다. 나는 그 할머니가 무척 궁금해졌다.

"미나코, 저 할머니하고 얘기해 보고 싶지 않니?"

"글쎄, 괜히 실례하는 건 아닐까?"

하지만 시간이 갈수록 호기심은 점점 커지기만 했다.

"미나코, 나 저 할머니한테 말 걸어 볼래."

"야야, 그런 건 멋진 남자들한테나 써먹는 거야."

나는 마침내 술기운을 빌려 옆자리로 가서 과감하게 말을 걸어 보았다.

"안녕하세요. 옆에 앉아도 될까요?"

할머니는 심드렁한 표정으로 고개를 끄덕였다.

"여기 혼자 오셨나요?"

"응."

"여기 자주 오시나 봐요?"

"오늘은 여기서 한 잔, 내일은 저기서 한 잔, 그렇지 뭐."

"와, 멋지다! 롯폰기를 잘 아시나 봐요?"

내가 긴자의 클럽에서 터득한 화술로 치켜세우자 할머니는 설핏 웃음을 보였다. 나는 이때다 싶어 대화거리를 하나하나 끄집어냈다. 그때마다 할머니는 일일이 반응하며 슬슬 마음을 열기 시작했다. 그러더니 저쪽에 혼자 앉아 있는 미나코를 가리키며 이리 오라고 손짓을 했다.

"동행을 너무 내버려두면 안 되잖아."

그러고는 바텐더에게 술을 더 주문했다. 술이 나오자 할머니는 잔을 채우며 말했다.

"홀짝홀짝하지 말고 벌컥벌컥 마셔! 팔팔한 것들이."

우리는 극구 사양했다. 아무래도 형편이 넉넉지 않아 보이는 노인한테 술까지 얻어 마시긴 좀 그랬다. 그러자 할머니는 "괜찮아!" 하며 숄더백에서 집히는 대로 돈을 끄집어냈다. 바텐더에게 내민 것은 놀랍게도 1만 엔짜리 지폐였다. 우리는 눈이 휘둥그레졌지만 바텐더는 익숙하다는 듯 미소를 지었다. 결국 우리 셋은 술잔을 치켜들고 건배했다.

"자, 그럼 여기서는 대충 마감하고 다음 장소로 이동!"

할머니는 벌떡 일어나더니 양손으로 우리를 잡아끌었다.

"어서 오십시오!"

문을 열고 들어서자 서너 명의 꽃미남들이 우리를 맞았다. 그곳은 남자 스태프들이 서비스하는 일종의 호스트 클럽이었다. 미나코가 내게 귓속말을 했다.

"호스티스가 호스트들한테 서비스를 받다니, 이런 걸 상황 역전이라고 하던가?"

나는 팔꿈치로 쿡 찌르며 웃었다.

그들의 서비스는 정중하다기보다는 친한 친구처럼 꾸밈이 없었다. 할머니는 여기서도 얼굴이 통하는 듯 거침없이 주문했다.

"동페리뇽으로 두 병!"

동페리뇽은 클럽 사와에도 있다. 브랜디나 위스키를 키핑하는 단골손님이 많아서 잘 나가진 않지만 화이트가 7만 엔, 로제가 15만 엔이나 하는 고급 샴페인이다.

'할머니, 무리하지 마세요'라고 말하려는 순간, 업소의 스태프 전원이 우리 주위로 모여들었다. 곧이어 그들 중 한 명이 마이크를 쥐고 큰 소리로 구호를 제창하자 스태프 전원이 '샴페인 콜!' 하고 복창했다. 고가의 샴페인을 주문한 손님에게 감사의 뜻을 표하는 퍼포먼스였다. 그 화려한 연출에 나는 깜짝 놀랐고, 미나코는 아이처럼 깔깔거렸다.

할머니는 계속해서 화려한 안주들을 주문했다. 그러면서도 정작 당신은 별로 입에 대지 않고 우리가 즐기는 모습을 흐뭇하게 감상했다.

그 뒤로도 할머니는 뭔가 아쉽다는 듯 우리를 데리고 몇 군데나 더 옮겨 다녔다. 크고 화려한 바, 숨은 맛집, 클럽의 VIP 룸……. 우리 셋은 마치 내일 세상의 종말이라도 올 것처럼 광란의 파티를 즐겼다.

자칭 '롯폰기 삼총사'인 우리 셋은 서로 약속을 하지 않더라도 자주 만났다. 미나코와 내가 바에 들어서면 먼저 할머니가 있는지 두리번거렸고, 할머니 역시 그랬다. 그러다 우리를 발견하기라도 하면 할머니는 남자처럼 손을 번쩍 들고 "어이, 아마리! 미나코! 이리로 와!" 하고 소리치곤 했다. 그럼 우린 할머니를 '맘mom'이라고 부르며 얼른 달려갔다.

맘은 항상 곤드레만드레 취한 채 젊은 남자의 시중을 받았다. 처음 만났을 때 혼자였던 것은 순전히 우연이었던 모양이다. 할머니 곁에는 항상 시중을 들거나 말벗이 되는 사람이 앉아 있었다. 그들은 대부분 클럽이나 맨즈 바 등에서 일하는 남자들이거나, 우리처럼 우연히 만난 사람들이었다. 어쨌거나 맘은 여러 명이 함께 마시고 노래하는 왁자지껄한 분위기를 좋아했다.

하지만 몇 번을 그렇게 만나도 맘이 어떤 사람인지, 가족은 어디에 살고 나이는 몇 살인지조차 알 수가 없었다. 아무래도 자신에 대해서는 얘기하기 싫어하는 눈치였다. 딱 한 번 혼잣말처럼 "나한테도 딸이 있었는데……"라고 말한 적이 있다.

혹시 가족을 잃고 혼자가 된 건 아닐까? 아니면 딸이 먼 나라로 이민을 떠난 건 아닐까? 그래서 그런 상실감 때문에 우리를 딸처럼 대해 주는 건 아닐까?

주말만 되면 나타나서 호화판으로 놀다 보니 우리 삼총사는 어느새 롯폰기에서 유명인이 되어 있었다. 주위에서는 우리 셋을 부자 엄마와 두 딸쯤으로 생각하는 것 같았다. 우리도 구태여 그 소문을 부정할 필요를 못 느끼며 마음껏 모녀 놀이를 즐겼다.

맘에 대해서 우리가 알고 있는 것은 아무튼 부자라는 사실뿐이었다. 롯폰기 곳곳에 부동산을 갖고 있다는 소문도 있었지만, 직접 사업을 해서 벌어들였는지 아니면 원래 부잣집 딸인지는 우리도 전혀 알 수 없었다. 맘은 함께 술을 마실 때마다 "성가시니까 너희들이 꺼내 계산해!" 하며 숄더백을 우리에게 그냥 맡기곤 했다. 처음 백을 열었을 때 나는 낮게 비명을 질렀다.

"어머, 세상에!"

백 속에는 카드와 지폐다발이 가득했다. 그러자 맘은 대수롭지 않다는 듯 이렇게 말했다.

"그런 건 다 종이 쪼가리일 뿐이야. 그런 게 아무리 많아도 행복을 살 순 없어."

그 한마디가 가슴을 아프게 찔렀다. 맘에 대해서는 여전히 아는 게 없지만, 언제나 돈을 물 쓰듯 쓰고 호화판을 누려도 왠지 쓸쓸하고 허전해 보이던 그 표정의 비밀을 조금은 이해할 수 있을 것 같았다. 결국 롯폰기의 화려한 파티들도 맘에겐 단순한 '시간 죽이기'가 아니었을까? 그렇게라도 하지 않으면 도저히 따분

하고 쓸쓸해서 견디기 힘들 만큼 마음속에 커다란 구멍이 뚫려 있는 게 아닐까?

그때 맘이 '내친 김에'라는 듯 이야기를 잇기 시작했다.

"너희들 몇 살이라고 했지? 스물아홉? 서른? 요즘 여자애들은 서른만 넘으면 나이 들었다고 한숨을 푹푹 쉰다며? 웃기지 말라고 해. 인생은 더럽게 길어. 꽤 살았구나, 해도 아직 한참 남은 게 인생이야. 이 일 저 일 다 해보고 남편 자식 다 떠나보낸 뒤에도 계속 살아가야 할 만큼 길지. 100미터 경주인 줄 알고 전력질주하다 보면 큰코다쳐. 아직 달려야 할 거리가 무지무지하게 많이 남았는데, 시작부터 힘 다 쏟으면 어쩔 거야? 내가 너희들한테 딱 한마디만 해줄게. 60 넘어서도 자기를 즐겁게 해줄 수 있는 게 뭔지 잘 찾아봐. 그걸 지금부터 슬슬 준비하란 말이야. 내가 왜 이 나이 먹고서도 매일 술을 마시는지 알아? 빈 잔이 너무 허전해서 그래. 빈 잔에 술 말고 다른 재미를 담을 수 있다면 왜 구태여 이 쓴 걸 마시겠어?"

"맘, 그런 재미를 어디서 어떻게 찾아야 할지 알 수만 있다면 얼마나 좋겠어요?"

"닥치는 대로 부딪쳐 봐. 무서워서, 안 해본 일이라서 망설이게 되는 그런 일일수록 내가 찾는 것일 수도 있으니까."

나는 흥분해서 맘에게 라스베이거스 계획을 발설하고 말았다.

그러자 맘은 "미쳤군" 하며 폭소를 터뜨렸다. 그리고 잔을 휙 비우더니 내게 말했다.

"내가 롯폰기 술집에서 들었던 얘기들 중에서 제일 맘에 드는구면. 해봐, 저질러 봐. 만일 아마리 네가 그 계획을 포기한다면 죽어서도 후회할 거야."

포기라뇨, 절대 안 해요.

나는 고개를 절레절레 흔들었다.

그 뒤로 두세 번 더 만난 이후로 맘은 소리 소문 없이 롯폰기에서 자취를 감추었다. 늘 가던 곳들을 차례차례 다니며 수소문했지만, 맘은 이 화려한 욕망의 거리로부터 완전히 발길을 끊은 듯했다.

작별인사도 없이, 어디로 간다는 말도 없이 사라진 맘을 생각하며, 미나코와 나는 여러 가지 상상을 해보기도 했다.

"아주 괜찮은 남자친구를 만나서 함께 좋은 곳으로 여행을 떠났을지도 몰라."

"아니, 어쩌면 이민 간 딸을 만나러 갔을 수도 있지. 만나서 묵은 오해도 풀고 감동적인 해후를 하셨을 거야."

그러다가 맘이 내게 "해봐, 저질러 봐. 포기한다면 죽어서도 후회할 거야"라고 했던 마지막 한마디가 떠올랐다.

"어쩌면 당신 마음에 깊이 품고 있던 것들을 마지막으로 저질러 보기 위해 떠난 것일 수도 있어. 그게 뭐가 됐건 맘은 속 시원하게 저지를 거야."

나는 속으로 '맘, 파이팅!' 하고 외쳤다.

꿈을 가로막는 것은
시련이 아니라 안정이다

D-3개월.

라스베이거스로 가는 날이 점점 다가오고 있다. 여행 자금은 계속해서 악바리처럼 모으고 있고, 라스베이거스에 대한 자료 검색이나 블랙잭 연습도 하루 한두 시간씩 꼬박꼬박 해나가고 있다.

그런데 문제는 영어회화였다. 책이나 오디오로 공부하는 것은 아무래도 한계가 있었다. 나는 라스베이거스에 머무는 동안 벙어리가 되거나 더듬거리는 영어로 어설프게 시간을 보내고 싶지 않았다. 뿐만 아니라 지도책에 얼굴을 파묻고 다니며 여기저기 길을 물어볼 생각도 없었다. 호텔에서든 길거리에서든, 그리고 카지노에서든 자연스럽고 당당하게 즐기는 것, 거기까지가 내 계획에 모두 포함되어 있었다. 그러자면 무엇보다 언어 소통 문제가 확실하게 해결되어야 했다.

그런 어느 날, 미나코가 내 고민을 듣더니 뭐가 걱정이냐는 듯 말했다.

"롯폰기를 좀 더 학구적으로 활용하는 게 어때?"

아닌 게 아니라 롯폰기에는 각국의 대사관들이 많아서인지 아시아계, 유럽계, 아프리카계 등 다양한 외국인들이 모여들었다. 미나코는 그중에서 유난히 영어권 외국인들의 출입이 잦고, 음료 한 잔에 500엔 정도 하는 값싼 클럽으로 나를 데려갔다.

사실 롯폰기의 외국인이라고 하면 유흥에 빠져 약물에 손을 대는 불량스러운 이미지를 떠올리는 경우가 많다. 이곳에 드나들기 전엔 나 역시 그런 선입관을 가지고 있었다. 하지만 실제로 만나 보니 모국을 떠나 가족과 헤어져 생활하며 열심히 일하고 있는 사람들도 많았다. 따지고 보면 나도 그들과 별반 다를 것 없는 처지라 우리는 쉽게 친해질 수 있었다.

외국인들과 이야기를 하다 보면 한 가지 특이한 점을 발견할 수 있다. 그들은 모르는 사람을 처음 만난 자리에서도 자기 꿈을 당당히 얘기한다.

"내 꿈은 일류 주방장이 되는 거야!"

"난 서른 중반쯤에는 아마 히말라야를 트래킹하고 있을 거야.
틀림없어."

그들은 저마다 꿈의 밑거름을 다지기 위해 머나먼 타국에서
열심히 일하고 있었다. 처음에는 남과 다른 것을 두려워하지 않
고 당당히 자신의 의견을 말하는 그들에게 놀랐지만, 시간이 갈
수록 나도 서서히 적응이 되어 갔다. 그래서 대뜸 "네 꿈은 뭐
야?"라고 물을 때도 솔직히 마음을 털어놓을 수 있게 되었다.

"꿈이라기보다는, 라스베이거스에 가서 카지노에 내 인생 전
부를 걸고 한바탕 승부를 펼치고 싶어."

그렇게 말하면 다들 "워워!" 하고 놀라곤 했다. 반응은 제각각
이다. "그거 정말 멋진 꿈인데!"라고 엄지손가락을 치켜올리는가
하면, "너무 무모해. 일찌감치 꿈 깨셔!" 하며 고개를 절레절레
젓기도 한다. 찬성이든 반대든 나는 잠자코 듣는 편이지만, 이야
기가 진행될수록 자기들끼리 찬반양론으로 나뉘어 격론을 펼치
기도 한다.

"갬블은 야만이야!"

도박을 금기시하는 이슬람 친구가 단호하게 말한다.

"좋잖아! 꿈이 있다는 건!"

미국 친구가 나를 옹호하고 나서자 영국 친구도 가세한다.

"라스베이거스 좋지. 나도 한 번 가본 적이 있어."

나는 영국 친구가 정말 라스베이거스를 가봤는지 확인하기 위해 이것저것 꼬치꼬치 캐묻기도 했다. 그러자 그는 "가본 적도 없다면서 어떻게 그렇게 잘 알아!" 하며 놀라워했다. 사실 나는 라스베이거스에 관한 책을 너무 많이 읽어서 이젠 진짜로 가본 사람보다 더 자세히 알고 있었다.

그들은 내가 얼마나 결사적으로 라스베이거스를 공부하고 있는지 모른다. 가이드북을 읽으면서 실제로 여행하는 기분을 느끼고, 유명한 프로 갬블러가 쓴 책을 읽으며 정말 카지노의 흥분에 휩싸이는 식으로 '결전의 날'을 위해 이미지 트레이닝을 반복하고 있다는 사실을.

나는 롯폰기에서 만난 몇몇 영어권 사람들에게 일본어를 가르쳐 주겠다는 조건으로 영어 회화의 파트너가 되어 달라고 정식으로 부탁했다. 살아 있는 영어 회화가 필요한 나에게 그들은 아주 든든한 선생님이 되어 주었다. 그런 어느 날, 함께 어울리게 된 이탈리아 남자가 이렇게 말했다.

"라스베이거스에서 모든 걸 건단 말이지? 아주 독특한 발상이군. 아마리다워!"

"정말? 나답다고?"

"그래, 넌 용감한 도전자야."

정말 그럴까, 나는 용감한 도전자일까?

'남이 알고 있는 나'는, '내가 알고 있는 나'가 아니다. 나는 누드모델을 하면서 느꼈던 감정이 떠올랐다. 그렇다면 내가 알고 있는 나는 진짜 나일까? '나다운 것'은 뭘까? 이전의 나와 지금의 나는 뭐가 다를까?

❖ ❖ ❖

타냐는 러시아에서 온 스트립댄서였다.

"가족은 다 러시아에 있어. 나 혼자 돈 벌러 왔어. 난 옷을 벗고 돈을 받아."

그녀는 마치 '난 대기업의 여성 CEO야'라고 말하듯 당당했다.

"그렇구나. 나도 같아. 누드모델 일도 하거든."

우리는 그렇게 해서 친해졌다.

똑같이 '옷 벗는 일'을 하지만 타냐와 나의 몸매는 차원이 다르다. 그녀의 풍만한 가슴과 엉덩이, 잘록한 허리는 일본 여성으로서는 도저히 따라잡을 수 없는 그야말로 '신이 내린 몸매'였다. 글래머러스한 몸과는 달리 얼굴은 한없이 천진하고 귀여웠는데, 그 또한 매력적으로 느껴졌다. 게다가 성격까지 싹싹하고 다정해서 친구들도 많았다.

나는 누드모델답게 그녀가 어떤 식으로 '알몸 춤'을 추는지 궁금했다. 하지만 차마 물어볼 수는 없었다. 그런데 타냐 쪽에서 먼저 나를 초대했다.

"이번 주에 한번 보러 와. 공짜로 보게 해줄게."

"정말?"

나는 약속한 날 새벽 1시 경에 미나코와 함께 타냐의 쇼 클럽으로 향했다. 우리가 뒷문 부근에서 서성거리자 타냐가 "여기야, 여기!" 하며 손짓을 했다. 우리는 종업원 입구를 통해 몰래 극장 안으로 들어갔다. 우리가 최대한 돈을 아낀다는 사실을 잘 알고 있는 타냐가 그런 '변칙 입장'을 고안해 낸 것이다. 자리에 앉자 타냐는 음료를 내주고는 가게 안쪽으로 사라졌다.

클럽 안은 상상했던 것보다는 건전(?)했다. 관객층은 젊은 비즈니스맨 분위기의 남성 그룹이 많았지만, 간혹 여성의 모습도 눈에 띄었다. 다들 무대 코앞에 있는 객석에 앉아 댄스를 구경한다기보다는, 술 마시는 김에 여흥으로 댄스를 즐긴다는 느낌이었다.

곧이어 외국인 댄서들과 함께 타냐가 등장했다. 속옷 차림의 타냐는 음악에 맞춰 봉을 잡고 현란한 춤을 추기 시작했다. 빙빙 돌기도 하고 한 손으로 몸을 지탱하거나 다리로 봉을 휘감고 몸을 젖히는 등 고난이도의 아크로배틱 댄스가 이어졌다. 역동적이고 섬세한 동작이지만 손가락 하나, 발가락 하나까지 온 신경이 두루 미치고 있었다. 온몸에서 섹시한 아우라가 넘쳐 반짝반짝 빛이 날 정도였다. 나는 인간의 몸이 그런 동작을 만들어 낼 수 있다는 사실이 믿어지지 않았다. 그 순간 내 머릿속에는 매일매일 혼자서 땀을 뻘뻘 흘리며 수많은 동작을 연습하는 타냐의 모습이 떠올랐다. 그러자 더 이상 관객의 시선을 유지할 수가 없게 되었다.

내가 라스베이거스 여행 자금을 모으기 위해 한시적으로 누드 모델을 하듯이 그녀 역시 자기만의 간절한 목표를 위해 춤을 추고 있겠지? 아니, 어쩌면 그저 생계를 위해서일 수도 있을 것이다. 사실 그건 중요하지 않다. 내가 밤마다 거울 앞에서 포즈를 연구하듯이 타냐 역시 지친 몸으로 날마다 땀을 뻘뻘 흘리며 춤을 연습할 것이다.

직업에는 귀천이 없다지만 사회 통념으로 인한 선입견은 어쩔 수 없다. 그래, 직업에는 귀천이 있다. 하지만 저마다 흘리는 땀에는 귀천이 있을 수 없다. 그래서 나는 타냐의 외설적인 춤과 볼쇼이 발레단의 무용을 단순 비교할 수 없었다.

요염한 댄스가 계속되는가 싶더니 타냐가 윗옷을 벗고 순식간에 토플리스가 되었다. 타냐가 아름다운 가슴을 드러내자 나는 넋을 잃고 바라보았다. 무대에서 내려오는 타냐 앞에 팁이 건네졌다. 팁을 받아든 타냐는 감사의 표시로 손님의 얼굴을 양쪽 가

습 사이로 확 끌어안았다. 여기저기서 함성과 박수가 터져 나왔
다. 타냐는 장난스러운 미소를 짓더니 우리 쪽으로 다가왔다.

'어, 왜 오는 거야? 설마······.'

바로 그 순간, 타냐는 풍만한 가슴 사이로 내 얼굴을 확 품어
버렸다.

"으악!"

내가 소리를 지르자 사람들이 박장대소했다.

"좋겠다!"

미나코가 깔깔대자 타냐는 그녀에게도 여지없이 가슴 서비스
를 하더니, 귀여운 미소를 지으며 무대를 떠났다. 나는 탄력 넘
치는 타냐의 엉덩이를 망연자실 보고만 있었다.

"아마리, 미나코! 나의 레스토랑에 온 것을 환영합니다."

샴이 우아하고 정중하게 우리를 맞았다. 심야 만찬의 초대 손
님은 나와 미나코뿐이고, 시간은 이미 자정을 훨씬 넘은 새벽 2시
다. 우리는 샴이 직접 세팅한 테이블을 보고 감탄사를 마구 터뜨
렸다.

20대 중반의 샴은 인도에서 온 요리사였다. 인도에 있을 때는

궁중요리 레스토랑의 셰프였지만, 일본에 온 뒤로는 아직 허드
렛일만 하고 있다. 늦은 밤 오너와 주방장이 퇴근한 뒤에도 그는
혼자 남아 가게를 청소해야 한다. 그런 그가 어느 날 우리를 특
별 초대했다.

"가게 문 닫고 아무도 없을 때 놀러와."

모두가 퇴근한 그 시간에 몰래 자신의 요리를 선보이고 싶었
던 것이다. 물론 이러다가 들키는 날이면 즉시 해고다. 하지만 그
는 꿈을 위해 돈을 아끼고 있는 우리에게 요리를 해주고 싶어 했
다. 또한 평소 가게에서 만들지 않는 요리를 만들어서 우리의 평
을 듣고 요리 실력을 평가받고 싶다는 의도도 있었을 것이다.

우리가 자리에 앉자 샴은 가게 셔터를 내리고 클로즈 간판을
내건 뒤, 커튼을 쳐서 불빛이 밖으로 새지 않도록 만반의 준비를
마쳤다. 샴은 남은 식재료를 써서 자신의 오리지널 인도 요리뿐
만 아니라, 일식과 서양요리에서 영감을 얻은 다국적 퓨전 요리
까지 창작해 냈다. 맛은 물론 최고였다. 우리는 쉴 새 없이 젓가
락을 움직였다.

"샴, 맛있어! 감동적이야!"

"정말이지, 일류 셰프가 울고 가겠어!"

이건 결코 칭찬에 익숙한 호스티스의 접대용 멘트가 아니었다.
나는 진심으로 샴의 요리에 경탄해 마지않았다. 샴은 쑥스러워하

면서도 계속 칭찬을 듣고 싶은지 내 곁에 바싹 다가와 앉았다.

"샴, 이 정도 실력이면 직접 가게를 차려도 되겠는 걸? 청소나 주방보조로 남기엔 너무 아까운 실력이야."

미나코가 말했다.

"사실 처음엔 그런 꿈으로 일본에 왔어. 하지만 지금 하고 있는 일만으로도 인도에 있을 때보다 훨씬 보수를 많이 받거든. 그러다 보니 자꾸 나 스스로 계획을 미루게 되더란 말이지. 미나코, 아마리 너희들을 만나고 나서야 아차 싶었어. 고향에 있을 때 나한테 요리를 가르쳐 주신 선생님이 이런 말을 한 적이 있어. '적의 행군을 막으려면 술과 고기를 베풀어라.' 그게 무슨 말인지 이제야 알 것 같아. 평생의 꿈을 가로막는 건 시련이 아니라 안정인 것 같아. 현재의 안정적인 생활을 추구하다 보면 결국 그저 그런 삶으로 끝나겠지. 그래서 오늘 이 만찬을 계기로 다시 나의 오랜 계획을 실행에 옮기기로 했어."

우리는 샴의 말이 끝나기 무섭게 잔을 높이 들어 '일류 요리사 샴을 위하여!'라고 소리쳤다.

스물아홉 살이 될 때까지 끝없이 안정적인 생활만을 추구하며 살다가 결국 자멸해 버린 나로서는 샴의 이야기가 쓰디쓴 약처럼 느껴졌다. 지금 나의 생활은 확실히 안정과는 거리가 멀다. 나이에 맞게 안정된 생활을 하고 있는 사람들이라면 내가 품고 있는 라스베이거스 계획을 미친 짓이라고 단언할 것이다. 나 역시 그렇게 생각한다. 왜냐하면 라스베이거스는 나의 꿈을 위한 과정이 아니라 그저 '인생의 종착역'처럼 자포자기적인 목표이기 때문이다.

그래도 난 그 목표에 모든 것을 걸었다. 비록 평생의 꿈은 찾지 못했지만, 이 정도 목표만을 위해서라도 전력을 쏟아붓고 싶었다. 나 자신을 한계선까지 밀어붙이지 않고서는 도저히 살아 있다는 느낌을, 살고 싶다는 느낌을 받을 수 없을 것 같기 때문이다.

만찬이 끝나고 디저트를 먹다가 우연히 카드 게임 이야기가 화제에 올랐다. 그때 샴이 끼어들었다.

"나도 인도에서 친구들하고 밤새도록 카드 게임을 하곤 했어."

그 말을 듣자마자 나는 늘 갖고 다니는 카드를 핸드백에서 꺼냈다.

"블랙잭 알지? 한번 해볼까?"

스물아홉 살의 마지막 날, 최후의 승부를 어떤 게임으로 정할 것인가? 나는 이미 '블랙잭'으로 정해 놓고 있었다.

블랙잭은 카드를 분배하는 딜러 한 명과 플레이어가 몇 장의 카드를 합한 숫자로 머리싸움을 하는 게임이다. 룰은 간단명료하다. 분배받은 카드의 숫자를 더해 가며 21에 가까워지는 쪽이 이긴다. 21이 넘어가면 '버스트'가 되어 패자가 된다.

카드는 2에서 10까지는 숫자 그대로 세고, J(잭 11), Q(퀸 12), K(킹 13) 세 장의 그림 카드는 전부 '10'으로 세며, A(에이스)는 '1' 이나 '11' 중에서 자신에게 유리한 쪽으로 셀 수 있다. 이렇게 되면 '10'에 해당하는 카드가 압도적으로 많아지며 이것이 승패의 관건이다.

플레이어는 맨 처음 두 장씩 받게 되는 카드를 본 뒤 다시 한 장 더 추가하고 싶을 때는 '히트', 카드를 추가하지 않고 두 장만으로 승부할 때는 '스탠드'를 선택한다. 예를 들어 '7'과 '8'을 쥐었을 때 플레이어는 두 장을 합한 15로 승부를 할지, 아니면 다시 한 장의 카드를 추가할지 선택해야 한다. 만일 몇 장을 더 받건 6 이하만 되면 21에 좀 더 가까워질 수 있어 승률이 높아지지만, 반대로 6을 넘으면 버스트가 되어 패배하게 된다.

이때 딜러 측 카드는 한 장만 오픈되어 있는 상태(페이스 업)로 분배되기 때문에, 플레이어는 그 한 장을 힌트로 '히트'와 '스탠드'를 선택해야 한다. 한편 딜러 측은 선택의 여지없이 두 장의 합이 16 이하일 때는 자동으로 한 장을 더 뽑고 17 이상일 때는 자동으로 스탠드가 된다. 결국 버스트를 피하면서 어떻게 딜러보다 더 높은 숫자를 만들 것인가, 이것이 블랙잭의 전부이다. 블랙잭은 이처럼 단순한 게임이다. 플레이어는 카드를 더 받을 것인가, 말 것인가를 선택하기만 하면 된다. 하지만 그 '선택'이라는 심리의 세계로 들어가면 블랙잭은 더 이상 단순한 게임이 아니게 된다.

나는 어릴 때 식구들과 재미삼아 블랙잭을 해봤지만, 라스베이거스 행을 결심한 뒤로는 독학으로 철저히 연구하고 있었다. 나의 목표는 라스베이거스에서 원 없이 돈을 펑펑 써보겠다는 것이지, 결코 한 방에 다 날려 버리는 것은 아니다. 그건 근처 강가에서 돈다발을 죄다 날려 버리는 것과 다름없기 때문이다.

내가 진짜 원하는 것은 뒤집어진 한 장의 카드를 놓고 거액의 베팅을 할 것인가, 말 것인가 선택해야 하는 그 초긴장의 상태를 경험하는 것이었다. 그만큼 카지노에서의 매순간을 진지한 승부와 도전으로 채우고 싶었다. 그렇게 전력을 다하지 않는다면 죽을 때 분명 후회가 남거나, 아니면 죽는 것을 주저하게 될 것 같았다. 그래서 나는 더 철저히 카지노를 파고들었다.

그렇게 혼자 집에서 연습하거나 가까운 넷카페에서 웹 게임으로 맹훈련을 하긴 했지만, 실제로 사람들과 게임을 해본 적은 없었다.

"좋았어, 아마리! 우리 실전처럼 해보자!"

미나코와 샴은 아주 적극적이었다.

게임이 시작되자 딜러 역이 된 미나코가 단번에 칩을 회수했다.

"좋았어, 블랙잭! 싹 쓸었어!"

게임의 이름이기도 한 '블랙잭'은 A와 10 혹은 그림카드 두 장만으로 '21'이 된 경우를 말한다. 이 패는 아주 깔끔하면서도 굉장한 파괴력을 지닌다. 칩도 1.5배이며 무조건 이긴다. 만일 상대가 같은 블랙잭 패를 손에 쥐었을 때는 무승부가 되지만, 양쪽모두 블랙잭이 되는 경우는 매우 드물다. 나와 같이 플레이어 역을 하고 있는 샴이 말했다.

"블랙잭은 단순하면서도 아주 재미있어. 아마리가 왜 좋아하는지 알 것 같아."

"맞아, 하지만 내가 블랙잭을 선택한 이유는 꼭 재미 때문만은아냐."

"그럼?"

미나코가 나를 보며 눈을 깜빡거렸다.

"그건…… 오로지 운에만 맡기는 게임이 아니니까."

"운에 맡기는 게 아니라고?"

미나코와 샴이 동시에 반응했다.

"물론이야. 계산만 잘 하면 분명 이길 수 있는 게임이야."

카지노의 게임들은 대부분 장기적으로 보면 반드시 카지노 측에 유리하도록 되어 있다. 하지만 블랙잭만은 다르다. 플레이어 측의 선택지가 많기 때문에, 숫자만 잘 다루면 좀 더 유리한 기회를 가져올 수 있는 게임이다. 따라서 기본 전략에 충실히 따르면 승률은 오르기 마련이다.

이 게임에서 절대로 해서는 안 되는 것이 있다면 그것은 '버스트'다. 숫자의 합이 '21'을 넘는 순간, 무조건 패하기 때문이다. '한 장 만 더 채우면 21에 좀 더 가까워질 수도……' 하는 게 사람 마음이지만, 그렇게 욕심을 부리다 버스트가 되면 말짱 도루묵이다. 물론 이런 리스크는 딜러 측도 마찬가지다. 그러니까 자신이 버스트가 되기 어렵고 딜러가 버스트가 되기 쉬운 상황을 확률적으로 끌어내면 된다. 여기까지 설명하자 미나코는 눈이 휘둥그레졌다.

"우와, 대단해!"

나는 내친 김에 내가 지니고 다니는 기본 전략 일람표를 펼쳐 보였다. 거기엔 통계학에 근거한 딜러의 페이스 업 카드 수와 내가 가진 경우의 수, 그리고 그때의 상황에 취할 수 있는 최상의 전략이 빽빽하게 적혀 있었다.

"아마리! 너 정말 굉장하구나!"

미나코는 계속 감탄만 했다. 트럼프 게임뿐 아니라 갬블은 통계학과 관련이 있다는 것을 잘 알고 있는 샴도 이런 표는 처음 본다며 흥미진진한 표정을 지었다.

당연히 실전에서는 이런 표를 보면서 플레이할 수 없다. 그러니까 나는 이 표를 완벽하게 외워서 내 것으로 만든 다음, 현장에서 적시에 써먹을 수 있어야 한다.

전략은 스탠드와 히트 이외에도 더블다운, 스프리트 등이 있다. 더블다운이란 맨 처음 두 장의 카드를 보고 될 것 같다는 확신이 들면 베팅을 배로 늘릴 수 있는 룰이다. 그 대신 더블다운 선언을 한 다음에는 단 한 장의 카드밖에 뽑을 수 없다. 그리고 스프리트는 맨 처음 두 장의 카드가 우연히 같은 숫자일 경우, 처음 베팅한 칩과 같은 금액의 칩을 추가하면 카드 두 장을 나눠 각각 플레이할 수 있는 룰이다. 즉 한 번에 두 가지 승패가 가능하다는 얘기다. 그런데 미나코와 교대로 딜러 역을 맡은 샴이 뭔가 이상하다는 듯 고개를 갸웃거리더니 나에게 지적을 했다.

"있잖아, 아마리. 전략이 잘못된 것 같지 않아?"

과연 숫자의 나라인 인도 출신답다. 벌써 기본 전략이 머릿속에 다 들어 있다.

샴의 말대로 내 패의 합은 13, 딜러의 페이스 업 카드가 2일 때, 기본 전략에서는 '스탠드' 사인을 내야 할 상황에서 내가 '히트' 사인을 낸 것이다.

"위험해, 아마리. 버스트가 될 거야."

하지만 나는 아무렇지 않게 대답했다.

"이걸로도 문제없어."

샴이 투덜대며 또 한 장의 카드를 나에게 건넸다. 결과는 5가 나와서 합이 18, 버스트를 면하고 딜러를 이겼다.

"대단해, 운이 좋았어. 아마리."

나는 고개를 저었다.

"운이 아니라니까, 샴. 이건 카운팅이야."

그렇다. 내가 하고 싶은 것은 단순한 기본 전략만이 아니다. 그보다 더 고차원적인 '카드 카운팅'인 것이다. 이 비밀 전략이 내 운명의 열쇠를 쥐고 있었다.

극한까지 밀어붙이다

D-1개월.

나는 라스베이거스 행을 위한 최종 점검에 들어갔다. 지금까지 모은 돈은 목표했던 200만 엔에는 훨씬 미치지 못하지만 적어도 라스베이거스에서의 일주일은 가능하다. 물론 그러기 위해서는 나머지 한 달 동안 전력투구를 해야 한다.

내 머릿속에는 이미 라스베이거스의 골목골목까지 생생하게 입력되어 있고, 거의 모든 호텔과 상점들의 가격, 특징까지 세세하게 외울 수 있다. 영어회화도 관광지에서의 일주일 정도는 무난히 지낼 수 있을 만큼 자신감이 있었다. 딱 하나 아직 불안한 것은 역시 카드 게임이었다.

나는 일확천금을 노리는 게 아니다. 그러나 1년 동안 번 돈을 삽시간에 잃고 싶지도 않았다. 스물아홉 살이 끝나는 마지막 날, 나는 모든 것을 걸고 최후의 도박을 할 것이다. 그 게임에서 지든 이기든 정말 기념비적인 게임을 하고 싶었다. 그러자면 지금보다 훨씬 능숙해져야 한다.

디데이 한 달을 남겨놓은 시점에서 나는 매일 자정마다 샴과 미나코를 만나 카드 게임을 했다. 그들에게는 여흥일 수 있겠지만, 나에게는 최후의 결전을 위한 집념의 훈련 시간이었다. 몸은 지칠 대로 지치고 정신은 극도의 긴장으로 팽팽해진 상태에서 나는 나 자신을 한계점까지 밀어붙이고 있었다. 데드 포인트 (Dead Point)를 지나면 비로소 찾아온다는 러너스 하이(Runner's high)를 맛보고 싶었던 걸까? 나에게 어떤 일이 닥치든 그 황홀한 무아지경을 한 번이라도 느껴 보고 싶었다.

샴이 차례차례 젖히는 트럼프 카드를 보며 나는 즉석에서 계산을 하고 있었다.

'6, 5, 6, 7, 6…….'

늘었다 줄었다 하는 숫자들…… 52장의 카드를 다 젖혔을 때 그 수는 제로가 되었다.

"좋았어, 아마리. 잘했어."

샴은 주방에서 커피를 끓여 왔다. 나는 커피를 한 모금 마시고 한숨을 길게 내쉬었다. 역시 혼자 연습할 때보다 사람을 상대로 연습할 때 더 긴장된다. 망설이거나 오래 생각하다가는 카드를 젖히는 속도를 따라갈 수 없게 된다.

블랙잭 카운팅은 카드 계산이 전부다. 이 계산이 재빠르고 정확하지 않으면 카지노에서 이길 수 없다.

"너무 어려워. 머리가 다 지끈거리네."

옆에서 지켜보던 미나코가 혀를 내둘렀다. 확실히 카드 카운팅은 머리를 써야 한다. 하지만 이 방법은 다양한 카드 카운팅 방법 중에서도 아직 간단한 편이다. 더 들어가 보면 내가 손댈 수도 없을 만큼 엄청난 고난도의 전략도 있다.

원래 나의 전술은 비교적 쉬운 수법인 '하이 로(Hi-Lo)'다. 이 것은 트럼프를 하이 카드와 로 카드, 그 외의 카드 이렇게 세 종류로 나눠 계산하는 방법이다. 하이 카드인 10점 카드(10, J, Q, K)와 A는 마이너스 1로 센다. 그리고 2부터 6까지의 로 카드는 플러스1로 센다. 그 외의 카드는 제로이며 무시해도 좋다. 딜러와 플레이어에게 분배되어 나온 모든 카드를 이 계산법으로 더하고 빼가는 것이다.

블랙잭은 조커를 제외한 52장의 카드를 사용한다. 이것을 1덱

(묶음)만 사용하는 경우가 있는가 하면, 2덱 이상 사용하는 경우도 있다. 카지노에서는 6덱이나 8덱을 사용하는 테이블도 있지만 어느 쪽이든 카드 매수에는 한도가 있다.

보통 블랙잭에서는 한 번 승부가 아니라 몇 번의 승부가 끝난 다음 사용한 카드를 섞는다. 따라서 카드를 분배하는 동안 남은 카드 매수는 점점 줄어들게 된다. 즉 나온 카드를 모두 기억하고 있다면 남은 카드가 몇 장인지를 유추해 낼 수 있는 것이다. 하지만 1덱이라면 어떻게 해보겠지만, 모든 카드를 기억하여 순간적으로 남은 카드를 파악할 수 있는 사람은 드물다. 나 역시 그건 너무 어렵다.

카드 카운팅이란 이것을 간소화하여 지금 플레이어에게 유리한 카드가 남아 있는지, 딜러에게 유리한 카드가 남아 있는지를 산출해 내는 마법의 계산법이다. 플러스가 크면 플레이어에게 유리하고, 마이너스가 크면 딜러에게 유리하다고 할 수 있다. 상황에 따라 기본 전략과는 다른 전략을 취하든지, 아니면 베팅을 늘리거나 줄이거나 해야 한다.

"그러니까 A나 그림카드가 많이 남았을 때 테이블은 버스트가 될 확률이 높아지는 거야."

17 이상이 될 때까지 카드를 계속 뽑아야만 하는 딜러는, 12부터 16의 패에서 하이 카드를 뽑으면 버스트가 된다.

"플레이어의 메리트도 있어. 하이 카드가 많이 남았을 때를 노려 더블다운하면 효과적으로 이길 확률이 높아져."

베팅을 배로 하는 더블다운으로 승부를 걸어놓고, 로 카드가 나왔다고 후회하는 것처럼 어리석은 일도 없다. 또한 11에서 더블다운을 했는데, A나 2가 나왔다면 카드를 내동댕이치고 싶을 만큼 열이 뻗칠 것이다. 하지만 이겼을 때의 기쁨은 베팅과 마찬가지로 배가 된다.

이런 식으로 젖힌 카드를 보고 순간적으로 계산하는 연습도 좋지만, 그래도 가장 좋은 건 역시 실전이다. 미나코와 샴, 나 이렇게 셋이서 게임을 할 때는 3명 모두에게 분배된 카드를 순식간에 계산하지 않으면 안 된다. 실전에서 플레이어의 수는 최대 6명이다. 하지만 나의 카드 카운팅 능력은 아직 많이 모자란다. 3명이서 하는데도 자꾸 틀리곤 한다. 결전의 날은 이제 앞으로 1개월 뒤…… 나는 시간이 갈수록 초조해졌다.

좀 더 많은 자금을 모으기 위해 주 4일 근무인 클럽 사와의 일을 주 5일로 늘려 달라고 부탁하기도 했고, 휴일에는 누드모델 일을 들어오는 대로 다 받았다. 그러면서도 짬짬이 샴을 졸라 블랙잭 실전 연습을 계속했다. 보다 못한 미나코가 손사래를 쳤다.

"아마리, 좀 쉬어! 그렇게 몸을 혹사시키다간 라스베이거스에

도착하자마자 몸져눕게 될지도 몰라."

샴도 걱정스러운 듯 내 얼굴을 뚫어져라 쳐다봤다.

"그래, 아마리. 요즘 안색이 너무 안 좋아."

난 듣는 둥 마는 둥 시선을 딴 곳으로 돌렸다.

'시간이 없단 말이야. 시간이…….'

그 순간 갑자기 시야가 흔들렸다. 그리고 온 세상이 빠른 속도로 빙빙 돌기 시작했다. '어? 이상한데?' 하는 느낌과 동시에 나는 바닥에 쓰러지고 말았다.

"아마리!"

미나코와 샴의 비명이 아득하게 들려왔다. 나는 갑자기 전기가 끊긴 것처럼 깜깜한 어둠에 휩싸였다.

노련한 레이서는 가속페달보다 브레이크를 더 잘 쓴다

'여긴 어디지?'

희미하게 눈을 뜨자 새하얀 천장이 보인다. 새하얀 커튼과 새하얀 벽지…… 그리고 링거가 눈에 들어온다.

'아, 그래…… 병원이구나.'

나는 병원 침대 위에 누워 있었다. 차츰차츰 어젯밤 일이 떠오르기 시작했다.

'맞아, 쓰러졌었지…….'

내가 의식이 몽롱해지면서 쓰러지고, 미나코와 샴이 전화로 구급차를 부른 것까지는 어렴풋이 기억이 난다. 내가 병원에 실려 온 뒤로 무슨 일이 있었는지, 그리고 시간이 얼마나 지났는지는 알 수 없었다. 그때 간호사가 들어와 링거를 교체하고 체온을 쟀다. 나는 간호사에게 말했다.

"어떻게 된 건지 얘기 좀 해주세요."

간호사는 살며시 미소를 지으며 설명해 주었다. 나는 병원에 오자마자 CT 촬영과 혈액 검사를 받았다. 그리고 '피로 축적에 의한 중증 빈혈'이라는 진단이 내려졌다. 그러니까 나는 '과로'로 입원한 것이다.

"친구 분들은 아침에 가셨어요. 좀 있다 다시 오실 거래요. 그럼 편안하게 푹 쉬세요."

간호사가 병실을 나간 뒤 나는 물끄러미 창밖을 바라보았다. 밖에는 부슬부슬 비가 내리고 있었다. 풀잎 무성한 나무와 초록 풀들은 빗방울을 맞으며 하염없이 흔들리고 있었다. 나는 시간 가는 줄 모르고 그 모습을 바라보았다.

그때 고요하던 병실의 정적을 깨고 복도 쪽에서 다급한 발소리가 울렸다. 그리고 점점 가까워지는가 싶더니 벌컥 문이 열렸다.

"어떻게 된 거야, 아마리! 괜찮아? 괜찮은 거야?"

레이나와 치카, 메구미…… 전우애로 똘똘 뭉친 클럽 사와 동지들이 요란뻑적지근하게 들이닥친 것이다. 그들은 피아노 독주회에서나 볼 수 있는 커다란 꽃다발까지 들고 있었다. 같은 병실 환자들은 일제히 우리에게 시선을 집중했다.

"뭐야, 왜 쓰러졌던 거야? 지금 어때? 힘들진 않아?"

"응, 그냥 과로인 것 같아…… 이젠 괜찮아."

평소에도 내 걱정을 많이 해주던 치카는 거의 울기 직전이다.

"괜찮긴, 과로로 죽는 사람도 있다더라. 몸 좀 챙기고 살아!"

"알았어. 미안해."

나는 엄마한테 혼나는 아이처럼 고개를 푹 숙였다.

"원, 이렇게 말라서 어디…… 많이 먹고 푹 자."

레이나는 계속 내 손을 쥐고 있었다.

"응. 고마워."

"아마리, 아무 생각하지 말고 푹 쉬어. 이럴 때 쉬지 언제 쉬겠어? 그동안 너무 열심히 살았어."

메구미가 말했다. "너무 열심히 살았어"라는 그녀의 말에 갑자기 울컥했다. 태어나서 그런 말을 들어 본 적이 있었던가?

"어쨌든 아무 생각하지 말고 한동안 몸이나 잘 챙겨."

클럽 오픈 시간이 다가오자 그녀들은 재빨리 꽃을 꽂고 "또 올게!" 하며 다시 폭풍우처럼 사라졌다. 나는 그녀들이 흩뿌린 향수의 잔향을 맡으며 "고마워"라고 중얼거렸다. 그때 병실 한 구석에서 웬 남자 간병인이 웃으며 말했다.

"거 자주 좀 오시라고 해요. 병실 분위기가 다 환해지네."

나는 킥, 하고 웃었다.

그리고 얼마 안 있어 이번에는 미나코와 샴이 쳐들어왔다.

"일어났구나. 몸은 좀 어때?"

"응, 괜찮아. 걱정 끼쳐서 미안해."

"그런데 정말 과로가 맞는 거야?"

"응, 아무튼 너무 잘나가도 탈이라니깐."

내가 농담을 하자 미나코는 안심이다 싶은지 활짝 웃었다.

"다행이야. 안색도 좋아졌어. 병원 들어올 때까지만 해도 얼마나 무서웠는지 몰라. 너무 창백했거든."

"지금은 괜찮아. 응, 뭐랄까. 마귀를 떨쳐낸 것처럼 산뜻해."

"이렇게 푹 자본 거 아주 오랜만이지?"

정말 그런 것 같다. 돌이켜 보니, 지난 11개월 동안 한 번도 쉬어 본 적이 없었다. 아침부터 저녁까지 회사에 다니고, 밤에는 긴자의 호스티스, 주말에는 누드모델, 그 틈틈이 애프터와 영어 공부, 블랙잭 훈련……. 도대체 언제 잠을 잤었나 싶기도 했다.

라스베이거스 행을 정하고부터 지금까지 1분 1초도 헛되이 보낸 적은 없었고, 뒤를 돌아볼 여유도, 고민할 시간도 없었다. 계속 달리다 보면 딴생각할 겨를도 없고, 옥죄어 오는 불안에 발목 잡힐 일도 없을 것 같았다. 오직 목표만을 향해 한눈팔지 않고 달려왔던 11개월, 정말이지 나는 휴식 따위에 신경 쓸 여유가 없었다. 하지만 너무 많이 달린 것 같다. 몸이 보내는 비명을 알아

듣지 못하고 결국 결승점 앞에서 쓰러지고 만 것이다.

"예전에 카레이서를 취재하다가 이런 얘기를 들은 적이 있어."

미나코가 말했다.

"초보 카레이서들은 매순간 가속페달을 있는 힘껏 밟으려고만 한대. 하지만 노련한 카레이서는 가속페달보다는 브레이크를 더 잘 쓴다는 거야. 지금 너한테 딱 필요한 말 같지 않아?"

"난 브레이크가 있는지도 몰랐어."

"브레이크를 안 쓰면 차가 커브 길에서 전복되거나 엔진 과열로 폭발할 수 있어. 명심해, 너를 결승선까지 데려가 주는 건 네 몸뿐이야. 몸을 홀대하면 결국 몸이 너를 거부하게 될 거야. 하긴 나도 이런 말 할 자격은 없지. 공범이니까."

미나코는 화제를 돌리려고 머리맡에 놓인 화병을 들어올렸다.

"우와! 꽃 예쁘다."

"응, 좀 전에 클럽 사와 친구들이 다녀갔어."

"그랬구나."

'친구'라는 말이 내 입에서 이렇게 자연스럽게 나오다니.

그때 미나코가 내 쪽으로 돌아섰다.

"아마리, 난 언제나 네 편이야. 하지만 건강은 조심해. 네가 쓰러지면 슬퍼할 사람들이 많다는 걸 잊지 마."

"응, 고마워."

나는 또 한 번 가슴이 뜨거워졌다.

나를 걱정해 주는 사람들이라니…….

나는 스물아홉의 마지막 날을 원 없이 호화롭게 보내고, 서른 살 생일에 생을 마감하기로 했다. 그것을 위해 폭주족처럼 달려왔다. 하지만…….

자욱한 회색빛 구름 같은 것이 가슴 깊은 곳에서 스멀거린다. 그것을 없애려고 나는 머리를 흔들며 창밖으로 눈을 돌렸다. 회색빛 하늘 아래, 비를 맞은 초목이 조용히 흔들리고 있었다.

무수히 많은 사람의 손을 거쳐 왔을 이 5달러짜리 지폐가 갑자기 나를 뭉클하게 했다. 1년이라는 치열한 시간을 환전해서 여기까지 날아와 인생을 건 도박 끝에 5달러를 번 것이다. '……그래, 이긴 거야. 달랑 5달러지만 난 이긴 거야!'

타임 투 세이 굿바이

퇴원하고 다시 3평짜리 나의 원룸으로 돌아왔다. 오랜만의 휴식으로 인해 내 몸은 어느 때보다 가벼워졌다. 이제 다시 엔진을 재정비하고 라스베이거스를 향해 달려야 할 시간이다. 하지만 나는 파견사원 업무 외에는 일을 잠시 멈추기로 했다. 클럽 사와의 마담 역시 내 몸이 정상으로 돌아올 때까지 푹 쉬라고 말했다.

나는 현재까지 준비된 사항들을 하나하나 점검하기 시작했다. 여행자금은 더 이상 늘릴 수 없는 대신 일정을 좀 더 세밀하게 짜야 할 것이다. 가능한 한 쓸데없는 경비를 최소화하되 라스베이거스에서 누려야 할 것들은 과감하게 누려야 한다. 그것은 사치가 아니라 목적이다. 아니, 내가 스스로 허락한 사치 그 자체가 라스베이거스 행의 핵심이다.

블랙잭 연습도 지금 수준에서 만족하기로 했다. 지금 실력으로도 풋내기 관광객들보다는 훨씬 수준 높은 게임을 할 수 있으리라 판단한 것이다. 이제 더 이상의 욕심은 거둬들여야 한다.

나는 여행사를 순례하다시피 하면서 더 이상 어떻게 해볼 수 없을 만큼 철저하게 일정을 짰다. 그리고 그 일정에 맞춰 매일 밤마다 상상여행을 떠났다. 그것은 일종의 이미지 트레이닝으로, 나를 라스베이거스 거리에 세워 둔 채 발생 가능한 모든 상황을 상상해 보는 것이었다.

그렇게 하루, 또 하루의 시간이 흘렀다.

출발 날짜가 손에 잡힐 듯 가까워질수록 가슴이 두근거렸다. '정말 해낼 수 있을까?'라는 생각이 불현듯 머리를 스쳤다. 내가 생각했던 것과는 전혀 다른 의외의 상황이 닥치지는 않을까? 느닷없이 몸이 덜덜 떨릴 만큼 불안해지기도 하고, 어느 순간 미칠 듯한 황홀감에 몸서리치기도 했다.

서른 번째 생일을 일주일 앞둔 7월의 어느 날, 나는 라스베이거스로 향하는 비행기 안에 앉아 있었다. 4박 6일의 여행 일정

중 마지막 날, 나는 서른 살이 된다.

가방에는 여행자수표와 달러가 들어 있다. 1년 동안 파견사원, 호스티스, 누드모델로 일해서 번 돈은 모두 150만 엔, 그중 여행사에 지불하고 남은 전액이 고스란히 가방 안에 들어 있다. 계획대로라면 서른 번째 생일을 맞는 그날, 나는 완전히 빈털터리가 되거나 아니면 평생 만져 보지 못할 거금을 손에 쥐게 될 것이다.

어쨌거나 상관없다. 라스베이거스의 카지노에서 내가 진짜 얻고자 하는 것은 일확천금이 아니라 '느낌'이니까. 세상에서 가장 화려한 곳, 인간의 욕망이 가장 극명하게 표출되는 그 현장에서 나는 그 모든 느낌들을 흡수할 것이다. 그리고 미련 없이 세상을 떠날 각오까지 다 준비됐다. 그런 의미로 본다면, 나의 베팅액은 '나'라는 존재 자체인 셈이다.

라스베이거스까지는 직항 편이 없기 때문에 로스앤젤레스에서 갈아타야 한다. 비행기는 지금 막 LA공항을 이륙했다. 이변이 없는 한 이제 내가 딛게 될 땅은 라스베이거스가 될 것이다. 가슴이 터질 것만 같다.

더 이상 두려운 건 없었다. 롯폰기의 외국인 친구들과 영어로 수다를 떨 만큼 기본적인 회화에는 자신이 있었고, 서점이나 인터넷에서 관련서적과 가이드북을 읽고 또 읽었기 때문에 이젠 눈을 감고도 거리를 걸을 수 있을 정도였다. 오히려 지나치리만큼 철저하게 준비한 것이 순수한 감동을 방해하지는 않을까, 그런 묘한 불안감까지 들었다.

잠시 후 기내방송이 흘러나왔다. 맥캐런 공항이 가까워지고 있었다. 창밖을 보니 한낮의 태양이 내리쬐는 광활한 사막 한가운데에 돌연 신기루 같은 라스베이거스의 거리가 모습을 드러냈다. 쭉 뻗은 거리 양쪽에는 높다란 호텔과 다운타운이 자리하고 있다. 수많은 책에서 닳고 닳도록 봤던 풍경이 그대로 펼쳐졌다. 나는 정말 라스베이거스에 온 것이다. 흥분과 설렘이 극에 달했는지 몸이 뜨겁게 달아오르며 부들부들 떨려오기 시작했다.

비행기가 활주로에 내리고 문이 열렸다. 나는 후들거리는 다리로 1년 동안 간절히 바라고 바라던 땅 위에 내려섰다.

'자, 이제 시작이다. 후회 없이, 미련 없이 호화롭게 노는 거야.'

공항 터미널 빌딩으로 들어서는 순간, 요란한 소리가 여기저기서 울렸다. 슬롯머신이었다. 라스베이거스에서는 슬롯머신이 '당신을 환영합니다!'라는 멘트를 대신하는 것만 같았다.

수화물 찾는 곳에서 가방을 챙겨든 뒤, 나는 재빨리 터미널을 빠져나왔다. 바깥은 사막 특유의 강한 태양이 이글이글 타오르고 있었다. 섭씨 40도에 육박하는 더위 속에서 나는 순식간에 땀투성이가 되었다.

공항 셔틀 버스에 몸을 싣고 베네치안 호텔로 가는 동안, 거리를 가득 메운 엄청난 규모의 시설물에 나는 입을 다물지 못했다. 세계 최대의 호텔이자 카지노 리조트인 'MGM그랜드', 디즈니랜드의 신데렐라 성 같은 '엑스칼리버', 맨해튼의 고층빌딩을 재현한 '뉴욕, 뉴욕'……. 나는 그 어마어마한 건물들을 보며 '인간의 상상력'이란 것에 새삼 경탄했다.

　호텔에 도착하자 실제로 이탈리아의 베네치아에 온 것 같은 착각이 들었다. 호텔 앞에는 물이 흐르고 그 위로 곤돌라와 칸초네를 부르는 뱃사공, 그리고 산마르코 광장과 두칼레 궁전, 리알토 다리 등 물의 도시를 대표하는 풍경이 고스란히 펼쳐졌다.

　현란하고 호화로운 입구를 지나 로비로 들어서자 온통 프레스코화로 채워진 높다란 돔 형태의 천장이 보였다. 나는 이런 것에 아주 익숙한 척하려 애썼지만 소용없었다. 걸을 때마다 새롭게 나타나는 풍경 때문에 흘끔흘끔 둘러보지 않고는 도저히 견딜 수가 없었다.

　입실 수속을 마치고 카드키를 받아든 뒤 시큐리티 존을 지났다. 가는 길에 1만 평방미터가 넘는 거대한 카지노 플로어가 펼쳐졌다. 수천 대의 머신과 테이블이 들어차 있는 플로어는 두뇌 회로를 마비시킬 것 같은 전자음이 끝없이 울려 퍼지고 있었다.

　'이곳이 내 결전의 무대…….'

가슴 속에서 뜨거운 것이 끓어오르는 것을 꾹 참고 엘리베이터로 향했다. 도중에 쇼핑가가 있는 2층에 들르니, 그곳에도 운하가 흐르고 곤돌라가 떠 있었다. 올려다보니 실내인데도 푸른 하늘이 실감나게 펼쳐져 있었다.

여기저기 둘러보고 싶지만 일단 짐부터 풀어야 한다. 객실 층에 내려 긴 복도를 걸어 겨우 방문 앞에 이르렀다. 생애 최초로 들어가 보는 스위트룸, 단 며칠뿐인 짧은 시간이지만 내 인생의 마지막 성이 되어 줄 방이다.

베네치안 호텔은 모든 객실이 60평 이상의 넓은 스위트룸으로 이루어져 있다. 내 방은 최고 등급은 아니지만 거실과 침실이 분리되어 있고 욕실에는 소형 텔레비전이 딸려 있다. 충분히 넓고 우아하며 꿈꾸던 모든 것들이 갖춰져 있다. 나는 피로에 지쳐, 아니 감격에 겨워 침대 위로 몸을 던졌다.

라스베이거스는 아직 오후 3시, 일본과의 시차는 서머타임 때라 16시간이다. 얼른 거리로 나가고 싶은 마음이 굴뚝같았지만, 앞으로의 컨디션 조절을 위해 잠깐 잠을 자둘 필요가 있었다. 비행기 안에서도 잠을 못 자고 밤을 꼴딱 새우지 않았던가. 나는 나 자신에게 기꺼이 잠을 허락했다.

알람 소리에 눈을 떴다. 방은 깜깜한 암흑이었다.

'여긴 어디지?'

순간적으로 기억이 멈춰 버렸다. 내가 라스베이거스에 와 있다는 것을 깨닫기까지는 시간이 걸렸다. 다음 순간 나는 총알같이 일어나 커튼을 젖혔다. 안타깝게도 방향이 거리 쪽이 아니라서 라스베이거스의 밤거리는 제대로 보이지 않는다.

'얼른 나가자!'

나는 황급히 옷을 갈아입었다. 이 여행을 위해 나는 1년 동안 차곡차곡 옷을 준비해 왔었다. 나는 원래 옷을 아무렇게나 입는 스타일이었다. 하지만 스물아홉 살 이전까지 샀던 옷들보다 이 한 해 동안 장만한 옷이 훨씬 많고, 훨씬 비쌌다. 그중에는 긴자와 롯폰기에서 몇 차례 입어 본 것들도 있지만, 오직 이날만을 위해 아껴 둔 옷도 있었다.

산책할 때 입을 옷을 비롯해서 런치, 디너, 호텔 바, 카지노 등 상황과 장소가 바뀔 때마다 계속해서 옷을 갈아입을 작정이었다. 옷만 제대로 입어 줘도 마음의 자세가 엄청나게 달라진다는 그 분명한 진실을 이제 나는 알고 있다.

문을 열고 나와 길고 긴 복도를 걸어 호텔을 나섰다. 상점과 행인, 네온이 화려하게 빛나는 밤거리를 다양한 국적, 다양한 인종의 사람들이 활보하고 있다. 미국에서 가장 치안이 잘 되어 있다는 말을 증명이라도 하듯 여기저기 보안요원들이 서 있었다. 이런 길이라면 한밤중에 여자 혼자 걸어도 전혀 두려울 게 없을 듯했다.

나는 마치 집에서 바람 쐬러 나온 사람처럼 자연스럽게 걸었다. 그리고 가능한 한 감탄사를 입 밖으로 내지 않기로 굳게 마음을 먹었다. 터져 나오는 탄성마저 내 속에 꼭꼭 간직하고 싶었기 때문이다. 라스베이거스는 '인간이 밤을 지배했다'는 생생한 증거와도 같다. 세상의 그 어떤 사진도, 그 어떤 영상도 이곳을 제대로 표현할 수는 없다.

'이제 뭐 좀 먹어야겠다!'

눈이 먼저 포식했으니 이제 입과 배를 채워야 한다. 라스베이거스에서의 첫 식사를 어디서 시작할 것인가? 나는 오래전부터 이미 파리스 호텔 뷔페를 생각해 두고 있었다. 걷다가 에펠탑이 보이면 그곳이 파리스 호텔이다. 물론 파리의 에펠탑보다는 절반가량 작지만…….

유명한 뷔페답게 줄을 서서 기다린 끝에 나는 드디어 뷔페로 들어섰다. 어마어마한 요리와 다양한 디저트가 마치 작품 전시회처럼 펼쳐져 있었다. 그러나 가격은 의외로 저렴한 편이었다. 라스베이거스는 카지노에 돈을 쓰게 하려고 음식점 가격을 비교적 낮게 설정해 놓기 때문이다.

혼자서 뷔페라니, 1년 전의 나라면 주변의 이목에 신경 쓰느라 제대로 먹지도 못했을 것이다. 하지만 이제 그런 건 아무래도 괜찮다. 남이 어떻게 보든 상관없다. 중요한 것은 이 순간을 얼마나 즐길 수 있는가, 오직 그것뿐이다. 나는 최대한 천천히 요리를 음미했다. 그리고 뷔페를 나와 게으른 코끼리처럼 느릿느릿 걸어서 벨라지오 호텔로 향했다.

널따란 연못이 대지 면적의 절반을 차지하는 벨라지오는, 베네치안 호텔과 함께 마지막 순간까지 나를 갈등하게 만들었던 최고급 호텔이다. 결국 베네치안 호텔에 묵기로 결정하긴 했지만, 라스베이거스에서의 마지막 날까지 이곳을 매일매일 찾아오리라.

그때 연못에서 커다란 분수가 뿜어져 나오자 사람들이 일제히 환호성을 질렀다. 영화 〈오션스 일레븐〉의 라스트 신에서 봤던 것과 똑같이 벨라지오의 분수 쇼가 시작된 것이다. 사라 브라이트만이 부르는 '타임 투 세이 굿바이'에 맞춰 형형색색의 조명과 함께 분수가 춤을 추었다. 천 개가 넘는 분출구에서 뿜어져 나온 물줄기가 하늘 높이 솟구치며 매끄러운 곡선을 그렸다. 인간이 만들어 낸 물과 빛과 음악의 군무를 지켜보며 나는 생각했다.

'그래, 이제 안녕이라고 말할 시간이야.'

나도 모르게 볼 위로 뜨거운 눈물이 흘러내렸다.

지난 1년 동안 나는 아무리 힘들어도 결코 눈물을 흘리지 않았다. 훌쩍댈 시간마저 없었다. 하지만 지금 이 순간은 흐르는 대로 내버려두자. 분수의 물줄기에 푹 젖은 것처럼 얼굴이 온통 젖는다 해도 그냥 내버려두자.

Time to say goodbye…….
이제 나는 내가 알던 나로부터 영원히 떠난다.

스물아홉의 마지막 날

사진을 찍거나 기념품 가게를 기웃거리는 짓 따위는 하지 않았다. 그럴 시간도, 그럴 마음도 없었다. 나는 시시껄렁한 여가를 보내기 위해 여기 온 것이 아니다. 돌아가서 사람들에게 자랑하기 위해서 온 것도 아니다. 서른이 될 때까지 아무것도 채우지 못하고, 아무것도 느끼지 못했던 가엾은 내면의 감각들에게 그저 잔치를 베풀어 주고 싶었을 뿐이다.

'나'라는 주인을 잘못 만나 3평짜리 원룸에 갇혀 눅눅하고 음침하게 퇴화되고 있었던 나의 오감에게 나는 말했다.

'그동안 미안했어. 늦었지만, 그리고 이번 한 번뿐이겠지만 누릴 수 있는 대로 누려 봐.'

나는 마치 일생일대의 전투에 뛰어들 듯 3일 동안 라스베이거스의 구석구석을 바람처럼 배회하기 시작했다. 거대한 로마제국 같은 시저스펠리스 호텔과 MGM그랜드, 엑스칼리버 호텔, 그리고 그 안에서 펼쳐지는 화려한 쇼를 구경하고 헬리콥터로 라스베이거스의 야경도 만끽했다. 스트라토스피어 전망대의 무시무시한 놀이기구와 지상 3,000미터 높이에서 점프하는 스카이다이빙, 그리고 프리먼트 거리에서 천만 개의 LED가 뿜어내는 빛과 소리의 쇼에도 매료되었다. 상상은 현실보다 과장된다고 하지만, 라스베이거스에서는 현실이 상상을 초월한다.

날이 밝을 무렵부터 늦은 밤까지는 그렇게 밖에서 온몸으로 라스베이거스의 공기를 흡수했고, 호텔 방으로 돌아와서는 결전의 날을 위해 잠들기 전까지 카드 카운팅의 최종 체크에 공을 들였다. 그리고 베네치안 호텔의 카지노를 수차례 들락거리며 사전 답사를 하고 또 했다. 블랙잭은 지역이나 호텔마다 미묘한 룰의 차이가 있기 때문에 미리 확인해 둘 필요가 있었다.

카지노의 분위기에 익숙해지려고 미니멈 5달러 테이블을 찾아 여러 게임을 해보기도 했다. 하지만 그토록 연습을 거듭했어도 실제 카지노의 분위기에 주눅이 든 탓인지 내 몸은 잔뜩 굳어 있었다. 플레이어와 딜러 사이에는 무엇이든 손으로 건네서는 안 된다는 원칙을 잊고, 현금을 카지노 칩으로 교환할 때 딜러에게 직접 돈을 건네는 초보적인 실수까지 저지르고 말았다.

'괜찮아. 이런 실수들도 미리 해보는 게 좋아. 마지막 날, 그날을 위해 모든 것을 익혀 두는 거야.'

그렇게 사흘을 보낸 뒤, 드디어 운명의 마지막 날을 맞이했다.

관광도 여행도 이제 다 끝났다. 이제 치열하고 뜨거웠던 나의 1년을 마감하게 될 최종 임무만 남았다. 오늘 밤은 라스베이거스에서 보내는 마지막 밤이자, 나의 스물아홉 살이 끝나는 마지막 밤이다.

나는 해 지기 전까지 오로지 카지노에만 집중하기 위해 베네치안 스파를 방문했다. 지금까지의 피로와 오늘의 긴장을 풀어야 했기 때문이다. 스파 입구에 들어서자 정면에 암벽등반용 클라이밍 벽이 펼쳐졌다. 이곳은 스파와 살롱 외에도 트레이닝 스튜디오, 피트니스 스튜디오, 그리고 수영장까지 갖추고 있었다.

피트니스에서 가볍게 몸을 풀고 사우나와 증기탕에서 땀을 뺀 다음, 욕조에 몸을 담그고 긴장된 근육을 최대한 이완시켰다. 그리고 100종류가 넘는 옵션에서 마사지 하나를 선택했다. 영화 배우처럼 핸섬한 남자 스태프에게 마사지를 받은 다음 살롱에서 네일 케어까지 했다. 그렇게 몸도 마음도 상큼하게 가다듬은 뒤 4층에 위치한 옥외 수영장으로 향했다. 탈의실에서 비키니를 꺼내든 순간, 나는 오랜 버릇처럼 잠시 망설였다.

'괜찮아. 넌 지금 최고로 아름다워.'

나는 자신에게 그렇게 말했다. 내 체중은 이제 47킬로그램까지 와 있었다. 1년 사이에 25킬로그램 넘게 살이 빠진 것이다. 이제 나는 예전의 내가 아니다. 누구 앞에서도 당당할 수 있다. 나는 태어나서 처음으로 비키니를 입고 사뿐사뿐 수영장으로 나갔다.

❖ ❖ ❖

사막 한복판의 인공 오아시스 주변에는 열대의 나무와 아름다운 구조물들이 나란히 하늘을 향하고, 수면은 새파란 하늘빛으로 찰랑찰랑 빛나고 있었다. 나는 선글라스를 쓰고 비치체어에 드러누워 칵테일과 샌드위치를 주문했다. 주변에는 이런 호화판에 아주 익숙해 보이는 부류의 사람들이 연인끼리, 혹은 가족끼리 와서 한껏 즐기고 있었다.

'저들 눈에도 내가 자신들과 같은 부류처럼 보일까? 내가 이 짧은 순간을 위해 1년 동안 칙칙한 3평짜리 원룸에서 살면서 하루 20시간 넘게 일했다는 사실을 짐작이나 할까?'

그런 생각이 들자 기분이 묘해지면서 약간 쾌감이 일었다. 최고급 룸에 머물며 카지노에서 아무렇지도 않게 거금을 날리는 사람들에게 150만 엔이라는 나의 전 재산 따위는 돈도 아닐 테지. 하지만 아무래도 상관없다. 돈이 많건 적건 간에 이 순간의 행복이 중요할 뿐이다. 더구나 지금 내가 누리는 사치는 죽을힘을 다해 발버둥친 대가로 얻은 것이 아닌가?

호스티스로 일하면서 호화로운 레스토랑이나 부자들이 노는 곳에 따라가 본 적은 있지만, 이만큼 만족스러웠던 적은 단 한 번도 없었다. 고생해서 얻은 만큼 나는 지금 최고의 시간을 누리고 있는 것이다. 나는 라스베이거스의 햇볕 아래서 유유자적 헤엄을 치거나 파라솔 아래 드러누워 잠을 자며 꿈같은 시간을 보냈다. 서서히 저물어 가는 해를 바라보며 칵테일을 마시고 있는데, 누군가 영어로 말을 걸어왔다. 키가 큰 백인 남자였다.

"어디서 오셨나요?"

롯폰기의 클럽에서도 몇 번인가 작업을 걸어오는 사람은 있었지만 그것과는 차원이 다르다. 꿈에 그리던 리조트의 상큼한 푸른 하늘 아래, 맷 딜런을 닮은 꽃미남 외국인이 말을 걸어오고 있지 않은가! 나는 두근거리는 가슴을 누르며 서툰 영어로 대답했다.

"일본이요. 당신은?"

"와! 일본? 저는 뉴욕에서 왔어요. 가족과 함께인가요?"

"아뇨, 친구요."

순간적으로 거짓말을 했다. 주위는 온통 커플과 친구, 가족뿐이다. 여자 혼자 여행 왔다고 하면 괜히 이상한 생각을 품을지도 모른다.

"그래요? 저도 친구랑 왔는데. 그 친구는 지금 카지노에 있어요. 친구 녀석은 이렇게 가슴이 확 트이는 수영장을 놔두고 완전히 카지노에만 빠져 있답니다. 그런데 혹시 학생이세요?"

역시 동양인은 어려 보이는 모양이다. 내일이면 서른이 되는 나를 학생으로 보다니, 나는 그냥 "예스"라고 대답했다.

"저는 로브라고 합니다. 변호사죠."

얼핏 장난기가 많아 보였지만, 얘기를 나눠 보니 똑똑하고 신사적인 데다 아주 매력적이기까지 했다. 로브는 "혹시 괜찮다면……" 하고 본론으로 들어갔다.

"오늘 저녁 함께 하는 거 어때요?"

세상에 이런 횡재가! 20대의 마지막 밤을 이렇게 멋진 사람과 함께 할 수 있다니.

나는 속내를 감추고 여유롭게 "그렇게 하죠"라고 대답했다.

우리는 오후 6시에 호텔 로비에서 다시 만났다. 라스베이거스에서의 마지막 저녁 식사를 위해 나는 아껴 둔 핑크색 시폰 원피스에 숄을 걸쳤다. 로브는 군청색 재킷에 한층 더 예의를 갖춘 모습으로 나타났다.

나는 그를 따라 아늑한 분위기의 이탈리안 레스토랑으로 들어 갔다. 레스토랑 입구는 '알 만한 사람은 다 안다'는 느낌을 노린 건지 일부러 찾기 어렵게 해놓은 것 같았다. 호텔 안에만 16곳이 나 되는 레스토랑 중에서 이렇게 구석진 곳에 보물 같은 최고급 레스토랑이 있다는 사실을 나는 마지막 날에야 알게 됐다. 라스 베이거스에 도착한 뒤로 뷔페나 패스트푸드, 패밀리 레스토랑은 다녀 봤지만, 입구에서부터 고급스러운 느낌이 확 풍기는 정통 레스토랑은 처음이었다.

계단 아래로 곤돌라가 떠다니는 운하를 바라보면서 우리는 코스 요리를 즐겼다. 마치 영화 속 주인공이 된 듯했다. 맛있는 요리와 우아한 음악, 눈앞에는 매력적인 남성…… 이 완벽한 분위기에서 대체 무엇이 더 필요할까.

식사가 끝나자 로브는 "바에서 한잔 더 할까요?" 하며 나를 (본격적으로) 유혹하기 시작했다. 사실 라스베이거스의 야경이 보이는 호텔 바에 구미가 당기긴 했다. 만일 이런 일이 어제 생겼더라면 난 응했을지도 모른다. 하지만 오늘 밤, 나에겐 해야 할 일이 있었다.

"정말 미안해요. 전 이제 가봐야 해요."

나는 정중하게, 그러나 단호히 거절했다.

나의 스물아홉도 이제 몇 시간밖에 남지 않았다. 신데렐라의 마법이 풀리기 전에 임무를 완수해야 한다. 로브는 꽤나 아쉬워했고 나 역시 미련이 있었지만 어쩔 수 없었다. 나는 연락처도 교환하지 않고 어떤 약속도 하지 않았다.

서른 살이 되는 내일…… 어쩌면 나는 이 세상에 없을지도 모르니까.

주저할 때가 바로
승부를 걸어야 할 때

    나는 다시 객실로 올라가 옷장을 활짝 열었다. 그리고 이 순간을 위해 오래전부터 준비해 둔 의상을 꺼내 침대 위에 펼쳐 놓았다. 나는 결전의 장으로 떠나는 전사의 심정으로 천천히 옷을 갈아입었다. 노출이 심한 검정 드레스에, 이미테이션이지만 화려한 목걸이를 하고 굵은 반지를 꼈다. 머리는 정성껏 말아 올리고, 긴자에서 갈고 닦은 솜씨로 눈부시게 화장까지 했다. 그리고 마지막으로 거울 앞에 섰다.

    거기, 익숙하면서도 낯선 여자가 서 있었다. 그녀는 아름다웠지만 위험해 보였고, 행복해 보였지만 동시에 슬픔도 간직하고 있었다.

"나의 20대여, 이제 안녕."

나는 시계를 꺼내 11시 59분에 울리도록 알람을 맞춰 놓았다. 이 알람이 울리면 라스베이거스의 일정과 더불어 나의 스물아홉 살도 끝을 맞이하게 될 것이다. 블랙잭 게임에서 거금을 따건 빈 털터리가 되건 나는 11시 59분에 미련 없이 일어설 것이다. 나의 목표는 그 시각까지 계속 게임을 하는 것이다.

모든 준비를 마친 뒤, 나는 조용히 문을 닫고 카지노를 향해 천천히 걸음을 옮겼다. 요란하고 화려한 카지노 플로어에 들어서는 순간 온몸의 신경이 곤두섰다. 하지만 나는 침착하게, 수수께끼의 동양 미녀 같은 이미지를 그대로 유지한 채 가슴을 펴고 사뿐사뿐 걸었다. 사람들의 시선이 느껴졌다. 나이 지긋한 백인 여자가 "정말 아름다워요!" 하고 말을 건네기도 했다. 나는 마치 귀부인처럼 우아하게 목례를 했다.

2천 대가 넘는 게임 머신과 130대의 게임 테이블을 갖춘 넓디넓은 카지노 플로어에는 수많은 사람들이 북적이고 있었다. 나는 다른 곳에는 눈길조차 주지 않고 오직 블랙잭 테이블만을 둘러보았다. 칩을 산처럼 쌓아 놓은 플레이어의 주변에는 수많은 구경꾼들이 운집해 있었다. 몇 개의 테이블 중에서 딜러의 느낌이 가장 좋은 곳을 정한 뒤, 나는 잠시 구경꾼들 틈에 섞여 살펴보기로 했다.

어제까지는 미니멈 5달러짜리 칩으로 연습을 해왔지만, 실전인 오늘은 그 열 배인 50달러부터다. 현재 환율은 1달러에 약 100엔, 즉 일본 엔으로 최소한 5,000엔부터 걸어야만 한다. 상당한 고액의 테이블이다. 어떻게 거느냐에 따라 내가 1년 동안 벌어들인 액수 따윈 순식간에 날릴 수도 있다. 베팅 금액이 적은 테이블은 룰을 잘 모르는 초보자가 플레이하기 때문에 딜러와 잡담을 나누는 등 화기애애한 분위기이지만, 베팅 금액이 큰 테이블에서는 플레이어와 딜러는 물론 구경꾼마저 긴장감이 감돈다.

'좋아, 인생을 걸기엔 아주 적합한 무대야.'

잠시 살펴보는 중에도 플레이어는 연신 들고나며 사라져 간다. 나는 딜러가 셔플하는 순간부터 카운팅을 시작해 봤다.

'5, 6, 7, 8······.'

수를 세는 동안 점점 플러스가 늘어 플레이어에게 유리한 상황이 전개되었다. 나는 마음을 정한 후 테이블의 가장 왼쪽 자리에 앉았다.

"체인지 플리즈."

그리고 엔화 20만 엔에 해당하는 2,000달러를 카지노 칩으로 바꿨다. 가슴이 터질 듯이 쿵쾅대기 시작한다.

자, 드디어 시작이다!

❖ ❖ ❖

50달러를 베팅하자 슈(shoe : 카드를 한 덱 이상 보유하기 위한 딜링 박스)에서 두 장의 카드가 분배되었다. 이 테이블의 슈에는 6덱이 들어 있다.

'내 손에 들어온 패의 합은 14, 그리고 딜러의 페이스 업 카드는 6이니까……'

아직 머리 움직임이 둔하다. 그사이 다른 플레이어가 익숙한 손놀림으로 신호를 보냈다. 나도 당황해서 집게손가락으로 테이블을 두드리며 '히트' 신호를 보냈다.

'아차!'

너무 긴장한 탓인지 실수를 저지르고 말았다. 수중의 카드는 7이 두 장, 그렇다면 카드를 둘로 나누는 '스프리트' 사인을 냈어야만 했다. 하지만 이미 늦었다. 무정하게도 테이블에서는 또 한 장의 카드가 분배되고 있었다. 그런데 내 패를 확인하는 순간 구경꾼 사이에서 '원더풀!' 하는 탄성이 새어나왔다.

이럴 수가, 세 번째 카드 역시 7이었다. 모두 합해 21이 되는 쓰리세븐! 좀처럼 나오지 않는 최고의 패였다.

'이건 기적이야!'

태어나서 한 번도 느껴 본 적 없는 흥분과 설렘이 온몸을 휘감았다.

"오! 멋지군요!"

옆에서 플레이하던 뚱뚱한 백인 남자의 눈이 휘둥그레졌다. 나는 애써 여유로운 태도로 미소를 지었다. 뺨에 경련이 일어날 지경이었다.

30초도 안 되는 이 한 번의 승부로 50달러가 두 배인 100달러로 변한 것이다. 나는 끝까지 포커페이스를 유지하고 있는 딜러에게 팁을 내놓았다. 팁 사회인 미국답게 카지노에서도 크게 땄을 때나 테이블을 벗어날 때에는 신세를 진 딜러에게 팁을 주는게 매너다. 나는 비록 최소액만 베팅했기 때문에 크게 딴 것은 아니지만, 이 아름다운 패에 대한 기념과 감사의 의미로 팁을 내놓은 것이다.

'좋은 징조일까, 혹시 나의 운을 너무 일찍 써버린 건 아닐까?'

진귀한 쓰리세븐 덕분에 이제 모두들 '이 여자, 보통 아닌데' 하는 눈빛으로 보기 시작했다. 그저 요행일 뿐이었는데, 설마 충분히 카운팅을 하고 만반의 태세를 갖춘 뒤 실전에 돌입한 '프로 겜블러'로 여기는 건 아니겠지. 어쨌거나 분위기가 달아오르자 여기저기서 구경꾼들이 모여들기 시작했다. 그들의 시선은 대부분 나에게 고정되어 있었다.

'어떡하지?'

남들의 시선은 익숙하지 않을 뿐더러 게임에도 방해가 된다. 딜러와 플로어에서 구석구석 눈을 번득이며 감시하고 있는 피트 보스(카지노 최고 감독자)에게 카드 카운터(블랙잭 게임에서 승산의 이동에 따라 베팅 형태를 바꾸며, 게임에 사용된 모든 카드를 암산하는 게임자)로 찍히면 이 소중한 기회마저 박탈당할 우려가 있기 때문이다. 라스베이거스에서는 카운팅이 사실상 금지되었지만, 현재까지는 아직 그렇게 엄격하지 않았다. 그래도 카지노 측에서는 카드 카운터들을 눈엣가시 같은 존재로 여긴다. 카운팅을 하고 있다는 사실이 들통 나면 그 자리에서 쫓겨날 수도 있는 것이다.

카지노에서는 카운팅에 대한 대비책도 강구하고 있는데, 예를 들어 '잦은 셔플'을 들 수 있다. 일반적으로 카드를 70~80퍼센트 정도 분배하고 나서 전부 셔플하도록 하지만, 카운터가 있다는 의심이 들면 50퍼센트나 그 이하에서 셔플을 한다. 그렇게 되면 애써 계산한 카운트가 다시 원점으로 되돌아간다. 극단적인 경우 매번 셔플하게 된다면 카운팅의 효과는 전혀 기대할 수 없게 된다. 하지만 실제로는 게임 진행이 더뎌져 수익률이 내려가기 때문에 셔플을 그렇게 자주 하지는 않는다.

카운터가 들통 나는 포인트는 먼저 시선의 움직임에 있다. 보통 사람은 자신의 카드만으로도 벅차지만 카드 카운터는 다른 플레이어의 패나 히트한 카드까지 꿰뚫고 있기 때문이다.

'티 안 나게, 티 안 나게…….'

나는 마음속으로 주문을 외며 티 나지 않게 딜러와 다른 플레이어의 카드를 재빨리 읽어 나갔다. 하지만 사람들의 시선이 나의 일거수일투족에 집중될수록 긴장 때문에 점점 힘들어졌다. 그렇게 경직된 상태에서 게임이 몇 차례 진행되는 사이, 커다란 금반지를 낀 아시아계 남자가 내 옆에 떡하니 자리를 잡았다.

"체인지 플리즈."

그는 칩을 교환한 뒤 내게 물었다.

"어디서 오셨나요?"

"일본이요."

"그렇군요. 저는 중국입니다. 함께 즐겨 볼까요?"

그의 대범한 미소가 내 마음을 푸근하게 했다.

'그래, 철저히 즐기자.'

일생일대의 큰 무대가 아닌가, 위축되기에는 너무나도 아까운 시간이다. 나는 고도의 테크닉을 지닌 카드 카운터가 아니다. 멍청하게 실수도 잘 저지른다. 하지만 뭐 어떤가? 과감하게 부딪쳐 보는 거다. 나답게 거침없이 승부를 즐기자.

구경꾼들은 점점 내 편이 되어 나를 응원해 주고 있었다. 덩달아 나도 점점 타인의 시선과 응원을 은근히 즐길 수 있을 정도로 평정을 찾기 시작했다. 나는 지나가는 웨이트리스를 불러 오렌지 주스를 주문하고 팁으로 1달러를 건네는 여유까지 생겼다.

　카지노에서 플레이하는 사람이라면 누구든 칵테일이나 맥주를 공짜로 마실 수 있다. 술을 좋아하는 사람이라면 더없이 행복한 일이겠지만, 사실 플레이어의 판단력을 흐리게 하거나 대범하게 만들어 계속해서 돈을 쏟아붓게 하기 위한 전략이다. 나는 주스를 단숨에 들이켜고 숨을 크게 내쉰 뒤, 파이팅을 외쳤다.

　'좋아! 시작해 볼까?'

　나는 본격적으로 게임에 집중하기 시작했다.

　칩을 놓고 신호를 보낸다. 세세한 동작 하나하나 우아하고 침착하게, 그러나 머릿속은 초고속으로 풀가동하고 있다. 게임이 시작되자 세 명의 플레이어에게 각각 카드가 분배되었다.

　현재 카운트는 플러스 3이다. 오른쪽 끝에 앉은 부인의 패는 8과 7, 다음 한 장이 2가 나와 합이 17로 스탠드, 그리고 옆자리의 중국 남자는 4와 8, 딜러의 페이스 업 카드를 보고 히트를 선택하자 세 번째 카드는 4, 네 번째는 6이 나오는 바람에 합이 '22'로 버스트가 되고 말았다. 나의 패는 J와 9, 합이 19로 스탠드, 그리고 딜러의 페이스 업 카드는 9, 페이스 다운 카드를 젖히자 5가 나오고 세 번째 카드는 Q가 나와 버스트가 되었다.

정리해 보자. 이번 판에서 카운트는 토털 플러스 6, 슈 속의 카드는 반 이상 분배되었을까?

'슬슬 승부수를 띄워 보자.'

나는 얼굴에 표시가 나지 않도록 침을 꿀꺽 삼켰다. 그리고 베팅액을 100달러로 올렸다. 100달러는 긴자에서의 하루치 급여다. 하지만 이제 그런 쩨쩨한 생각은 하지 않기로 한다. 이 자리에서 내가 가진 스킬, 운, 재산, 인생, 모든 것을 아낌없이 내놓는 것이다.

내게 분배된 카드는 7과 5, 합이 12, 그리고 딜러의 페이스 업 카드는 5. 나는 손바닥을 아래로 향해 좌우로 흔들어 스탠드 사인을 냈다. 생각대로 딜러는 K를 빼내어 버스트가 되었다. 페이스 다운 카드는 10이었다. 내가 이겼다.

'좋았어!'

나는 마음속으로 쾌재를 불렀다. 다른 플레이어의 카드를 포함하여 카운트는 6으로 변함이 없다. 승부는 계속되었다. 나는 다시 100달러를 걸었다.

이번에는 나의 패가 5와 8로 합이 13이다. 딜러의 페이스 업 카드가 J라서 버스트를 기대하며 스탠드했지만, 딜러는 운 좋게 5가 나와 페이스 다운 카드 6과 합해 '21'이 되었다. 이번엔 나의 패배다. 나는 탄식하거나 화내지 않고 포커페이스를 그대로 유지했다.

주사위를 수백 번, 수천 번 흔들다 보면 1부터 6의 숫자가 나올 확률이 각각 1/6에 가까워지듯 블랙잭의 카운팅도 게임이 거듭되면 될수록 평균치에 가까워진다. 그러니 단 한 번의 승부로 일희일비할 필요는 없다. 승부니까 당연히 질 때도 있다. 패배를 줄이고 승리할 타이밍을 가늠하여 한 번 크게 걸어 보자.

플레이어는 끊임없이 들어오고 나가지만, 나는 강태공처럼 흐르는 강에 낚싯대를 드리우고 단 한 번의 기회를 노리고 있다. 플레이어는 각양각색이다. 시종일관 깐깐한 표정으로 침묵을 지키는 노인이 있는가 하면, "라스베이거스에는 자주 오나요?" 하며 서글서글하게 말을 건네는 쾌활한 청년도 있다.

나는 신경을 빼앗기지 않고 계속해서 카운팅을 했다. 히트와 스탠드를 반복하자 나의 칩도 늘었다 줄었다를 반복한다. 카운트도 오르락내리락 한다. 칩이 떨어질 때마다 나는 몇 번이나 추가로 환전을 했다.

밤이 깊어지면서 카지노에는 사람들이 점점 많아졌다. 인파가 절정에 달했을 무렵, 나에게 최대의 기회가 주어졌다. 서서히 늘고 있던 카운트가 드디어 플러스 10을 넘은 것이다.

'이때다!'

나는 과감하게 500달러를 베팅했다.

뒤에 선 구경꾼들이 웅성거리기 시작했다. 곧이어 분배된 카드는 5와 6으로 11, 이제 10점짜리 하이 카드가 나오면 21이 되는 찬스 카드다. 딜러의 페이스 업 카드는 K였다. 하이 카드가 아직 많이 남아 있는 지금의 상황이라면 더블다운을 해야만 한다. 하지만 그렇게 하려면 500달러를 더 베팅하지 않으면 안 된다. 즉 합계 1,000달러를 걸어야 하는 것이다. 이기면 두 배, 지면 1,000달러를 순식간에 날리게 된다.

'더블다운을 할 것인가, 말 것인가.'

나는 스스로에게 되물었다. 하지만 나의 손은 이미 500달러 칩을 쥐고 있었다.

'주저할 때가 바로 승부를 걸어야 할 때!'

그래, 여기서 걸지 않고 어떻게 승부를 기대하겠는가? 막판의 담력은 누드모델로 배양된 나의 무기가 아니겠는가. 내가 500달러 칩을 추가하자 '와!' 하는 탄성이 울려 퍼졌다. 곧이어 세 번째 카드가 주어졌다. 나의 시선은 물론 모두의 시선이 카드에 집중되었다.

…… 하이카드 10이 나왔다. 합이 21! 그리고 딜러는 Q가 나와 페이스 다운 카드인 4와 합해 24가 되어 버스트!

"원더풀!"

여기저기서 박수갈채가 터져 나왔다. 나는 심장이 터질 것만 같았다. 가까스로 진정한 뒤 나는 딜러에게 팁으로 200달러를 건네주었다. 귀부인이라도 된 양 우아하고 품위 있게. 그러자 어느 틈엔가 옆자리로 옮겨 온 영국 신사가 어깨를 으쓱하며 물었다.

"그렇게 쓰면 남편이 뭐라고 하지 않나요?"

나는 웃으며 "네, 괜찮아요"라고 대답했다. 내가 부잣집 안주인으로 보이는 모양이다. 어떻게 생각하든 나는 지금 이 순간을 누구보다 확실히 즐기고 있었다. 긴장 때문이 아니라 기쁨에 겨워 몸이 떨린다. 뇌 속에서 아드레날린이 한꺼번에 방출되어 찌릿찌릿 저릴 정도로 흥분이 된다.

자, 이제 또 다른 한 판이 시작된다. 나는 세상의 소리와 단절된 채 점점 게임의 세계로 빠져들었다.

새로운 시작은
5달러로도 충분하다

시간이 얼마나 흘렀을까.

손목시계의 알람 소리에 나는 불현듯 현실 세계로 돌아왔다. 너무 집중한 탓인지 머리가 지끈지끈 쑤신다. 시계는 정확히 11시 59분을 가리키고 있었다. 오후 8시부터 4시간 동안 꼼짝 않고 게임에만 몰두하고 있는 사이 벌써 자정이 다 된 것이다. 나는 시계에서 눈을 떼지 못했다. 그리고 마침내 시간이 바뀌었다.

'12:00'

이제 새로운 하루가 시작됐다.

내가 느꼈던 모든 설렘과 두려움과 기쁨도 이제 모두 '어제'가 되어 흘러가 버렸다. 다시 오지 않을 내 인생의 진정한 하루가 끝난 것이다. 게임오버.

"고마웠어요."

나는 미련 없이 자리에서 일어났다. 그리고 수중의 칩을 모두 회수했다. 환전을 몇 번이나 거듭했는지, 이제 얼마를 따고 얼마를 잃었는지 가늠조차 할 수 없었다. 서둘러 칩을 현금으로 바꾼 뒤, 나는 롯폰기의 맘처럼 돈다발을 되는대로 마구 백에 쑤셔 넣었다. 피곤했다. 얼른 방으로 돌아가고 싶었다. 모든 사고와 감각이 정지된 기분이었다. 길고 긴 복도를 지나 방으로 돌아오자마자 나는 그대로 침대 위에 고꾸라지고 말았다.

⋯⋯모두 끝났다. 인생의 대승부도 끝나고, 나의 20대도 영원히 끝나 버렸다. 머릿속엔 수많은 생각과 감정들이 터질 듯이 들어차 있었다. 나는 그 생각들을 잠시 보류하기로 했다. 하지만 잠시 후 호기심이 밀려왔다.

'얼마나 잃었을까?'

나는 백을 열어 침대 위에 거꾸로 뒤집었다. 100달러짜리 지폐가 와르르 쏟아졌다. 방금 지나간 마지막 하루, 아니 지난 1년 내 인생의 총결산이다. 나는 지폐를 한 장 한 장 세기 시작했다.

한 장, 두 장, 세 장⋯⋯ 내가 카지노에 가지고 갔던 액수는 총

1만 달러였다. 100달러 지폐로 세면 딱 100장이다.

스물하나, 스물둘, 스물셋…… 참 신기했다. 공공요금도 제때 못 내던 내가 지폐 다발을 세고 있다니. 일흔일곱, 일흔여덟, 일흔아홉…… 지폐는 아직 몇 장 더 남아 있다. 이제 곧 답이 나온다. 백 장에서 멈추면 나의 패배, 넘으면 나의 승리다.

아흔일곱, 아흔여덟, 아흔아홉, 그리고…… 백!'

이럴 수가, 정말 100장이란 말인가? 나는 믿을 수가 없었다. 카지노에 가지고 갔던 것과 딱 맞아떨어지는 액수였다.

'아냐, 그럴 리가 없어.'

나는 다시 천천히 돈을 셌다. 그러나 이번에도 역시 거짓말처럼 100장이었다. 우연치고는 정말 기가 막힌 우연이었다.

'뭔가 잘못된 게 아닐까?'

나는 다시 백을 뒤집어 탈탈 털었다. 그러자 꼬깃꼬깃한 지폐 한 장이 더 나왔다.

'더 있었어!'

나는 허겁지겁 지폐를 펼쳤다. 그것은 5달러짜리 지폐였다.

'5달러…….'

100달러 지폐가 100장이니까 최종적으로 1만 5달러! 결국 내가 딴 돈은 달랑 5달러였다. 이것이 내 성과의 전부였다. 물론 딜러한테 기세 좋게 건넸던 팁을 포함하면 더 땄을지도 모른다. 하지만 지금 내 수중의 순이익은 5달러뿐이다.

나는 꼬깃꼬깃한 5달러 지폐를 물끄러미 들여다보았다. 지폐 속 링컨의 얼굴도 꼬깃꼬깃 주름져 있었다. 갑자기 그가 내게 말을 건넬 것만 같다.

"승리를 축하한다, 아마리!"

무수히 많은 사람의 손을 거쳐 왔을 이 5달러짜리 지폐가 갑자기 나를 뭉클하게 했다. 1년이라는 치열한 시간을 환전해서 여기까지 날아와 인생을 건 도박 끝에 5달러를 번 것이다.

'……그래, 이긴 거야. 달랑 5달러지만 난 이긴 거야!'

나는 지폐를 양손에 번쩍 들고 불빛에 비췄다. 고작 햄버거 하나 정도의 가치일 뿐이지만, 지금의 나에겐 세상에서 가장 의미 있는 종잇조각인 것이다.

느닷없이 웃음이 터져 나왔다.

'……이겼다! 인생 최대의 승부에서 승리한 거야!'

나는 큰 소리로 미친 듯이 웃으며 침대에 흩뿌려진 100달러 지폐를 위로 내던졌다. 지폐가 너울대며 내 머리 위로 쏟아졌다. 그것은 돈이 아니라 마치 팔랑팔랑 춤추는 파티용 색종이 같았다. 나는 계속해서 머리 위로 돈을 뿌렸다. 그리고 휘날리는 지폐 속에서 나에게 소리쳤다.

'Happy birthday to me!'

♦ ♦ ♦

D+1일.

라스베이거스에서의 시간은 모두 끝이 났다. 다음 날 아침 눈을 떴을 때, 침대 위에는 100달러짜리 지폐들이 어지럽게 널려 있었다. 나는 부스스한 얼굴로 일어나 창문을 활짝 열었다. 사막의 더운 바람이 방 안으로 쏟아져 들어왔다.

'이제 뭘 해야 하나.'

연극이 다 끝난 뒤 혼자 무대 위에 서 있는 느낌이었다. 지난 1년 동안 단 하루도 계획 없이 눈을 뜬 적이 없었다. 늘 해야 할 일이 있었고, 시간은 언제나 부족했다. 그런데 지금 이 순간, 나는 영원처럼 무한한 시간 속에 서 있다. 문득 〈바람과 함께 사라지다〉에서 스칼렛 오하라가 했던 마지막 대사가 떠올랐다.

'Tomorrow is another day.'

나는 다시 말을 바꾸어 조용히 속삭였다.

"Today is another day."

그리고 가방을 열어 플라스틱 통을 꺼냈다. 그것은 바로 이 시간을 위해 꼭꼭 숨겨 두었던 강력 수면제였다. 나는 테이블 위에 약통을 올려놓았다. 그리고 침대 위에서 꼬깃꼬깃한 5달러짜리 지폐를 찾아 약통 옆에 나란히 놓았다. 그런 다음, 나는 멀찌감치 떨어져서 약통과 5달러를 한참 동안 바라보았다.

　예정대로라면 나는 지금 통에 든 알약을 모조리 입 안으로 털어 넣어야 한다. 그럴 각오로 오늘 이 순간까지 내처 달려온 것이다. '기꺼이 죽겠다'라는 각오가 없었으면, 나는 지난 1년 중 단하루도 온전히 살아 내지 못했을 것이다. 계획했던 모든 일들을 완수했고, 목표했던 결승선까지 완주한 지금, 나에겐 최후의 선택만이 남았다.

　'어째서 5달러를 땄을까?'

　어제의 치열한 게임에서 획득한 5달러짜리 지폐가 갈수록 커다란 의미로 다가왔다. 날고 긴다는 카지노의 딜러와 대결해서 몽땅 털리기는커녕 5달러를 땄다는 것이 도대체 어떤 의미일까? 솔직히 나는 완전히 잃거나 대박을 터뜨리는 것, 그 두 가지 경우의 수만 생각했었다. 하지만 내 예상은 보기 좋게 빗나가고 5달러라는 수수께끼만 남았다.

　불현듯 내 마음 깊은 곳에서 이런 목소리가 들려왔다.

　'사실은 비긴 것이다. 하지만 너에게 5달러를 남겨 준다. 그러니 이제 다시 너의 게임을 시작하라.'

　나는 그 5달러를 '새로운 시작'의 상징으로 해석했다. 500달러도 아니고 5천 달러도 아니다. 달랑 5달러이기 때문에 더욱 의미가 큰 것이다. 그것으로 충분하다.

체크아웃 시간이 다가왔을 때, 나는 화장실로 들어가 플라스틱 통에 들어 있는 하얀 알약들을 모두 변기에 쏟아붓고 물을 내렸다. 나 스스로 정했던 약속들이 알알이 쓸려 내려갔다.

나는 이제 더 이상 죽지 않기로 했다. 카지노에서 이겼기 때문이 아니다. 다만 이번에는 '죽지 않는 쪽'을 선택한 것이다. 1년 전 3평짜리 원룸에서 식칼을 손목에 갖다 댔을 때의 나와 지금의 나는 같은 사람이 아니다.

내가 알던 그녀는 어제 죽었다. 이로써 나는 '또 다른 오늘'을 얻었고, 인생의 연장전을 이어가게 되었다.

서른 살 첫날, 내가 받은 선물은 '생명'이었다.

'끝이 있다'라는 것을 인식하는 순간, 인생의 마법이 시작된다

D+2일.

나는 집으로 돌아왔다. 내가 나에게 걸었던 1년간의 마법은 이제 다 풀렸다. 마차는 호박으로, 라스베이거스의 궁전은 3평짜리 원룸으로 변했다.

방 안에는 떠나기 전과 다를 바 없이 후덥지근한 공기와 눅눅한 냄새가 고여 있었다. 나는 커튼을 젖히고 창문을 열었다. 그리고 먼 산을 바라보았다. 문득 장자의 호접몽이 떠올랐다.

'내가 라스베이거스의 나를 꿈꿨던 것일까, 아니면 라스베이거스의 내가 지금의 나를 꿈꾸고 있는 것일까?'

나의 목표와 모든 계획은 라스베이거스까지였다. 나는 거기서 죽으려 했고, 그 다음은 없었다. 그래서 지금 내가 숨 쉬고 있는 이 순간은 인생의 '덤'이다. 다시 포맷한 머릿속에는 아무런 계획도, 목표도 들어 있지 않았다. 하지만 하얗게 비어 있는 내면의 허공 속에서 알 수 없는 에너지가 느껴졌다.

'뭔가 달라졌어.'

그날 오후, 나는 클럽 사와를 찾아가 마담에게 일을 그만두겠다고 말했다. 라스베이거스라는 목표가 시효를 다했으니 더 이상 호스티스를 해야 할 이유가 없었다. 마담은 '왜?'라고 묻지 않았다.

"처음부터 알았어. 아마리가 여기서 쭉 일하지는 않을 거라는 걸. 손님들도 그래서 아마리를 좋아했던 것 같아."

"무슨 뜻인지……."

"말하지 않아도 알 수 있는 게 있잖아. 가슴속에 아주 분명한 무언가를 품고 있으면 반드시 표시가 나게 돼 있어. 사람들은 그런 힘에 마음이 끌리거든."

그러면서 마담은 내 손을 꽉 쥐며 "힘차게 살아요"라고 말했다. 그 순간 나는 클럽이라는 직장을 버린 대신 '인생의 언니'를 얻게 되었음을 깨달았다.

"자주 놀러올 거지? 손님이 아니라 친구로."

"그럼요. 제가 친구라고 말할 수 있는 사람들은 죄다 여기 있잖아요."

마침 레이나와 치카, 메구미가 떼거지로 몰려왔다.

"아마리, 왜 가? 가지 마!"

이 소중한 친구들과 헤어지기는 싫었지만 영원한 이별은 아니다. 가는 길은 달라도 앞으로 쭉 인연을 이어갈 수 있을 것이다.

다음 날, 나는 모델 에이전시를 찾아가 "그동안 고마웠어요"라고 말했다. 돌이켜 보면 태어나서 처음으로 남들 앞에서 옷을 벗는 그 순간부터 나의 자신감이 표출되기 시작한 것 같다. '해보기 전엔 절대로 알 수 없는 것'이 있다는 것, 그리고 '사람은 뭐든지 할 수 있다'는 것도 그때 알았다.

다음으로 찾아간 곳은 파견회사였다. 회사를 그만둬야 할지 말아야 할지에 대해서는 약간의 망설임이 있었다. 요즘처럼 취업난이 심각한 시기에, 그래도 근무조건이나 급여를 볼 때 이만한 회사를 찾기도 쉽지 않았기 때문이다. 하지만 나는 모든 것을 새롭게 시작하고 싶었다.

그런데 아이러니컬하게도 회사를 그만두겠다고 하자 '정사원으로 입사할 생각은 없나요?'라는 제의가 들어왔다. 정말 뜻밖이었다. 지난 1년 동안 한눈팔지 않고 시간을 쪼개 가며 일만 하던 나를 두고 회사에서는 '별종이지만 일 잘하는 슈퍼 파견사원'이란 평가를 해왔던 것이다.

"대단히 감사합니다만, 다른 계획이 있어서요."

회사를 그만두던 날, 나는 과감하게 사장실 문을 두드렸다.

"퇴직 인사드리러 왔습니다."

그러자 K사장은 놀라는 눈치였다. 일개 파견사원이 사장에게 퇴직 인사를 하러 오다니, 특이할 법도 했을 것이다. 사장은 잠시 의아한 표정을 짓더니 문득 생각난 듯 말했다.

"혹시…… 아마리?"

나는 대답 없이 미소를 지으며 "그동안 감사했습니다"라고 말했다. 그리고 꾸벅 인사를 하고 사장실을 나왔다.

그가 나를 알아봤을까? 나를 아마리라고 확신했을까? 그건 모르겠다. 하지만 구태여 확인하지 않는 편이 서로에게 낫다는 것을 알고 있었다.

1년 동안 나를 목표 지점까지 갈 수 있게 해준 모든 수단들과 작별한 뒤, 나는 다시 벌거벗은 기분으로 세상 앞에 섰다. 아직은 어떤 길로 가야 할지 알 수 없다. 하지만 분명한 것은, 길이 아주 많다는 것이다.

D+1년

다시 1년이 흘렀다. 서른한 살.

나는 지금 오다이바의 전경이 한눈에 내려다보이는 인텔리전트 빌딩 창가에 서 있다. 그사이 나는 파이낸셜플래너 자격을 취득했고, 세상 물정 어두운 엄마까지도 이름을 알고 있는 글로벌 회사에서 정사원으로 일하고 있다.

하늘에는 라스베이거스를 떠올리게 하는 한여름의 태양이 눈부시게 타오르고 있다. 빛과 열기를 피해 모두가 그늘을 찾고 있지만, 해바라기는 태양을 향해 고개를 꼿꼿이 세운 채 꿋꿋하게 서 있다. 그리고 멀리 공원의 숲속에서는 일주일밖에 못 산다는 매미가 끝없이 울부짖고 있다. 하늘 아래 모든 것들이 자신에게 주어진 생을 온몸으로 살아가고 있다.

나 또한 스스로 정한 시한부의 삶이 끝나던 날부터 쭉 남은 생을 살아가고 있다. 이것은 인생의 연장전이며, 목숨이 다하는 날까지 계속될 것이다.

나는 지금도 가끔 라스베이거스에서의 6일을 떠올리곤 한다.

기나긴 인생에서 6일이라는 시간은 아무것도 아닐 수 있다. 그 시간 동안 방바닥에 드러누워 만화책을 볼 수도 있고, 술에 취해 비틀거릴 수도 있으며, 우리에 갇힌 짐승처럼 자포자기하며 지낼 수도 있다. 예전의 나는 수많은 세월을 그렇게 휴지조각처럼 살았었다. 남은 인생마저 계속 그럴 거라면 그냥 죽는 것과 다를 게 하나도 없었다. 그래서 나는 나 자신에게 '라스베이거스에서 아낌없이 불태우고 죽으리라'는 주문을 걸었고, 매일매일 디데이를 향해 카운트다운을 가동했다. 그리고 그 마법은 통했다. 이제 나는 마법을 믿는다.

인생에서의 마법은 '끝이 있다는 것'을 의식하는 순간부터 시작된다는 것을 나는 몸으로 깨달았다. 그 사실을 알기 전까지 나는 '끝'을 의식하지 못했고, 그래서 시간을 헛되이 흘려보내기만 했었다. 아무런 비전도 없이 노력은커녕 비관만 하며 그저 되는 대로 살았었다. 하지만 D-365, D-364, D-363······ 카운트다운이 시작되면서부터 나는 치열하게 내달릴 수 있었다.

생각해 보면 정말 난폭한 방식의 자기개혁이었지만, 말 그대로 죽을힘을 다했기 때문에 라스베이거스 행 비행기에 오를 수 있었다. 그리고 그 사막의 판타지 공간에서 보냈던 20대의 마지막 6일이 나를 바꿔 버렸다.

나는 단 6일을 위해 1년을 살았고, 삶을 끝내기 위해 6일을 불태웠다. 그 끄트머리에서 '20대의 나'는 죽고 30대의 내가 다시 살아났다. 이제부터 맞이하게 될 수많은 '오늘들'은 나에게 늘 선물과도 같을 것이다. 나는 죽는 순간까지 '내일'이란 말을 쓰지 않을 것이다. 앞으로 나의 인생은 천금 같은 오늘의 연속일 테니까.

삶이 있는 한 희망은 있다. - 키케로

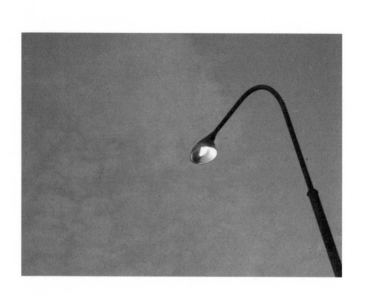

장은주

동의대학교를 졸업하였으며, 일본어 통번역 프리랜서로 활동하다가 활자의 매력에 이끌려 번역의 길로 들어섰다. 옮긴 책으로는 『중년수업』 『어느 날, 내가 죽었다』 『살면서 포기해야 할 것은 없다』 『인생에 대한 예의』 『상대를 꿰뚫어 보려면 디테일이 답이다』 『병에 걸리지 않는 면역생활』 등이 있다.

스물아홉 생일, 1년 후 죽기로 결심했다

초판 1쇄 발행 2012년 7월 20일   초판 44쇄 발행 2014년 5월 7일

지은이 하야마 아마리 옮긴이 장은주
펴낸이 연준혁

출판 6분사장 이진영
편집장 정낙정
편집 박지수 최아영
제작 이재승
표지이미지출처 shutterstock

펴낸곳 ㈜위즈덤하우스
출판등록 2000년 5월 23일 제 13-1071호
주소 경기도 고양시 일산동구 정발산로 43-20 센트럴프라자 6층
전화 031-936-4000 팩스 031-903-3895
홈페이지 http://www.wisdomhouse.co.kr 전자우편 wisdom6@wisdomhouse.co.kr
종이 월드페이퍼 | 인쇄·제본 ㈜현문 | 특수가공 이지앤비_특허 제 10-1081185

값 12,800원
ISBN 978-89-5913-689-6 03830

국립중앙도서관 출판시도서목록(CIP)

스물아홉 생일, 1년 후 죽기로 결심했다 / 하야마 아마리 지음 ; 장
은주 옮김. ― 고양 : 위즈덤하우스, 2012
    p. ;   cm

원표제: 29歳の誕生日、あと1年で死のうと決めた
원저자명: 葉山アマリ
일본어 원작을 한국어로 번역
수상: 일본감동대상 대상, 2010
ISBN 978-89-5913-689-6 03830 : ₩12800

일본 문학[日本文學]

838-KDC5
895.686-DDC21   CIP2012002937

Paul Verlaine and
the decadence
1882–90

Philip Stephan

Northeastern University

Paul Verlaine and the decadence 1882–90

Manchester University Press

Rowman & Littlefield

© 1974 Philip Stephan

Published by
the University of Manchester
at the University Press
Oxford Road, Manchester M13 9PL

UK ISBN 0 7190 0562 0

USA

Rowman & Littlefield
81 Adams Drive, Totowa, N.J. 07512

US ISBN 0 87471 563 6

Library of Congress cataloguing-in-publication data

Stephan, Philip
    Paul Verlaine and the decadence, 1882–90.

    Bibliography: p.
    1. Verlaine, Paul Marie, 1884–1896. 2. French
poetry—Nineteenth century—History and criti-
cism. I. Title.
PQ2467.S8   841'.8   74–8190
UK ISBN 0 7190 0562 0
US ISBN 0 87471 563 6

Printed in Great Britain by
Western Printing Services Ltd, Bristol

Contents

Acknowledgements

For this book I owe a heavy debt to many persons and institutions. My particular thanks go to the Horace H. Rackham School of Graduate Studies for the use of the University of Michigan library; to the Association pour la Conservation et la Réproduction Photographique de la Presse, Paris, for microfilm copies of many of the periodicals cited in this work; and to Harvard University for use of the Widener and Houghton libraries; without these institutions this book could not have been written. I am also indebted to the staffs of the Bowling Green State University and the Northeastern University libraries and the Boston Public Library. The generosity of the Committee on Faculty Leaves and Research of Bowling Green State University and that of the Faculty Research Fund and the University Research Council of Northeastern University played their role. I wish to thank Professor Louis Cooperstein, Chairman of the Modern Languages Department of Northeastern University, for his encouragement and assistance, and my wife for much patience, encouragement, and collaboration. Finally, I express my special thanks to Professor Georges Zayed, of Boston College, and to others for generously reading the manuscript and for their helpful suggestions. This book contains material which appeared in different form in the following periodicals, to whose editors I am indebted for permission to reproduce it: *Romance Notes*, *French Review*, *Modern Language Quarterly*.

Introduction

The year 1882 was a critical one in the career of Paul Verlaine and also, to a lesser extent, in the history of French poetry. For Verlaine, it was the year in which he returned to Paris with his mother and definitively settled in the capital. He had left ten years before in the company of Arthur Rimbaud, amid substantial scandal, and the intervening decade had been spent in wandering with him through northern France, Belgium, and England, in a two-year prison term for shooting Rimbaud in the wrist, and in a succession of teaching jobs. Not only had he been absent from the literary centre of France and ostracised on account of his behaviour, during this period he had published nothing in periodicals, and the two collections of verse he did publish apparently were not distributed for sale. Thus, except for some loyal friends of his own generation and a few persons who had seen reviews of *Romances sans paroles* (1874) and *Sagesse* (1881), Verlaine was virtually unknown to the reading public.

For French poetry it was a time of transition and of impending change, even if 1882 might be less significant than subsequent years. The principal currents in French verse were Romanticism and the Parnassian movement, and in most cases the same individuals who had first led those movements were still actively composing verse. Victor Hugo was the acknowledged master of French poetry, and in spite of his eighty years he continued his various activities with unabated vigour. Between 1877 and 1883 he published two enlarged editions of *La Legende des siècles* and three new collections of verse; after a jubilee performance of *Hernani* in 1880, he published *Torquemada* in 1882. Juliette Drouet, the actress who played in *Lucrèce Borgia* in 1833 and whose love he celebrated in 'Tristesse d'Olympio', was still alive and lived near by. For his eightieth birthday a crowd of 600,000 admirers gathered before his town house on the Avenue d'Eylau. In 1886 Anatole France recommended Lamartine as a model of poetic clarity.[1] Théophile Gautier, of the red waistcoat and green trousers,

[1] 'Voyez Lamartime. Il est le plus grand de nos poètes comme il en est le plus

was dead, but Théodore de Banville was still alive, who always claimed to belong in spirit to the proud generation of _Hernani_ (although he was only seven years old in 1830). Among the Parnassians, Leconte de Lisle was still the most distinguished figure (in 1894 Verlaine would succeed him as 'Prince of Poets'). It was only in 1878 that he published a definitive edition of his _Poemes barbares_ with forty-five new poems added. He was working on translations from the Greek (_Sophocle_, 1877; _Euripide_, 1885), and his _Poèmes tragiques_ did not appear until 1884. José-Maria de Heredia's _Trophées_ would finally appear in 1893. Although Hugo simply outlived the Romanticism associated with his name, Leconte de Lisle's continuing activity indicates that the Parnassian movement was alive and productive at the same time that French symbolism was coming into existence. Banville, Heredia, Verlaine, Mallarmé, and Laforgue all published poems within a few months of each other in the same magazine,[2] and many of the decadent poets published Parnassian-style verse in reviews devoted to change in poetry. A study of decadence and of Verlaine's role in the movement, therefore, involves considering the relationship between the Parnassian tradition and the new currents in French poetry.

---

simple.' 'Le Symbolisme—décadents et déliquescents—simples observations sur un manifeste de M. Jean Moréas', _Le Temps_, 26 September 1886.

[2] This was _La Revue Indépendante_, which, besides numerous poems by Verlaine, Mallarmé, Laforgue, and others, also carried Banville's 'Populus' (n.s., III, 7, May 1887, 249–51) and Heredia's 'A une ville morte' (n.s., II, 4, February 1887, 200) and 'Hortorum Deus' (n.s., VI, 17, March 1888, 422).

Chapter I
French poetry in 1882

Of four poets commonly associated with symbolism, Baudelaire, Verlaine, and Mallarmé all had poems in at least one of the three editions of the *Parnasse contemporain* (1866, 1869–71, 1876), and Rimbaud submitted verse to it, which was refused, in 1870. So they deserve to be called Parnassians as well as symbolists. Terms like 'Parnassian' and 'symbolist', which summary treatments of French literary history describe as antithetical, actually are not mutually exclusive. Edmund Wilson takes too narrow a view of Parnassian poetry when he states that its creators 'seemed to have taken for their aim merely to picture historical incidents and natural phenomena as accurately as possible in impassive perfect verse'.[1] Although Gautier's hard, statuesque poems and Leconte de Lisle's purposeful elephants do, to be sure, represent one aspect of Parnassian verse, more generally those poets sought the goals of careful versification, exact expression, and absence of sentimentality. In seeking those goals Baudelaire and poets like him developed suggestive, indirect means of expression which are now much admired. Nevertheless, as can be seen in Leconte de Lisle's 'Midi' or 'La Robe du centaur', even seemingly objective description still permits the poet to evoke the fervour of an emotional experience by the use of striking imagery or by portraying its effects on the participant. Writers too young to have submitted work to *Le Parnasse contemporain*, and doubtless as impatient as Edmund Wilson with some kinds of Parnassian verse, were nevertheless well aware of their filiation with the older group. When Catulle Mendès' *Legende du Parnasse contemporain* appeared in the same year as Verlaine's *Poètes maudits*, a reviewer compared the Parnassians to the decadents of his own day, noting that both were in revolt against an obsolete tradition.[2] Even the writer who characterised Parnassian poetry as 'une lamentable kyrielle de vers trop rimés, d'où rien ne se dégageait, ni pensée, ni coeur, ni âme . . . un défilé de banalités paradoxales, écrites au métronome, et conçues dans une arrière-boutique d'éditeur', conceded that a poem of Charles Cros in the *Parnasse contemporain* was enough to redeem all the rest.[3] More typical of the younger generation's attitude is Téodor de Wyzewa's statement that contemporary poetry (i.e. that of Mallarmé and the decadents) was created by the Parnassians: Gautier, Banville, Leconte de Lisle, and Verlaine. Instead of taxing them with lifeless verse, he gives them credit for having disencumbered poetry of superfluous functions, so that it could better fulfil its true role of evoking in the souls of readers emotions akin to music.[4]

Typical of this concurrency of Parnassian and decadent verse is a poem which appeared in *Le Chat Noir* just as Verlaine was returning to Paris:

La Sieste du lion

> Gorgé de chair vivante et de sang étourdi
> Sur le sol calciné par les feux du midi
> Dans le désert, en plein soleil, devant son antre,
> Ce lion s'est couché tout du long sur le ventre.
> Somnolent, il digère, et des frémissements
> De la queue à la gueule agitent par moments
> Sa robe fauve, car il rêve des cavales
> Bondissantes, il voit leurs jambes, ses rivales
> En vitesse, il croit suivre en bonds géants leur vol.
> —Et ses ongles d'acier égratignent le sol.   [Charles Morice, 22 July 1882]

In the same magazine we also find Georges Henry Bertin's 'Une Heure au désert', dedicated to Leconte de Lisle (3 February 1883), Félix Decori's 'La Sultane' (17 June 1882), and Louis Brechemin's 'Sonnet' (*ibid.*); all three have in common the objective descriptions, rich rhymes, and hot desert sun so typical of Parnassian verse. Even in *Le Decadent* a few years later there are Léo d'Orfer's 'Chanson' (18 September 1886), with its leonine rhymes, and Delphin de Girard's 'Endormement' (6 November 1886), which reminds us of Leconte de Lisle. In *La Basoche*, a decadent periodical in Belgium, Catulle Mendès' 'Victoire d'Indra' (I, 8, June, 1885, 278–280) expresses the common Parnassian theme of Hindu mythology.[5] Of more interest than the continued presence of impassible, descriptive verse are poems in which the Parnassian manner is nevertheless used to express purely subjective viewpoints. Edmond Haraucourt's verse in *Le Chat Noir* illustrate this tendency. In two sonnets the quatrains give a scenic description and the tercets make a personal interpretation.[6] In 'La Cité morte' Haracourt devotes nine quatrains to describing an abandoned city, to which he compares his heart in two final quatrains. The style is generally

Parnassian, although, in the last line of the quotation, the similes suggest the influence of Victor Hugo:

Sous la tranquillité d'un ciel platement bleu
Où l'air dort, sans chaleur et sans force vitale,
Une ville déserte, aux murs pâlis, s'étale
Triste comme la Mort et grande comme Dieu.   [27 May 1882]

In many such Parnassian descriptions the poet's choice of theme or his interpretation of a scene look forward to attitudes of the decadents. There is often a tension between the old and the new as poets, writing in the style they learned from Leconte de Lisle or Gautier, strive nevertheless to introduce novel themes and points of view. Maurice Millot describes the passage of a train in precise, objective language ('Le Train', *Chat Noir*, 20 January 1883). In Mélandri's 'Un Fait-Paris' (*ibid.*, 12 August 1882), which describes how a drunken coachman commits suicide by throwing himself under a horse tram, the effort to raise a *fait-divers* to a poetic level by realistic, objective treatment is in contrast with the clichés of Parnassian diction. Edmond Haraucourt's 'En Crète' (*Chat Noir*, 16 September 1882) recapitulates the loves of Pasiphaë and the bull; the purely decadent theme of sodomy with an animal, the Parnassian anecdote from classical antiquity and description of sun-bathed Crete, and the Baudelairean treatment of Pasiphaë, panting with desire, show how traditional Parnassian diction and décor can serve as the vehicle for a new sensibility.

Of the poets who published in the *Parnasse contemporain* it is Charles Baudelaire who most strongly influenced the young poets of *Le Chat Noir* and *La Nouvelle Rive Gauche*. Although in 1882 he was still unknown to the general public, and traditional and academic critics denigrated his poetry, he always had a small circle of followers. As early as 1869 a hostile critic noted that Baudelaire had enthusiastic disciples among the Parnassians,[7] and an anonymous reviewer observed in 1872, 'Dans la postérité, comme parmi les contemporains, la gloire de Baudelaire sera fondée principalement sur le suffrage des esprits d'élite. . . .'[8] Some of those 'elite minds' were teenagers who, having grown to manhood, would help create the symbolist movement. Among them was Arthur Rimbaud, who praised Baudelaire in his 'Lettre du voyant' of 1871, and whose poetic theories would exert an important influence on symbolism. By 1881 Barbey d'Aurevilly presents Maurice Rollinat as a disciple of Baudelaire, and in August of 1882 the Belgian poet Emile Verhaeren writes admiringly of Baudelaire.

While Rimbaud prized the author of *Les Fleurs du mal* as a seer, Barbey d'Aurevilly and Verhaeren deal rather with the decadent aspects of his sensibility. [9] For Verhaeren, Baudelaire's hypersensitivity makes him the poet of modern times: 'Et pourtant Baudelaire est reconnu comme poète essentiellement actuel, ayant mieux que personne traduit l'âme de son temps.'[10] And Barbey d'Aurevilly, Rollinat and Verhaeren were not alone in their admiration. In a *Journal* entry for 6 June 1883 Edmond de Goncourt notes learning from a schoolboy caller 'qu'à l'heure actuelle, les intelligents, les piocheurs, les lettrés du collège sont divisés en deux camps: les futurs normaliens qui appartiennent à About et à Sarcey, et les autres sur lesquels Baudelaire et moi, serions les deux auteurs qui ont le plus d'action'.[11] Echoes of such homage occur frequently in the pages of literary magazines, where minor poets, often provincials like Rimabaud and Verhaeren, express their reverence for *Les Fleurs du mal* by imitating them in their verse.

Le Chat Noir printed some poems ascribed to Baudelaire: 'Les Chats' in the issue of 28 January 1882, a so-called 'Sonnet inédit' on 26 June 1886, and a poem from a projected drama, 'Chanson du scieur du long.' on 31 July 1886.[12] Many poems in *Le Chat Noir* and in other magazines recall Baudelaire by their language and techniques or by their ghoulishness and determined depravity. In 'Le Crâne' Fernand Crésy writes of his dead cousin, stating that the cypress have taken root in her belly and made resin of her blood, but that he has saved her skull from the worms. These details of physical decay are, of course, typical of Baudelaire, as are the word *spleen* and the alliterations in the last tercet:

Et, mêlant dans mes spleens moroses
Le gracieux au solonnel,
J'ai ceint son front chauve de roses.   [*Chat Noir*, 10 June 1882]

Albert Aurier, writing in *Le Decadent* four years later, contemplates the skull of his mistress and draws the cheerful conclusion 'La Catin ne peut plus me gratifier de cornes!' ('Contemplation', 12 June 1886). In 'Vision funèbre' Aurier pushes the macabre past the limits of taste: he begs pardon of his dead wife, for while her best friend and he were paying their respects to her corpse laid out in state, he was overcome by a hallucination, mistook the friend for his wife, and possessed her on the very *lit mortuaire* (26 June 1886)! How much of this sort of ghoulishness can be attributed to Baudelaire, and how much is owed to Maurice Rollinat? The latter's *Les Névroses*, with their exaggerated Baudelaire-anism, had appeared in 1883 and gone through three more editions by

1885, and his poetry would have been familiar to readers of *Le Chat Noir*. Aurier's genius seems to have been even more malleable than that of the other minor poets we have to discuss, reflecting whomever he had read most recently. In one poem ('A Mallarmé', *Decadent*, 24 April 1886) he imitates Mallarmé, then six weeks later he again turns to Baudelaire: 'Car ce parfum de femme était plus désirable, / Emanant de ce corps en habit de garçon!' ('Pantalon de satin', *ibid.*, 5 June 1886). Baudelaire's influence is also evident in Paul Vorsin's 'Nocturne visiteuse' (*ibid.*, 28 August 1886), which describes awakening in an army barracks bathed with moonlight, and in the opening line of 'Phryne': 'O reine des langueurs, de la volupté molle, / Et des brûlantes nuits sous l'alcôve de sang' (*ibid.*, 18 September 1886). Louis Le Cardonnel's 'Impression de pluie' recalls Baudelaire's 'Spleen' poems: 'Mon coeur exaspéré, mon coeur se sent plus vieux, / Par ce lugubre temps, par ce temps pluvieux' (*Chat Noir*, 2 December 1882).

These selections represent echoes of Baudelaire's language and sometimes tasteless handlings of his themes. Another kind of influence is represented by two poems, less directly imitative, which suggest that a few poets analysed Baudelaire's verse more closely than the others did, isolated some of his techniques, and freely adapted them to their own use. In 'Adultère' Edmond Haraucourt begins with a rather facile statement of Baudelaire's idea that part of the pleasure of love consists in doing wrong: 'Je t'apprendrai l'amour stérile, et le secret / Des bonheurs trop savants qu'ignore l'hymenée,' (*Chat Noir*, 15 July 1882). He goes on to reproduce a wide range of Baudelaire's rhythms: the run-on line, above; in the tercets, the accentuation of *Viens!* by placing the cesura after the first syllable, the mute *e*'s in the first two lines, and the contrast of an irregular, broken line with the flow of a regular alexandrine. In the phrase *L'immense volupté* the long, harmonious nasal vowel of *immense* emphasises the sharp sounds and rapid rhythm— and hence the meaning—of *volupté*:

> Viens! Ce que tu rêvas sans le pouvoir connaître,
> Je te le donnerai! Tu te sentiras naître;
> Tes grands yeux dessillés verront dans l'infini:
>
> Et tous deux, emportés sur un rêve sublime,
> Nous aurons pour bénir encor l'amour béni,
> L'immense volupté qu'on appelle le crime!

The seventeenth-century word order, *sans le pouvoir connaitre*, and the creation of suspense by postponing the final thought, are typical of

Baudelaire. Of course, the less servile the imitation, the less certain the influence of one poet on another. Haraucourt could have acquired the resources of French prosody from any good poet—Victor Hugo, too, uses the devices we have described; nevertheless, in view of the Baudelairean theme and a few echoes of his diction, it is tempting to think of *Les Fleurs du mal* as Haraucourt's source.

In 'Spleen' Baudelaire transforms one concrete object into another which images his mood: the low sky becomes a pot lid, the earth a dungeon, the rain prison bars, and so on. In the same way, Louis Brechemin compares his mistress to ancient idols, then the doors of the salon become city gates opening out on desert sands, and his mistress becomes a sphinx:

Sonnet

Avec la majesté des idoles antiques,
Entrant dans la clarté des lustres du salon,
Telle qu'une crinière au cou d'un étalon
Vos cheveux tombaient pleins d'effluves magnétiques.

Et les portes soudain se changeaient en portiques,
Au loin se dessinait le dos d'un mamelon.
Et le sable doré comme un corps de frelon
Se déroulait sans fin en plaines fantastiques.

C'était le grand désert. Levés vers l'horizon
Vos regards étoilant votre riche toison
Sondaient l'inaccessible énigme de l'espace.

Sphinx, votre silhouette, au fond, se détachant
Superbement, ainsi qu'une ombre de rapace,
Se fondait lentement dans le soleil couchant.

[*Chat Noir*, 17 June 1882]

There are other Baudelairean touches, such as the treatment of the lady's hair, but the important lesson that Brechemin has learned, perhaps from *Les Fleurs du mal*, is the handling of images and the sudden, fanciful change in perspective. These, rather than shocking treatments of sex and death, are the essential message of *Les Fleurs du mal* which enabled Baudelaire's progeny to look forward to creating a different poetic idiom.

What direction poetry would take seemed less pressing, however, than the more basic question of whether poetry could survive at all before the colossus of the best-seller novel, as it was represented by

Emile Zola and Georges Ohnet. Although he was the greatest publishing success of the century[13] and was decorated for his achievements by
the French government in 1883, today Georges Ohnet has sunk into a
well earned oblivion. The formula of hackneyed characters in conventional plots and the consistent triumph of virtue in the ten volumes
of his *Batailles de la vie* won him a vast public; by 1884–85 *Le Maître
des forges* had gone through 250 editions, *Serge Panine* and *La Comtesse
Sarah* 150 each, and *Lise Fleuron* 100. *Serge Panine* was crowned by the
French Academy. Serious men of letters, to the contrary, regarded him
with undisguised scorn. To the typical decadent writer, whose work,
if published at all, appeared in small editions and was ridiculed by
academic critics, Ohnet's success seemed all the more ironic. A more
practical consideration was that, by saturating the market with enor-
mous sales, such novelists made it all the harder for unknown authors
to obtain an audience. Léo Trézenik's doubts as to whether the 124
copies of *Les Sytres*, Jean Moréas' first volume of verse, would find
purchasers, and whether, even if they were sold, the purchasers would
find time to read them among so much literature emanating from the
presses, were in sarcastic contrast to M. Ohnet's vast sales.[14] The death,
during his military service in North Africa, of an unpublished young
writer named Bobillot drew enough attention for a publisher to print
some of his works. Does this mean, *Lutèce* scornfully asked, that there
should be a special receptacle into which departing conscripts could
drop their manuscripts, in case they, too, should enjoy such posthumous
discovery?[15]

The comments of critics who deplored public taste and the con-
sequent neglect of worthy authors sound surprisingly familiar to us
today. It is difficult to keep up with the vast amount of material
published in the average week; a vulgar crowd gobbles up the work of
cheap popular novelists without regard for truth or beauty; only a
few poets struggle against this lamentable situation by writing works
of truth and beauty.[16] Poetry alone reveals some sign of originality,
and then only in language and style, for it still expresses the same
hackneyed ideas.[17] Poetry, in fact, is dead; originally designed as an
aid to memory in the days before written language, it no longer
serves a purpose, in spite of the rare individuals who persist in writing
it.[18] In consideration of the way Zola, Ohnet and Co. have reduced
literature to a commercial exploitation of mass taste, art should be made
the heritage of a cultural elite, a priesthood inaccessible to the common
herd.[19]

While the success of Georges Ohnet does not concern us further, the naturalist novel, as it was handled by Zola and by the brothers Jules and Edmond de Goncourt, is of considerable relevance to the history of decadent poetry.

In 1882 Emile Zola was at the high point of his career, and his *groupe de Médan* (named after his suburban home on the Seine) comprised the naturalist school. The critical and financial success of *L'Assommoir* in 1877 established Zola as a leading novelist; in 1880 *Nana* and *Les Soirees de Médan*, an anthology of short stories by Zola and his disciples which illustrated the principles of naturalism, confirmed his position; and *Germinal* in 1885 was also a success. In contrast, the crudity of *La Terre* in 1887 produced an adverse reaction, and the resulting controversy harmed Zola's reputation and dispersed the Médan group. Chronologically, therefore, the activity of Zola and his followers approximately coincides with that of the decadents. There were, of course, other naturalists, such as Alphonse Daudet, but the two names which occur most often in decadent criticism are Zola and Edmond de Goncourt. (Flaubert had died in 1880, and although the decadents respected his artistry, he was seldom discussed in relation to their own work.)[20]

Naturalism has traditionally, and in general correctly, been considered the antithesis of symbolism, since it is the fruit of science and of positivism, and symbolism is a Romantic, subjective reaction against positivism. This simplified view, however, does not take into account the diversity of the various currents which composed each of the two movements. Upon looking more closely, modern scholars have differentiated between decadence and symbolism by the former's cordial attitude toward naturalism,[21] and critics of the period saw more similarity than difference between naturalism and experimental verse. In 1885 Jules Lemaitre wrote that the impressionist rendition of sensation was common ground to naturalism in the novel, impressionism in painting, and Parnassian poetry, so that a typical literary review would contain 'côte à côte une Nouvelle naturaliste, une fantaisie mystique, un roman pessimiste, des vers gravement lascifs et d'autres vers purement inintelligibles, où le poète a voulu exprimer l'inexprimable et "suggérer" des sensations ou des sentiments'.[22]

Writers of the period seem never to have held any prejudice against naturalism as a literary doctrine: it was accepted that the contemporary novel would seek to render even rather sordid realities as accurately as possible, and such passages were felt to be aesthetically pleasing. We see this mutual acceptance in the relations between naturalist critics and persons involved with decadent poetry.[23] Henry Céard and Paul Alexis, both contributors to *Les Soirées de Médan*, handled book reviews for the first series of *La Revue Indépendante*, a magazine that was essentially decadent and symbolist in its orientation, yet catholic enough to fit Lemaitre's description perfectly; Adrien Remacle, one of the few decadents named in the 'Préface' to *Les Deliquescences d'Adoré Floupette*, favourably reviewed Daudet's *Sapho*.[24] Although the symbolist critic Téodor de Wyzewa, important for his espousal of Mallarmé's and Laforgue's poetry and for his definition of the symbolist aesthetic, was disappointed in the performance of the members of the Médan group, he still observed, 'Le naturalisme leur donnait une esthétique restreinte mais sûre et précise: ils l'ont abandonné sans adopter en échange une direction plus nette.'[25] Rather, it is in reviews of Zola's novels that we meet hostile attitudes, and even in his case, reviews varied according to the particular novel and the individual reviewer. '. . . Mallarmé, the most rarefied and recondite of French poets, wrote Zola a congratulatory letter as soon as *L'Assommoir* appeared.'[26] Léo Trézenik, editor of *Lutèce*, felt that Zola's work had been declining since *L'Assommoir*, and he gave *Germinal* a poor review;[27] Hector Chainaye in *La Basoche*, to the contrary, was enthusiastic over *Germinal*,[28] and an anonymous notice in *Le Chat Noir* (perhaps by Paul Alexis?) praised it.[29] Reviews of Zola often give the impression that jealousy of his commercial success lay behind at least some of the hostile criticism. A typical lampoon opens with facetious remarks about his income before going on to accuse him of having removed the fig leaf and done vivisection on female flesh.[30] Thus, it was toward Zola, not naturalism, that ill-will was expressed.

Essentially, naturalists and decadents worked alongside each other as friends and collaborators. Robert Caze, Jean Ajalbert, Jean Lorrain and Laurent Tailhade, to name but a few, wrote decadent verse and naturalist novels. More interesting is the fact that in several instances it was naturalist novelists, disciples of Zola, who defined decadence and symbolism in critical articles.[31] Louis Desprez wrote one of the first studies of Verlaine's poetry; Joris-Karl Huysmans' novel, *A Rebours*, as we shall see, described the principles of decadence for the general public. Paul Adam's first novel, *Chair molle*, was typically naturalist: the history of a prostitute in the best tradition of French social realism, it got him a condemnation for *outrage a la pudeur*. As critic and editor, on the other hand, in 1886 Adam helped found *Le*

Symboliste, where his article 'La Presse et le symbolisme' distinguished the symbolists' aims from those of the decadents.

It is therefore hardly surprising to find that, beginning in 1882, magazines like *La Revue Indépendante, Le Chat Noir, Lutèce* (until 30 March 1883 *La Nouvelle Rive Gauche*), or *La Basoche* in Belgium were congenial to naturalism and to decadence equally. *La Revue Indépendante* included poetry by Verlaine, Mallarmé, Laforgue, Banville, and Heredia; short 'slice of life' sketches, such as Huysmans' 'L'Avenue de la Motte-Picquet', Paul Hervieu's 'Attentat à la pudeur', or Frantz Jourdain's 'Ouvriers du bâtiment'; and articles or sketches by Edmond de Goncourt and Emile Zola. In so far as smaller formats permitted, other magazines were equally eclectic. In its two weekly pages of text *Le Chat Noir* published criticism by Paul Alexis and decadent verse. In *Lutèce* and *La Basoche* poetry and naturalist prose, fiction or criticism, appeared side by side. It was only in 1886 that magazines like *Le Symboliste* or *Le Décadent* would be narrowly sectarian.

Naturalism and decadence are not at all the same thing, since the former proposed to analyse contemporary society (in Zola's case, the recently contemporary society of the Second Empire) with scientific rigour and, it was implied, little sympathy, and the latter sought to express the sentiments of 'modern' man, who was likened to the ancient Romans of the decadence. Impressionist painting, with its analysis of the effects of light on contemporary, non-academic subjects, is something else again. Nevertheless, each of these movements dealt, either incidentally or as its primary goal, with the contemporary milieu; and all three believed in portraying the subject as it is perceived by our senses, rather than in analysing it rationally; and finally, because of their choice of subject-matter and methods of expression, all three found themselves working in defiance of academic convention. Thus, in spite of obvious differences in their techniques, materials and technical goals, on at least one level the three arts shared a common aesthetic philosophy.[32] Furthermore, the notion of transposition of the arts had been in the air since Victor Hugo and Romanticism, so that Gautier and the Goncourts could create effects of sculpture and painting in literature, and symbolist theoreticians could discuss music as the goal of poetry. The same individuals wrote poetry, fiction, and art criticism impartially, and in many cases painters and writers were personal friends. Zola, Huysmans and minor naturalists like Paul Adam and Félix Fénéon defended the impressionist painters in their art criticism; Manet was friendly with both Zola and Mallarmé and painted their portraits; Verlaine's brother-in-law, Charles de Sivry, was a composer; Verlaine knew the composer Chabrier, and he had a close friendship with the painter F.-A. Cazals.

Jules Lemaitre was correct in identifying sensation as the element common to poetry, the novel, and painting.[33] Impressionism, as the name implies, sought to render sense impressions at the expense of form, volume and subject-matter. Decadence in literature was defined, as we shall show in our next chapter, in terms of modern man's hypersensitive perception of experience. The high esteem in which the decadents held the Goncourts was partly due to the brothers' successfully reproducing sensation. In criticism, writers recognised that the cause of the *avant-garde* was common to themselves and painters, since both had to deal with a traditionally-minded public hostile to unusual ideas.[34] Although the novel, with its appeal to a mass audience, might seem less revolutionary than impressionist painting or decadent verse, Georges Ohnet's commercial triumph, which outstripped Zola's, suggests that in the mind of the common reader there was a sentimental tradition with which naturalism clashed. The frequency with which even the more liberal Third Republic prosecuted novelists for *outrage à la pudeur* and *outrage à l'armée* indicates that the State itself stood behind certain taboos. Jules Lemaitre reproached the naturalist novel with having abandoned moralism and idealism, and Ferdinand Brunetière compared it to vaudeville.[35] Finally, owing to their experiences shared as friends and as middle-class Parisians, and owing to their concern with modernity, all the artists were interested in a common subject-matter. Manet and Degas regarded themselves as illustrators of contemporary Parisian scenes, a viewpoint which distinguishes them from the other impressionists, while bringing them closer to the novelists.[36] Degas, for instance, made drawings to illustrate Edmond de Goncourt's novel *La Fille Elisa*. When Claude Lantier, the painter in Zola's *L'Oeuvre*, looks upstream from the Pont des Saints-Pères, he has 'pour premier plan le port Saint-Nicolas, avec sa grue, ses péniches qu'on décharge, son peuple de débardeurs'; consequently, Zola's description of Claude's painting suggests Monet's *Deschargeurs de charbon*.[37] Zola's treatment of Claude Lantier's career in *Le Ventre de Paris* and *L'Oeuvre* brought him into direct contact with the world of artists, although the milieu of the novels antedates that of the impressionists. Henri Mitterand shows that Manet had first made the acquaintance of Zola's character Nana in the final chapters of *L'Assommoir* in 1876, and, perhaps finding that she resembled Henriette Hauser, entitled his painting of Henriette

Nana. Zola, in turn, borrowed the motif of Manet's painting, an actress undressing before a gentleman in black, for the scene in chapter 5 of *Nana*, where the actress does her *toilette* before Count Muffat in her dressing room at the Variétés.[38] Some of these similarities of subject-matter were merely casual, brought about by social and personal contacts among intellectuals, but the constant presence of painting in literature shows that writers, at least, consciously appropriated the domain of impressionism.

As for the poets, it is clear that by 1882 they owed as much to the naturalist novel and to impressionist painting as they did to Baudelaire's 'Tableaux parisiens' for their presentations of their urban milieu. Jean Moréas summarises his description of a working-class scene in 'Square des Batignolles' with the verse '—On dirait un tableau du grand maître Manet' (*Chat Noir*, 24 February 1883). A series of 'Sonnets-Montmartre' in *Le Chat Noir* (beginning 28 January 1882) draw brief sketches of life in the quarter: Raymond de Cazba's 'Le Modèle' treats an impoverished artist's model posing in the unheated studio (28 January 1882), and the anonymous 'L'Ambulant' is about a street musician (11 February 1882). Adolphe Vautier's 'Crépuscule' describes sunset over the capital in terms of the activity in the streets and in the cafés:

C'est l'heure où, chez les mastroquets,
Plus culottés que les vieux bouges,
Des consommateurs aux nez rouges
Etranglent de verts perroquets.   [25 February 1882]

In the last line, the use of the slang terms *étrangler* (to drink several glasses in succession) and *perroquet* (a mixed drink of pastis and crème de menthe) is a device borrowed from the novel. Parodies of Zola in *Le Chat Noir* mimic his use of colloquial language.[39] A few years later, Jean Ajalbert's long poem *Sur Les Talus*[40] recounts in free verse a love idyll on the fortifications outside Paris, an adventure based on a personal experience. The length of the narrative led a reviewer to comment that it would have been better cast as a novel.[41] and, as was done with novels by Daudet, Goncourt and Zola, Ajalbert later reworked it into a play.

Decadent critics acclaimed the novels of Jules and Edmond de Goncourt with enthusiasm. Jules died young in 1870, but at the moment which concerns us Edmond was carrying on their work by himself, publishing *La Fille Elisa* in 1877 and *Les Frères Zemganno* in 1882;

beginning in 1885, he, too, held weekly receptions in his *grenier* at Auteuil. Even the usually reserved Téodor de Wyzewa writes of 'cette précision et cette puissante vérité de vie qui ont fait de *Chérie* le plus prodigieux roman de notre temps'.[42] Like Zola and Huysmans, the Goncourts subscribed to the *école du document*, sought to *faire vrai*, and wrote art criticism; but in what seems to have been the crucial distinction between them and the Médan group, they wrote as painters painted, introducing the impressionist style, or *écriture artiste*, into literature, and they stressed the rendering of physical sensation. Moreover, characters in their novels suffered from the psychological aberrations of 'modern' man, of *fin-de-siécle* man worn out by centuries of civilisation. Their actresses, clowns, painters, and bourgeois seemed closer to writers, who were themselves middle-class, than did Zola's workmen, peasants and miners. Laforgue underlines this point in a letter in which, despite some glaring chronological discrepancies, he likens the mood of Corbière's verse to certain Goncourt novels.[43]

Zola's pessimism and his handling of diseased heredity parallel the Goncourts' decadent outlook, and in treating the milieu of painters he imitates the style of painting. Without using the Goncourts' *écriture artiste*, he describes scenes, especially in *L'Oeuvre*, in impressionist terms of light,[44] apparently in conscious imitation of painting, for he has been quoted as saying, 'Je n'ai pas seulement soutenu les impressionnistes. Je les ai traduits en littérature, par les touches, notes, colorations, par la palette de beaucoup de mes descriptions.'[45] Hence the consistent failure of decadent critics to recognise in his work the same decadent traits that they hailed in the Goncourts' appears all the more unreasonable; personal prejudice and an inability to challenge current opinion seem to have been the basis of this attitude. Its arbitrary nature is brought out in a *Journal* entry by Edmond de Goncourt. Referring to *L'Oeuvre* (which, egotistically, he regarded as a plagiarism of his own *Manette Salomon*), he writes:

C'est particulier chez Zola, comme le dialogue est toujours d'un manoeuvre, jamais d'un artiste. La langue de l'artiste peut être émaillée de jurements, peut être canaille, mais elle a sous les jurements, sous la canaillerie de l'expression, quelque chose qui la distingue, qui la sépare, qui la relève de la langue des charpentiers, et ce sont toujours des charpentiers qui parlent dans *L'Oeuvre*.[46]

In any case, it was the Goncourts, not Zola, whom the decadents regarded, along with Baudelaire, as their literary ancestors. Before

examining how the idea of decadence was interpreted and brought
into focus by the critical essays of Théophile Gautier and Paul Bourget,
we must show how it had originated and had been gaining ground in
the course of the preceding hundred years.

Notes

1 Edmund Wilson, *Axel's Castle* (New York: Scribner's, 1931), p. 7.
2 Léo Trézenik, 'Chronique lutécienne: les parnassiens', *Lutèce*, 2–9 November
   1884.
3 Louis Marsolleau, 'Charles Cros, poète', *Chat Noir*, 19 September 1885.
4 'M. Mallarmé', *Vogue*, I, 11 (5–12 July 1886), 362–3.
5 *Cf.* André Fontainas' use of Scandinavian mythology, reminiscent of
   Poèmes barbares, in 'Gerda' and 'Freya', *Basoche*, I, 4 (March 1885), 179–82
   and 196.
6 'Le Nénuphar', *Chat Noir*, 30 December 1882, and 'La Lune', 6 January
   1883.
7 See A. E. Carter, *Baudelaire et la critique française, 1868–1917* (Columbia:
   University of South Carolina, 1963), p. 30.
8 *Ibid.*, p. 43.
9 See *ibid.*, pp. 50 and 55.
10 *Ibid.*, p. 56.
11 *Ibid.*, p. 58.
12 'Les Chats', *Oeuvres complètes*, Y.-G. Le Dantec and Claude Pichois, eds.
   (Gallimard, 1961), p. 63; 'Sonnet inédit', p. 158; and 'La Chanson du scieur
   du long', p. 566. Baudelaire did not compose the latter, but intended to use
   it in *L'Ivrogne*.
13 Jules Lemaitre, 'Georges Ohnet', *Les Contemporains*, first series, twenty-
   third edition. (Société française d'imprimerie de la librairie, n.d.), pp.
   337–55.
14 Léo Trézenik, 'Chronique lutécienne: à propos des Syrtes', *Lutèce*, 21–8
   December 1884.
15 Edouard Norès, 'Place aux jeunes', *Lutèce*, 14–21 June 1885.
16 Charles Morice, *La Littérature de tout à l'heure* (Perrin, 1889), pp. 1 *et seq.*
17 Téodor de Wyzewa, 'Les Livres', *Revue Indépendante*, I, 2 (December 1886),
   186–7.
18 Louis Villatte (Anatole Baju), 'Chronique littéraire', *Décadent*, 24 April
   1886.
19 Pierre Vareilles (Anatole Baju), 'Décadence', *ibid.*
20 Although Flaubert was one of des Esseintes' favourite modern writers,
   J.-K. Huysmans devotes only eighteen lines to him in *A Rebours*, as opposed
   to seventy for the Goncourts and twenty-nine for Zola (Fasquelle, 1955,
   pp. 223–8). Emile Hennequin, whose articles on Edmond de Goncourt and

Huysmans in *La Revue Indépendante* emphasise decadent aspects of their work, does not treat Flaubert as decadent in *La Revue Contemporaine* ('Gustave Flaubert, étude critique', III, 2, 25 October 1885, 137–74), even under the rubrics *Le style* and *Pessimisme*. Either Hennequin did not think Flaubert was decadent, or he could not say so in the conservative *Revue Contemporaine*. (Participants in the decadent movement adopted a different tone when writing in that magazine.) Ernest Raynaud describes Flaubert as a worthy predecessor of the Goncourts, but less innovative than they. As a heroine Emma Bovary resembles the decadent type but lacks Mme Gervaise's strength of character. See 'Les Origines du mouvement décadent: les frères de Goncourt', *Décadent*, 1–15 and 15–30 January 1889.

21 Both Pierre Martino, in *Parnasse et symbolisme*, eleventh edition (Colin, 1964), p. 144, and Albert-Marie Schmidt, in *La Littérature symboliste* (Presses universitaires, 1963), p. 54, make this distinction.

22 'La Jeunesse sous le Second Empire et sous la Troisième République', *Revue Politique et Littéraire* (*Revue Bleue*), XXXV, 24 (13 June 1885), 743.

23 See also our article 'Naturalist influences on symbolist poetry, 1882–6', *French Review*, XLVI, 2 (December 1972), 299–311.

24 'La *Sapho* de M. A. Daudet', *Revue Indépendante*, I (May 1884), 144–9.

25 'Les Livres', *ibid.*, n.s. II, 5 (March 1887), 321–2.

26 Martin Turnell, *The Art of French Fiction* (London: Hamilton, 1959), pp. 93–4; see also Elliott M. Grant, *Emile Zola* (New York: Twayne, 1966), p. 84.

27 For *Germinal*, see 'Chronique lutécienne' and 'Zola romantique', 5–12 April 1885; for Zola's decline, see Henri Heltey (like 'Léo Trézenik', one of Léon Epinette's several pen names), 'Chronique lutécienne: un décadent', *Lutèce*, 10–17 January 1886.

28 '*Germinal*', I, 6 (April 1885), 205–17.

29 'Les Nouveaux-nés', *Chat Noir*, 14 March 1885.

30 'Bulletin littéraire du *Chat Noir*', *Chat Noir*, 5 January 1884.

31 For a thorough treatment of the role of critics in the simultaneous rise of impressionism and symbolism, see Jacques Lethève, *Impressionnistes et symbolistes devant la presse* (Colin, 1959), and 'Quand Verlaine, Huysmans et Moréas partaient en guerre au nom des 'Poètes maudits', *Figaro Littéraire*, 11 April 1959, pp. 6 and 11.

32 For parallels between art and literature, see Helmut Hatzfeld, *Literature through Art; a New Approach to French Literature* (New York: Oxford University Press, 1952), and Ruth Moser, *L'Impressionnisme français; peinture, littérature, musique* (Geneva: Droz, 1952).

33 'Et l'on voit aussi comment le naturalisme, et la poésie parnassienne, et l'impressionnisme s'appellent et s'engendrent. Quand on renonce à ce qui avait été presque le tout de la littérature classique et de la littérature roman-esque, à la peinture de la vie morale et à l'idéalisation de l'homme, que reste-t-il que la sensation, l'impression pittoresque et sensuelle? L'art nouveau

se réduit peut-être à cette recherche inventive de la sensation rare.' 'La Jeunesse sous le Second Empire et la Troisième République', pp. 742–3.

34 Lethève, who, oddly enough, rejects transposition of the arts, sees public traditionalism as the chief bond between the two groups: 'Il se trouve ensuite qu'ils sont heurtés à la même incompréhension de la part du public; c'est qu'ils rompaient également, peintres ou poètes, avec la tradition de l'école. L'apparence de leurs oeuvres déroute totalement le public . . .' *Impressionnistes et symbolistes*, p. 12. *Cf.* Helen Trudgian's observation: 'Cette façon d'identifier sa [Huysmans'] propre cause avec celle du mouvement artistique contemporain, constitue une véritable originalité dans la critique d'art. Elle fait que les tâtonnements de la jeune école sont enregistrés par Huysmans dans les *Salons* avec une minutie qu'on chercherait vainement ailleurs.' *L'Evolution des idées esthétiques de J.-K. Huysmans* (Conard, 1934), p. 101.

35 For Lemaitre, see note 33 above. Brunetière sees 'une remarquable affinité du roman naturaliste pour le vaudeville et la grosse farce' in 'Revue littéraire: les petits naturalistes', *Revue des Deux Mondes*, LXIV (1 August 1884), 697 *et seq.*

36 See Phoebe Pool, *Impressionism* (New York: Praeger, 1967), pp. 118–20 and 144: 'Actresses, barmaids, skaters and courtesans are all as brilliantly and dispassionately observed [by Manet after the 1870's] as the women in Maupassant's stories' (p. 144).

37 Emile Zola, *Les Rougon-Macquart*, Henri Mitterand, ed., IV (Gallimard, 1966), pp. 216 and 1457. For thorough treatments of *L'Oeuvre* see Patrick Brady, *L'Oeuvre de Emile Zola; roman sur les arts* (Geneva: Droz, 1968), and Robert J. Niess, *Zola, Cézanne, and Manet; a Study of L'Oeuvre* (Ann Arbor: University of Michigan, 1968).

38 *Les Rougon-Macquart*, II (1961), p. 1663. Mitterand also sees Zola's portrait of Clorinde Balbi serving bar at a charity sale (*Son Excellence Eugène Rougon*, II, p. 332) as a source for Manet's *Bar des Folies Bergères*.

39 See Paul Signac, 'Mounard, dite la *Trique*', *Chat Noir*, 11 February 1882, and 'Une Crevaison', 25 March 1882. In his edition of *L'Assommoir* Mitterand publishes a glossary of slang terms, II, pp. 1597–601.

40 (Tresse and Stock, 1886); *Revue Indépendante*, n.s., IV, 9 (July 1887), 67–89.

41 Téodor de Wyzewa, 'Les Livres', *Revue Indépendante*, n.s., V, 12 (October 1887), 2–3.

42 *Ibid.*, n.s., III, 7 (May 1887), 211.

43 'Correspondance', *Lutèce*, 4–11 October 1885.

44 Brady, pp. 355–7. For rendition of light effects in *L'Oeuvre* see Niess, pp. 244–5.

45 Henri Hertz, 'Zola, témoin de la vérité', *L'Europe*, III, 83–4 (November–December 1952), p. 32.

46 *Journal*, 23 February 1886, quoted by Brady, p. 359.

Chapter II
The idea of decadence

Montesquieu refers to decadence in the title of his *Grandeur et decadence des Romains*, in which he demonstrates that it was the enervating effects of civilisation and the relaxation of republican virtues which brought about the collapse of the Roman empire. Jean-Jacques Rousseau holds an equally jaundiced view, arguing in his *Discours sur les sciences et les arts* that it was civilisation, with its restrictions and artificial conventions, that corrupted man and did for the noble savage.[1] Both Montesquieu and Rousseau anticipate the Romantic outlook, which, besides listening to its heart rather than to its mind, preferred the country to the city and extolled the virtues of whatever is natural. 'As a result, the badness of civilisation and the virtues of nature became part of a new sensibility, which we usually call Romantic; so much a part of it, in fact, that any revolt against Romanticism—when it came—was bound to be a revolt against the primitive and the natural. The cult of decadence is just such a revolt.'[2]

A pet notion of the Enlightenment was that of progress, which, contradicting Montesquieu and Rousseau, held that man, aided by his own reason and profiting from his collective past experience would inevitably grow toward a better life. Positivism was the nineteenth century's own version of progress, for it placed confidence in technology and the scientific method as means of improving man's lot. So it appears that in both the eighteenth and nineteenth centuries French thinkers had a choice of—or perhaps we should say, were torn between—two conceptions of the human condition, one pessimistic, one optimistic. At a practical level these contradictory ideas were not mutually exclusive: Romantics who lamented the loss of Eden still worked for social improvement, and decadents who decried modern times looked hopefully to the future.

To an important degree the key to this ambivalence was perverseness, which caused man to devote his attention to what he found repellent, or at least to do the opposite of what was expected of him. An early reaction against Rousseau's ideas was expressed by the

Marquis de Sade, who argued that nature is destructive and anti-human, and who advocated resisting nature by cultivating the artificial. He contended even that unnatural sex practices are a useful antidote to nature's threat to man.[3] The cult of the artificial and of sexual perversion has a great deal to do with decadence. So does Romanticism's tendency, apparent early in its history, to revel in its own sufferings. Chateaubriand's René, the Lamartine of *Méditations poétiques*, and Musset suffered from their ill-fated loves, yet rather than seeking effective relief, they cultivated their misfortune as a source of inspiration. Decadent critics would refer back to the *mal du siècle* as an antecedent of their own pessimism. Romanticism also liked what is extravagant, grotesque, and, finally, even ugly. We see this in the mixture of the sublime and the grotesque in Victor Hugo's *theorie du drâme* and in the character Quasimodo in *Notre Dame de Paris*. Thus decadence was both a revolt against one kind of Romanticism and a continuation of another Romanticism's perversely deliberate choice of what is unpleasant—what Mario Praz has called 'Beauty of the Medusa, beloved by the Romantics Beauty tainted with pain, corruption, and death—we shall find it again at the end of the century . . .'[4]

These remarks will help explain the readiness of nineteenth-century French intellectuals—philosophers, historians, artists, and writers—to accept the thesis that their country was degenerating and, furthermore, their willingness to live in a time of impending doom. Social thinkers, in fact, interpreted contemporary events as evidence of decline. 'Frédéric Ozanam, a distinguished Catholic historian of democratic convictions, declared in 1852 that the best minds of his time believed in decadence, and that the idea of progress had become a discredited notion.'[5] Claude-Marie Radot's *Decadence de la France* (1850) 'had the merit of presenting the first systematic analysis of various symptoms of social and political disorganization from which, it was held, French society was suffering'.[6] After observing factors like the slow population growth, the decline of the merchant marine and armed forces, the backwardness of French agriculture, and an increase in the crime rate, Radot came to the conclusion that France was decaying as a nation. The agitated and often unfortunate course of French history from the defeat at Waterloo in 1814 to the Great War a century later tended to bear out these bleak observations. At the end of the century the philosophical pessimism of Friedrich Hegel and Arthur Schopenhauer gained wide acceptance among French intellectuals and thus reinforced such a dark interpretation of history.

The notion of decadence involves a sustained paradox, for, unable to choose between two opposing ideas, it cordially accepts both. Decadent thinkers accepted Rousseau's idea that nature is good and civilisation bad, yet they enthusiastically preferred the artificial: such perverse enjoyment of what is thought to be evil characterises decadence.[7] With respect to the interpretation of history, some French writers accepted that their nation was declining, yet the idea of living in a decadent civilisation appealed to their Romantic sense of exoticism, local colour, and the grotesque. 'Like French writers of the *fin de siècle*, these last representatives of French Romanticism no longer dreamed of distant lands more virtuous and more vigorous than their own, but of societies more vicious and more decadent.'[8] Thomas Couture's *Romains de la décadence* attracted considerable attention at the Salon of 1847. The hero of Théophile Gautier's *Mademoiselle de Maupin* craved release in the debauchery of ancient Rome, and in the preface Gautier exclaimed: 'Tibère, Caligula, Néron, grands romains de l'Empire, ô vous que l'on a si mal compris et que la meute des rhéteurs poursuit de ses aboiments, je souffre de votre mal et je vous plains de tout ce qui me reste de pitié!'[9] The author of *Salammbô* wrote to Louise Colet, 'Que ne donnerais-je pas pour voir un triomphe! Que ne vendrais-je pas pour entrer dans Subure, quand les flambeaux brûlaient aux portes des lupanars et que les tambourins tonnaient dans les tavernes.'[10] At the end of the century there grew up a veritable cult of late classical antiquity, which is reflected in the titles of popular novels: Jean Lombard, *L'Agonie* (1888) and *Byzance* (1890); Anatole France, *Thaïs* (1890); Paul Adam, *Les Princesses byzantines* (1893); Pierre Louys, *Aphrodite* (1896); Jean Richepin, *Contes de la décadence romaine* (1898). Sinkiewicz' *Quo Vadis* enjoyed considerable success in France after being translated in 1896.[11] After having seen classical antiquity spurned because of its associations with French literary classicism, later Romantics rediscovered imperial Rome on their own terms.

Decadent Rome became pertinent to them as Frenchmen found in it analogies with their own world. As early as 1834 Désiré Nisard, in his *Etude de moeurs et de critique sur les poètes de la décadence*, slightingly compared Romantic poetry to Latin poetry of the Silver Age. A critic with strong classical taste, Nisard was merely trying to belittle Romantic poetry and its facile effects by showing how Latin poetry of the late Empire had expressed the same tastes,[12] but the analogy he drew remained. In 1862 Sainte-Beuve compared Flaubert's style in *Salambô* to that of decadent Latin.[13] Balzac called Paris, as a centre of depravity, the heiress of Ninevah, Babylon, and ancient Rome.[14] In what apparently was pure coincidence, Victor Hugo in 1837 compared himself to Virgil and, by extension, Paris to Rome:

> O Virgile! ô poëte! ô mon maître divin!
> Viens, quittons cette ville au cri sinistre et vain
> Qui, géante, et jamais ne fermant la paupière,
> Presse un flot écumant entre ses flancs de pierre,
> Lutèce, si petite au temps de tes Césars,
> Et qui jette aujourd'hui, cité pleine de chars,
> Sous le nom éclatant dont le monde la nomme,
> Plus de clarté qu'Athène et plus de bruit que Rome.
> . . .
> J'ai trouvé, dans une ombre où rit l'herbe fleurie,
> Entre Buc et Meudon, dans un profond oubli,
> —Et quand je dis Meudon, suppose Tivoli!—
> . . .[15]

Hugo, who has just acquired a country home, sings the beauties of nature in appropriately Romantic fashion; but he also makes devices like calling Paris 'Lutèce', carriages 'chars', and of equating Parisian landmarks with Roman ones; in fifty years poets will resume this translation, only insisting on depravity and decadence as the areas of contact between the two cities. After the similarities which French classical writers in the seventeenth and eighteenth centuries saw between themselves and ancient Rome, and after Madame de Staël's interpretation of Romanticism as a Nordic art replacing Mediterranean classicism, the comparison of nineteenth-century Paris to decadent imperial Rome appeared inevitable.[16] Following the unbroken line of the *Ancien Régime*, the political instability of the nineteenth century, with its succession of empires, monarchies, and republics, seemed to parallel the disintegration of central authority in the ancient Roman State. The Second Empire and the Roman empire invited comparison: both enjoyed social brilliance, economic expansion, and military grandeur; both, on the other hand, suffered from moral profligacy and political corruption; and both fell before invading hordes of blond, barbaric Teutons.

The growing acceptance of what were seen as the values of decadent Roman culture can be traced in the manner of comparing contemporary French and late Latin styles. Nisard's comparison of 1834 was intended as an affront; Sainte-Beuve's of 1862 was only slightly pejorative; and by 1843 Gautier asserted that in the *lycée* he had sought to imitate the metres of decadent Latin poets.[17] When in 1857 Baudelaire actually included such a poem, 'Franciscae meae laudes', in his *Fleurs du mal*, he clearly stated his intent:

> Ne semble-t-il pas au lecteur, comme à moi, que la langue de la dernière décadence latine,—suprême soupir d'une personne robuste déjà transformée et préparée pour la vie spirituelle,—est singulièrement propre à exprimer la passion telle que l'a comprise et sentie le monde poétique moderne? . . .[18]

In 1864 Mallarmé wrote of long days spent with his cat and with an author of the late Empire, for he liked all that can be subsumed in the word *chute*, and he found voluptuous pleasure in reading 'la poésie agonisante des derniers moments de Rome'.[19] Finally, in the 1880's decadent verse deliberately mimics late Latin by means of turgid, ornate style and by neologisms formed on Latin models: *plangorer, rutiler, langourosite, déliquescent, incandescent, torrescent*. In the minds of French writers, the diction characteristic of late Latin underwent a complete rehabilitation, from a measure of inferiority to a standard of excellence. By the same token, the very word 'decadence' acquired a double meaning: it could still denote decline, but it also came to designate the best of its kind.[20]

Translating the idea of decadence into creative works of literature took on a rather specialised character, for writers of the 1880's did not themselves draw the analogy between modern Paris and ancient Rome or deduce its consequences: it was done for them. The major step, by which this analogy was translated into specific literary techniques and attitudes, was accomplished by essays of two influential critics, Théophile de Gautier and Paul Bourget.

Gautier's 'Notice' to the 1868 edition of *Les Fleurs du mal* is less than original, since it adds little to what he had been saying for some time, but it was a significant document because of the influence it had on Baudelaire's admirers.[21] Gautier himself was better known than Baudelaire, and this edition was the only one extant between Baudelaire's own revised edition of 1861 and the Nouvelle Revue Française edition of 1918. Thus, for the half-century during which Baudelaire moved from obscurity to recognition as a major poet, readers of *Les Fleurs du mal* probably read Gautier's essay too, and this essay made an exclusively decadent interpretation of Baudelaire's poetry. The biased, polemical quality of Gautier's presentation immediately becomes apparent, for upon opening the pages of this edition to his 'Notice' we meet, not Baudelaire, but various works of art. After stating that

he first met Baudelaire at the Hôtel Pimodan, Gautier promptly
digresses to a pair of comely models and the works of art for which
they posed, so that the initial paragraph, 'La première fois que nous
recontrâmes Baudelaire', actually deals with titles of paintings and the
description of a statue. Thus art is substituted for reality in thoroughly
decadent fashion. This artificiality is maintained in the second paragraph, where the poet's physiognomy is described in terms of works
of art or of artifacts like tobacco, perfumes, and rice powder:

> Son aspect nous frappa: il avait les cheveux coupés très ras et du plus beau
> noir; ces cheveux, faisant des pointes régulières sur le front d'une éclatante
> blancheur, le coiffaient comme une espèce de casque sarassin; les yeux,
> couleur de tabac d'Espagne, avaient un regard spirituel, profond, et d'une
> pénétration peut-être un peu trop insistante; quant à la bouche, meublée de
> dents très blanches, elle abritait, sous une légère et soyeuse moustache om-
> brageant son contour, des sinuosités mobiles, voluptueuses et ironiques
> comme les lèvres de figures peintes par Léonard de Vinci; le nez, fin et
> délicat, un peu arrondi, aux narines palpitantes, semblait subodorer de
> vagues parfums lointains; une fossette vigoureuse accentuait le menton
> comme le coup de pouce final du statuaire; les joues, soigneusement rasées,
> contrastaient, par leur fleur bleuâtre que veloutait la poudre de riz, avec les
> nuances vermeilles des pommettes; le cou, d'une élégance et d'une blancheur
> féminines . . .[22]

Baudelaire is again presented as in a painting when Gautier quotes from
Banville's description of a portrait by Emile Deroy. Balzac, too, had
described his characters as figures in paintings; so, the device was not
new; but for young decadents who perhaps did not know Balzac as
well as they did the Goncourts and who anyway regarded art as a
mode of life, Gautier's description must have seemed altogether
appropriate, even if not original. Still more allusions to paintings
follow: decorations in the Hôtel Pimodan done by pupils of Lesueur
or Poussin, painters like Fernand Boissard who were members of the
circle at the Hôtel Pimodan, Baudelaire's art criticism and his admiration for Constantin Guys, the realist school of painting led by Courbet
and Manet. For writers who were interested in transposition of the
arts and in imitating subjects and effects of painting in their poems, all
these references would have made Baudelaire seem like one of their
own number. Other passages call Baudelaire the poet of the artificial,
for whom 'la *dépravation*, c'est-à-dire l'écart du type normal, [qui] est
impossible à la bête', is a sign of man's superiority over nature (p. 32)—
an assertion which recalls the Marquis de Sade's notion that man should

assert himself against nature. All this is convincingly argued, for the 'Notice' is as much a work of propaganda as of literary criticism; 'Gautier, vieux feuilletonniste rompu à toutes les finesses du métier, s'est ici surpassé: son oeuvre volumineuse ne contient rien de mieux.'[23]

Turning to his style, Gautier explains that Baudelaire has not taken the great masters of the past for his models because they had the good fortune to arrive at the dawn of human experience, when 'les grands lieux-communs qui composent le fond de la pensée humaine étaient alors dans toute leur fleur, et ils suffisaient à des génies simples parlant à un peuple enfantin' (pp. 18–19). Now, however, these *lieux-communs*, like coins worn smooth by the many hands that have held them, no longer suffice to express the complexities of nineteenth-century life. Inevitably, therefore, Baudelaire writes during the sunset of literature and so is constrained to adopt a manner suitable for portraying those effects peculiar to the end of day. This premise leads to the heart of Gautier's essay, a discussion of the decadent style:

> Le poète des *Fleurs du mal* aimait ce qu'on appelle improprement le style de décadence, et qui n'est autre chose que l'art arrivé à ce point de maturité extrême que déterminent à leurs soleils obliques les civilisations qui vieillissent: style ingénieux, compliqué, savant, plein de nuances et de recherches, reculant toujours les bornes de la langue, empruntant à tous les vocabulaires techniques, prenant des couleurs à toutes les palettes, des notes à tous les claviers, s'efforçant à rendre la pensée dans ce qu'elle a de plus ineffable, et la forme en ses contours les plus vagues et les plus fuyants, écoutant pour les traduire les confidences subtiles de la névrose, les aveux de la passion vieillissante qui se déprave, et les hallucinations bizarres de l'idée fixe tournant à la folie. Ce style de décadence est le dernier mot du Verbe sommé de tout exprimer et poussé à l'extrême outrance. On peut rappeler, à propos de lui, la langue marbrée déjà des verdeurs de la décomposition et comme faisandée du Bas-Empire romain et les raffinements compliqués de l'école byzantine, dernière forme de l'art grec tombé en déliquescence; mais tel est bien l'idiome nécessaire et fatal des peuples et des civilisations où la vie factice a remplacé la vie naturelle et développé chez l'homme des besoins inconnus. Ce n'est pas chose aisée, d'ailleurs, que ce style méprisé des pédants, car il exprime des idées neuves avec des formes nouvelles et des mots qu'on n'a pas entendus encore. [p. 20]

Baudelaire prefers the Latin style of Apuleius, Petronius, Juvenal, St Augustine and Tertullian to that of Virgil and Cicero; Gautier pursues this motif of Roman decadence by stating that Baudelaire's preference for the artificial is also that of 'les civilisations très avancèes ou très corrumpues' (p. 31), and by calling the hypocritical reader addressed in 'Au lecteur' a 'Néron bureaucrate, Héliogabale boutiquier' who 'rêve platement les férocités et les débauches romaines' (p. 35).

The thesis that the nineteenth century was an old, jaded culture whose perception was subtler than that of previous ages, and the corollary that it needed a nicer literary style to express its experience adequately, are both questionable: today the early part of the century seems, if anything, like an age of youthful enthusiasm, and the similarity between the Romantic style in French and Silver Age Latin seems more metaphorical than stylistic. Nevertheless, no one seems to have questioned this line of reasoning. The greater part of Gautier's essay deals factually with other aspects of Baudelaire, such as his prose poems and his translations of Poe; its significance for the history of decadence is that he states the case for decadence so persuasively. His argument for a different style to meet the special needs of an old civilisation—although simply a restatement of the Romantic tenet that a new sensibility requires a new style—became a cliché of decadent criticism.

A brief look at comments other poets made about Baudelaire will illustrate the general acceptance of Gautier's interpretation. Barbey d'Aurevilly wrote in 1881, 'Baudelaire et Poe . . . étaient enfin la poésie du spleen, des nerfs et du frisson, dans une vieille civilisation matérialiste et dépravée . . . qui est à ses derniers râles et à ses dernières pâmoisons . . .'[24] In the same year Paul Bourget characterised Baudelaire as decadent: 'Il s'est rendu compte qu'il arrivait tard dans une civilisation vieillissante, et . . . il s'en est réjoui . . . Il était un homme de la décadence, il s'est fait un théoricien de décadence,'[25] and he devoted a chapter of his essay to Baudelaire's style. In 1882 Emile Verhaeren observed: 'Nul poète ne sent d'une façon plus aiguë, avec des nerfs plus surexcités; il pousse tout à l'outrance, il semble avoir des sens spéciaux pour subir les morbidesses, les mélancolies, les navrements, les désespoirs. . . . Sa langue . . . est trempée dans le mysticisme. . . . Elle est admirable pour exprimer les doléances et les misères, les affaissements et les ennuis. . . .'[26] Thus, except that Verhaeren attributes Baudelaire's style to the Middle Ages (another period of corrupt Latin style?), by 1882 Gautier's views of Baudelaire's morbidly sensitive nature, and of his language as a specialised vehicle of expression, had acquired rather general currency among the generation of writers who would become known as decadents.

As was the case with Baudelaire, the brothers Jules and Edmond de Goncourt were a principal influence on this generation, and the decadence of their novels was carefully explained in an admiring and

widely read essay. Paul Bourget, its author, had apparently read
Gautier's 'Notice', for there is the same insistence that the nineteenth
century was old and tired,[27] the same attention to the Goncourts' cult
of art and to their specialised style. (Bourget also did an essay on
Baudelaire, the third part of which is entitled 'Théorie de la décadence.'[28]
Thus anyone who missed Gautier's essay could have read much the
same thing in Bourget's.) A brief quotation will show how the major
lines of Bourget's interpretation follow those of Gautier's:

> En plein milieu du second Empire, ils étaient l'un et l'autre des hommes de
> lettres de 1880. Chez eux commençait de s'accomplir l'influence de l'object
> d'art sur la littérature, et cette influence est aujourd'hui un fait capital . . .
> Sous cette influence ils créaient une forme particulière de roman, qui se
> trouve capable d'exprimer mieux qu'aucune autre les maladies morales de
> l'homme moderne, et, pour écrire ce roman, ils inventaient et mettaient en
> pratique une sorte de style si entièrement neuve que les meilleurs juges de
> leur époque en furent étonnés.[29]

Like Gautier, Zola, and, indeed, many prose writers of the period
who had to earn their living through journalism, the Goncourts knew
the world of painters and wrote art criticism. Their *L'art au dix-huitième
siècle* and *La Femme au dix-huitième siècle* reflected contemporary taste,
and they were among the first Frenchmen to join in the vogue for
Japanese art in the latter part of the century; in this they anticipated
the impressionists, whose paintings recall the handling of space and the
use of blank areas in Japanese prints. It is the Goncourts' transposition of
impressionist painting into literature and their general aestheticism
which seem to have distinguished them from Zola in the minds of the
decadents. While the Goncourts are no longer as highly esteemed as
they were in the 1880's, modern scholarship still recognises the significance of their style: 'The Goncourts were the pioneers of modern
prose. . . . Next only to Flaubert and perhaps to Chateaubriand, they
were the most decisive influence in nineteenth-century narrative prose,
and it is safe to say that without them, the development of French
literary style would have taken a different course.'[30]

The Goncourts were the first to recognise the importance of their
contemporaries' nervousness and to claim that a morbidly hypersensitive nature was actually a form of superiority.[31] 'Songez que
notre oeuvre, et c'est peut-être son originalité durement payée, repose
sur la maladie nerveuse,' they wrote to Zola in 1870.[32] Morbidity is a
characteristic of their novels: in *Renée Mauperin* (1864) the heroine
dies of heart disease, *Germinie Lacerteux* (1864) analyses a case of

nymphomania and hysteria, and *La Faustin* (1881) relates the life of a
Comédie française actress whose lover Georges Selwyn, dies of a
hereditary nervous disease. Mario Praz identifies him as the very type
of the English sadist.[33] The aestheticism and artificiality inherent in
the profession of acting can be considered decadent. The artistic
personality is generally decadent, for the acuity of perception which
allows a painter, for example, to render extremely subtle nuances of
colour, light, or atmosphere is the same pathological sensitivity which
causes him to suffer unduly from the abrasions of daily life.[34] Bourget
demonstrates the relationship which links style. hypersensitivity, and
modernity:

> Cette rhétorique, issue de la peinture et de la sculpture, est un instrument
> merveilleux pour exécuter certaines analyses, celles, par exemple, des
> troubles du système nerveux. Sous l'influence de ces troubles, l'émotion
> morale est accompagnée d'un cortège de fortes impressions physiques, et,
> comme cet énervement est la maladie même de l'époque, les frères de
> Goncourt ont employé leurs procédés de style avec un bonheur rare dans les
> fortes études de détraquements qui s'appellent *Manette Salomon, Madame
> Gervaisais, Germinie Lacerteux*. Ces monographies de névroses n'auraient
> jamais pu être rédigées dans la langue que nous a transmise Voltaire . . .[35]

Again we meet the basic, if debatable, premise of decadence, that
modern man feels more intensely than his ancestors did, even to the
point of sickness. The point at issue is not whether the Goncourts really
depicted this syndrome more accurately than, say, a Flaubert or a
Zola, but that, on the basis of these notions, decadent criticism ranked
the Goncourts as the most accomplished novelists of their time, and
that a critic whose other judgements were generally sound could write:

> J'admire seulement avec quelle finesse il [Edmond, this article having been
> written seventeen years after Jules' death] a, seul de tous les romanciers
> peut-être, fait vivre des personnages non abstraits et généraux, mais
> spécialement contemporains. Le côté moderne des caractères, seul il est
> parvenu à le marquer toujours, sans déformer l'ensemble vivant des âmes et
> des attitudes. Les héros de Balzac, de Flaubert, de M. Zola et de M. Bourget
> sont, avant tout, considérés dans leur aspect humain et général: la *Faustin*,
> surtout *Chérie*, sont des âmes spécialement prises dans notre vie actuelle.[36]

The same panegyric tone characterises Emile Hennequin's 'Les Romans
de M. Edmond de Goncourt', in *La Revue Independante*,[37] and Ernest
Raynaud's 'Les Origines du mouvement décadent: les frères de
Goncourt,' in *Le Décadent*.[38]
  Zola, too, presents his characters in terms of the decadence of modern

man. In *L'Oeuvre* Claude Lantier describes the parents of Régine Margaillan as too enervated by declining heredity to bear a robust child: '. . . ils l'ont si mal fichue à eux deux, lui le sang gâté par des générations d'ivrognes, elle épuisée, la chair mangée par tous les virus des races finissantes',[39] and he iterates the Paris–Rome metaphor when he says of Mathilde Jabouille's succession of lovers, 'c'était renouvelé des Romains'.[40] In *Mes Haines* Zola writes, 'Mon goût, si l'on veut, est dépravé. J'aime les ragoûts littéraires fortement épicés, les oeuvres de décadence où une sorte de sensibilité maladive remplace la santé plantureuse des époques classiques.'[41] *Les Rougon-Macquart* is the case history of pathological heredity, as the novel studies the descendents of the alcoholic Macquart and the neurotic, hysterical Adélaide Fouques Rougon. As Koenraad Swart observes, Zola's analysis of the corruption of the Second Empire, with its portrayal of various types of degeneracy, bears out the decadent thesis that the decline of the nineteenth century was caused by luxury and hereditary tendencies.[42]

Where Zola differs from the Goncourts is that, however methodical and specific his tableau of degeneration and depravity, he presents it with disapproval; he sees civilisation as crumbling, but in expiation of its sins, and in order to give way to a higher and morally better order, whereas the Goncourts identify themselves with the hysteria and degeneration of their characters.

Zola's attitude becomes clear in a curious essay of *Mes Haines*. The opening lines could just as well have been written by the Goncourts:

> Qu'il me soit permis de parler du'n sujet qui intéresse toute notre généra-tion d'esprits affolés et hystériques. Le corps, comme aux meilleurs temps du mysticisme, est singulièrement en déchéance chez nous. Ce n'est plus l'âme qu'on exalte, ce sont les nerfs, la matière cérébrale. La chair est endolorie des secousses profondes et répétées que le cerveau imprime à tout l'organisme. Nous sommes malades, cela est bien certain, malades de progrès. . . . Cette victoire des nerfs sur le sang a décidé de nos meours, de notre littérature, de notre époque tout entière.[43]

Nevertheless, Zola's purpose is quite opposite from theirs, for in fact the essay is his review of a book on physical fitness, and Zola deplores the fact, the truth of which he does not question, that modern civilisa-tion has emphasised the nerves and mind at the expense of the body, that it is no longer possible for the whole city to turn out on the drill field for gymnastics, as in the time of the ancient Greeks, and, finally, that the epigraph of the book, *Mens sana in corpore sano*, is an ideal unattainable for his contemporaries. So, from an identical initial observation of facts, Zola's deduction is quite the contrary of the Goncourts'. In the novels, Zola's recurrent use of the sexual act to symbolise healthy, vital regeneration is in direct contrast with the decadent preoccupation with the same act, which was taken in every sense except that of normal love and reproduction. There is in *Les Rougon-Macquart* a natural vitality foreign to the artificiality of decadence, an artificiality which is present in the works of the Goncourts, and perhaps it was this vitality which decadent critics sensed with dislike when they accused Zola of obscenity and crudity.

Baudelaire, Gautier, and Jules de Goncourt, who lived and wrote under the Second Empire, were all dead by 1872, and so they had no personal contact with the generation of the 1880's. Edmond de Goncourt, on the contrary, was active throughout the decade; after 1885 many decadents were guests at his Sunday receptions in Auteuil. Paul Bourget, who was only thirty in 1882, was close in age to the writers we shall consider; as a member of the Hydropaths, an associate of Léo Trézenik, and a contributor to *La Nouvelle Rive Gauche*, he must have had personal contact with the poets of the new generation. Even so, his influence on the formation of the decadent sensibility was chiefly exercised through his *Essais de psychologie contemporaine* (1883) and his *Nouveaux Essais de psychologie contemporaine* (1885), which originally appeared in *La Nouvelle Revue*, starting with the one on Baudelaire (15 November 1881) and ending with the one on the Goncourt brothers (1 October 1885). Thus they were exactly contemporary with the activities of the decadent school in poetry. While *La Nouvelle Revue* was not specifically devoted to decadent aims, contributions by Jean Aicard, Jean Lorrain, and Gabriel Vicaire suggest that members of the movement were familiar with it. In any case there can be no doubt that the *Essais* were read and appreciated. Charles Morice wrote, '. . . M. Paul Bourget est assurément, pour l'aristocratique attitude du poète et pour l'exquise clairvoyance du critique, celui que ceux de demain écoutent avec le plus de sympathie.'[44] In reviewing the *Nouveaux Essais*, Léo Trézenik said that while they were not unduly original, their merit was to gather together and express clearly ideas 'qu'on retrouve là avec joie comme de vieilles connaissances.'[45]

In the 'Préface' to his *Nouveaux Essais* Bourget draws attention to the pessimism which he sees as a trait of contemporary youth:

> Le résultat de cette minutieuse et longue enquête est mélancolique. Il m'a semblé que de toutes les oeuvres passées en revue au cours de ces dix essais une même influence se dégageait, douleureuse et, pour tout dire d'un

mot, profondément, continuement pessimiste. Et, de fait, l'existence du pessimisme dans l'âme de la jeunesse contemporaine, est reconnue aujourd'hui
par ceux-là même à qui cet esprit de négation et de dépression répugne
le plus.[46]

He calls their attitude a 'reprise inattendue de ce que l'on appelait en
1830, le mal du siècle' (p. iii), pointing out that in essence decadence is
Romantic melancholy transposed into a contemporary setting; what
Adolphe by Benjamin Constant and *A Rebours* by Huysmans have in
common is 'une mortelle fatigue de vivre, une morne perception de la
vanité de tout effort' (p. iv). Bourget maintains that this attitude is not
just an imitation of Schopenhauer's pessimism, for the only doctrines
we accept are those germs we already carry within us, and pessimism
first became apparent with the generation that was young in 1855.

In conclusion, we shall indicate some decadent attitudes which were
not specifically developed by Gautier and Bourget. One of these is the
general notion of modernity: the 1880's were held to be the end-point
of a long degeneration, but they were obviously at the centre of an
exciting new world, too. Technological progress had been just as
dramatic as in our own time, and, when he was not decrying its effects,
the decadent marvelled at the urban, industrial society in which he
suddenly found himself. His wonder was expressed in literature and
the arts by the presence of city streets, workers' suburbs, railways, and
whatever else seemed to distinguish modern city life. Even suburban
commuting appears in decadent literature: the action of Ajalbert's *Sur
les Talus* takes place at the end of a tram route, Verlaine mentions
bateaux-omnibus on the Seine, Laurent Tailhade describes a typical
suburbanite.[47] There is also a tendency to social and political optimism,
since the decadent could not quite renounce the idea of progress. *La
Nouvelle Rive Gauche* espoused the cause of exploited department-
store employees, Zola came to the defence of Captain Dreyfus, and
editorials in *Le Décadent* maintained that life would be better in the
twentieth century than in the nineteenth. At the same time the decadent
was suspicious of change, since his premise was that *tout décade*. Along
with a general enthusiasm for things modern, therefore, decadence is
also characterised by a sometimes vigorous reactionism, with a tendency
for writers to employ the *particule nobilière* and to write of nobles and
the Middle Ages. *Les Rougon-Macquart* illustrates this ambiguous view
of modern times: Zola is modern in his subject-matter and in his
pseudo-scientific approach, yet the results of his inquest are un-
favourable to modernity; his treatment of the harsh, oppressed life of

the coal miners in *Germinal*, who find relief in drink, and in propagating children they are too poor to raise, is both an analysis and an indictment of industrialism. Gautier best explained the decadent's attitude towards modernity when he compared him to the bird who is both horrified and fascinated by the serpent which seeks to devour it.[48]

In religion, a few decadents echoed the anti-clericalism of the Voltairian tradition, but for many, anti-clericalism was represented by Flaubert's Monsieur Homais, and in reaction to this parody of modern liberalism they turned to Christianity.[49] Instance of this trend are Bourget's novels *Le Disciple* and *L'Etape*, and the stormy conversions of Verlaine and Huysmans. Roman Catholicism is a theme in decadent writing, particularly to the extent that the Church was seen as a mother of the arts, as a quiet sanctuary of *basse latinité* set off from the rest of the world. Mario Praz, in a different view, sees Catholicism as one side of a coin whose reverse is sadism, and he traces an oscillation between eroticism and mysticism back to Chateaubriand, whose Amélie took the veil to escape an incestuous love for her brother René.[50] From this brand of eroticism comes the common decadent theme of sexual perversion, too. Other sources are the popular belief that sodomy was widely practised in Greco-Roman antiquity or in very old civilisations, the writings of Marquis de Sade, and Romantic love of the grotesque.

Hesitation between opposite views also characterises decadent literary criticism. In one view, the growth of cheap literature which catered to the undiscriminating taste of the masses was regarded as a fruit of the industrial revolution, of popular education, and of the application of mass-production techniques to publishing. Georges Ohnet's novels were so considered. In reaction the decadent sought refuge in artistic purity and the quest of excellence.[51] Not a single decadent critic contested the thesis that poetry should be the province of a few initiates, to the exclusion of the general reader. Only the patient and cultivated reader who is willing to spend the necessary time, effort, and erudition will be able to appreciate the subtle evocations of a Baudelaire, a Verlaine, or a Mallarmé. In contrast to such exclusiveness, other decadent critics appealed to the evolution of art, arguing that what was good taste for one generation was undesirable for the next, and that literature must keep up with the times. Their reasoning was partly defensive, since the decadent writer was usually under attack for his novel manner; consequently, a consistent motif in their criticism is that the decadent writer is no different from the classic, the Romantic, or the Parnassian, whose writings were also criticised by their elders.

Notes

1 For thorough treatments of the idea of decadence, see A. E. Carter, *The Idea of Decadence in French Literature, 1830–1900* (Toronto University Press, 1958), and Koenraad W. Swart, *The Sense of Decadence in Nineteenth Century France* (The Hague: Nijhoff, 1964).

2 Carter, p. 4.

3 See *ibid.*, p. 5.

4 *The Romantic Agony*, Angus Davidson, trans., second edition (London: Oxford University Press, 1951), p. 45.

5 Swart, p. 86.

6 *Ibid.*, p. 89.

7 See Carter, pp. 4–5.

8 Swart, p. 77.

9 *Cf.* Flaubert in 1839: 'J'aime bien à voir des hommes comme ça, comme Néron, le marquis de Sade . . .' Both quoted by Jacques Lethève, 'Le Thème de la décadence dans les lettres françaises à la fin du XIXe siècle', *Revue d'Histoire Littéraire de la France*, LXIII, 1 (January–March 1963), 47–8.

10 Quoted by Lethève, p. 48.

11 See Lethève, p. 59.

12 See Swart, p. 78.

13 'Salammbô', *Nouveaux Lundis*, IV (Lévy, 1872), p. 92.

14 In *La Cousine Bette* (Garnier, n.d.), p. 325.

15 'A Virgile', *Oeuvres complètes; poésie*, II (Ollendorff, 1909), p. 406.

16 Paul Marrot's poem 'L'Enseigne' is an example of this comparison. The St-Denis and St-Martin gates, through which passed the victorious Louis XIV, suggest Roman triumphal arches; the refrain 'Ludovico magno' and other quotations of Latin inscriptions on the gates further Romanise the Sun King. Meanwhile, contrast is made with disreputable characters of modern Paris. *Chat Noir*, 16 December 1882.

17 'Je traitais les sujets de vers latins dans tous les métres imaginables et je me plaisais à imiter les styles qu'au collège on appelle de décadence.' Quoted by Lethève, pp. 47–8.

18 *Oeuvres complètes*, Y.-G. Le Dantec et Claude Pichois, eds. (Gallimard, 1961), p. 1525.

19 'Plainte d'automne', *Oeuvres complètes*, Jean Aubry and H. Mondor, eds. (Gallimard, 1945), p. 270.

20 See especially Anatole Baju's (alias Louis Villatte and Pierre Vareilles) editorials in *Le Décadent*. The novels of Zola, Ohnet, and their like are 'la

plus visible des décadences' ('Décadence', 24 April 1886); by contrast, 'Nous sommes des *Décadents*, puisque cette décadence n'est que la marche ascensionnelle de l'humanité vers des idéals inaccessibles' ('Aux jeunes', 10 April 1886).

21 For a discussion of this edition of *Les Fleurs du mal* and Gautier's 'Notice', see A. E. Carter, *Baudelaire et la critique française, 1868–1917* (Columbia: University of South Carolina, 1963), pp. 19–21.

22 'Charles Baudelaire', in Charles Baudelaire, *Les Fleurs du mal* (Lemerre, n.d.), pp. 2–3. Further references to this essay will be identified in the text by page number.

23 Carter, *Baudelaire*, p. 19.

24 *Ibid.*, p. 50.

25 *Ibid.*, p. 53.

26 *Ibid.*, p. 55.

27 See Carter, *Idea of Decadence*, p. 88, n. 83.

28 Paul Bourget, *Essais de psychologie contemporaine* (Lemerre, 1883), pp. 23–32.

29 Paul Bourget, 'MM. Edmond et Jules de Goncourt', *Nouveaux Essais de psychologie contemporaine* (Lemerre, 1886), pp. 138–9.

30 Stephen Ullmann, *Style in the French Novel* (New York: Barnes & Noble, 1964), pp. 144–5.

31 See Lethève, 'Thème de la décadence', p. 49.

32 Quoted by Bourget, *Nouveaux Essais*, p. 168.

33 See *Romantic Agony*, pp. 419–21, and Carter, *Idea of Decadence*, pp. 70–1.

34 'C'est que l'homme, en multipliant à l'infini ses émotions d'art, exagère à l'extrême la délicatesse de son système nerveux et finit par transporter l'excitation de sa nature esthétique dans les rencontres quotidiennes de toute l'existence'. Bourget, *Nouveaux Essais*, p. 155. See also Lethève, p. 49.

35 *Nouveaux Essais*, p. 192.

36 Téodor de Wyzewa, 'Les Livres', *Revue Indépendante*, n.s., III, 7 (May 1887), 211–12.

37 I, 1 (May 1884), 28–43.

38 1–15 and 15–31 January 1889.

39 Emile Zola, *Les Rougon-Macquart*, Henri Mitterand, ed., IV (Gallimard, 1966), p. 166.

40 *Ibid.*, p. 174.

41 Quoted by Mario Praz, pp. 309–10; see also p. 393, n. 37.

42 In *Sense of Decadence*, p. 108.

43 'La Littérature et la gymnastique', *Oeuvres complètes*, XL, Maurice Le Blond, ed. (Bernouard, 1928), p. 47.

44 'Paul Bourget', *Revue Contemporaine*, II, 1 (25 May 1885), 72.

45 'Chronique lutécienne', 13–20 December 1885.

46 *Nouveaux Essais*, p. iii. Subsequent quotations from the 'Préface' will be identified in the text.

47 For *Sur les Talus*, see chapter I, note 40; for Verlaine, 'L'Aube à l'envers', *Oeuvres poétiques complètes*, Jacques Borel, ed. (Gallimard, 1962), p. 375; for Tailhade, 'Rus', *Poèmes aristophanesques*, third edition (Mercure de France, 1910), p. 45.

48 'Charles Baudelaire', p. 24.

49 See Renato Poggioli, 'The autumn of ideas', *Massachusetts Review*, II, 4 (summer 1961), 659–60.

50 *Romantic Agony*, pp. 306–8.

51 Ernest Raynaud expressed it thus: . . . Il y avait, travaillant dans l'ombre, un petit groupe de jeunes gens, de tendances diverses, réunis par ce seul point commun: l'amour désintéressé des lettres et la haine de la littérature vénale. Cette haine allait si loin que tout talent préconisé par la foule, fût-il réel, leur était suspect. Par contre ils s'enthousiasmaient pour cinq ou six maitres méconnus: Verlaine, Mallarmé, Barbey d'Aurevilly, Huysmans, etc. —Pour accentuer leur mépris de toute spéculation commerciale, ils s'efforçaient de se rendre inaccessibles au public, en vêtant d'une forme laborieuse, des idées abstruses. N'ayant à compter avec personne, ils s'ingéniaient à n'écrire que pour eux, en gens qui se comprennent à demi-mot, à qui suffit une allusion.' 'Chronique littéraire', *Décadent*, 15–31 January 1888.

Chapter III

1882: change and decadence in French poetry

We return now to the situation of poetry in 1882, as it appears in the pages of *Le Chat Noir* and *La Nouvelle Rive Gauche*, both of which were appearing regularly by autumn of that year.

In the first number of *La Nouvelle Rive Gauche* (9 November 1882)[1] there is an eight-syllable sonnet by Georges Bouret, 'Les Broussailles'. It merely states that the poet likes to work without preconceived method, composing his verses from day to day; by the same procedure, his heart has become lost in the thickets of love. The second issue has a poem by Charles Morice, 'La Voix du temps', telling the struggles, joys, disappointments, and also the moral nobility of those who have passed by the spot and whose tales are echoed by the walls of the old houses. Form and thought are equally undistinguished:

> En s'appuyant du front au mur des maisons vieilles
> Aux dangereux ébranlements,
> On croit saisir un bruit confus de voix pareilles
> A de lointains chuchotements.

A week later, in the third issue, Morice has a sonnet of Parnassian inspiration which recounts in impeccable alexandrines how two fauns abducted the nymph Amadryade and violated her ('Les Faunes'). In 'Effect de printemps' Emile Taboureux states that love is born again in the spring, and in 'Sonnet vieux jeu' Léo Trézenik, who has suffered from love since the day he first saw his lady, begs her to come relieve his suffering, since 'Vous êtes trop bonne, Madame, / Pour vouloir la mort du pécheur.' In the fourth number, on the page facing Charles Morice's hostile article 'Boileau–Verlaine', appears a sacrilegious poem by Eugène Divet, 'Questions à la Vierge'. It almost seems as if the editors were themselves composing verse on short notice to fill its lean poetry columns while waiting for something better to be submitted. If we skip ahead to the issue of 5–12 January 1883, in which Verlaine appears for the first time with 'A Horatio' and 'Le Clown', the other two poems in that issue are another sonnet by Charles

Morice and Laurent Tailhade's 'Autumn's flowers' (*sic*). Thus in the first two months of its life *La Nouvelle Rive Gauche* published poetry which appears more as a dull, trite background against which the Verlaine-Morice correspondence over 'Art poétique' and the first appearance of poems by Verlaine stand out in bright relief, than as an intimation of poetic renewal. Still, the redeeming quality of some of the love poetry is that the poets try to rejuvenate their hackneyed subject by treating it ironically. Such seems to be Trézenik's intention in choosing a depreciating title, 'Sonnet vieux jeu', and a somewhat humorous tone. In several poems an ironic final line deflates the romanticism of the content. So in 'Amour filial' Trézenik drives with a prostitute who asks him to give the coachman a generous tip: '—Fais-le pour moi, c'est p'pa!' (8–15 December 1882); or Georges Rall's beautiful blonde mistress accepts his love while reading her newspaper, interrupting impatiently, 'Voyons, dépeche-toi, que je tourne la page!' ('Paroles d'amour', 8–15 December 1882). Such ironic final lines were not uncommon; what interests us in these poems is the effort to create an anti-romantic mood by quick shifts in style and viewpoint.

Even advertisements can be indicators of impending change; the first issue advertises, along with Marc champagne and Löwenbräu beer, these collections of verse: Charles Morice, *Vers pour les femmes*; Georges Bouret, *Les Broussailles*; and Léo Trézenik, *Les Gouailleuses*, *poésies fantaisistes*, now in their second edition. Again, the titles are hardly revolutionary, but mention of Morice's and Trézenik's publisher, Léon Vanier, foreshadows the days when *Lutèce* will regularly carry publicity for Vanier's editions of Verlaine, Mallarmé and Laforgue.

Le Chat Noir had been appearing for almost half a year, since 14 January 1882, when Verlaine returned to Paris. More modest in its aspirations than *La Nouvelle Rive Gauche*, *Le Chat Noir* was largely given over to humorous verse, ironically facetious editorial comment, and references to Montmartre cafés. Each issue has a full-page political cartoon, often scatalogically anti-Prussian, and a drawing by Willette of the activities of the black cat after which the magazine and café were named. There are also critical articles, such as Léon Bloy's studies of Maurice Rollinat and of Verlaine, and if the poetry is never as distinguished as that of *La Nouvelle Rive Gauche*, most minor poets of the decadent movement published there, and there were usually a greater number and variety of poems than in its Left Bank competitor. Like their colleagues of *La Nouvelle Rive Gauche*,[2] poets of *Le Chat Noir* write about the quarter in which they lived and the bohemian life they aspired to lead; in the first number Eugène Torquet announces his disdain for the mundane pursuit of wealth and his intention of being a poet, painter, or actor in his 'Ballade de la joyeuse bohême' (14 January 1882). There is a poem on 'Le Moulin de la Galette' by René Ponsard (18 March 1882), and a series of 'Sonnets-Montmartre' dealing with scenes of daily life in the quarter. Rodolphe Salis, the editor, founded a café called *Le Chat Noir*, where every Saturday there was a literary meeting at which poets were urged to read their poems from the orchestra platform: 'Nos différents collaborateurs sont les clients assidus du *Cabaret du Chat Noir*, 84, Boulevard Rochechouart.' The *Chat Noir* was a 'period' café in the style of Louis XIII ('Fondé, en 1114, par un fumiste'), and there is an advertisement for another such café, style of Henry IV, *La Grande Pinte* ('Musée intéressant, patron davantage'); this historicity doubtless accounts for the many poems in pseudo-Middle French, and for the magazine's cult of François Villon. A quotation from a typical archaic poem, 'Ballade des Assassins', will illustrate the use of Middle French and the bawdy quality of such verse:

> Merdauculatives guenilles,
> Guenipes aux regards malsains,
> Gaupes, gouges, vadrouilles, filles
> Dont s'honorent nos traversins,
> Souffrez que notre main caresse
> La gélatine de vos seins,
> Tirependières en détresse,
> Sous les bosquets des Assassins.[3]

Poems in remote dialects of French are a feature of *Le Chat Noir*; there are as many poems in *français populaire* as in Middle French, and we even find an example of *petit nègre*:

> Lisette quitté la plaine,
> Moé perdi bonher a moué;
> Gié a moué semblé fontaine
> Dipi moué pas miré toué.
> Le jou, quand moé coupé canne
> Moé songé zamour à moué;
> La nuit, quan moé dans cabane
> Don dormir moé quiembré toué.[4]

There is a little bit of everything in *Le Chat Noir*; much of the humorous verse is merely silly, and much of the serious verse richly deserves the oblivion which has overtaken it. Nevertheless, as we saw in some of the poems derived from the Parnassians, there are hints of a different poetic sensibility, and for this reason it is equally interesting to look at some of the humorous verse. 'Le Homard' ('Sonnet à la Coppée', 4 March 1882) tells about an outing by a young couple; the style clearly mocks François Coppée's sentimental treatment of everyday life in *Les Humbles*. When we consider the role of parodies in the decadent movement and Corbière's success with parodies of Romantic poets, it almost seems odd that there are not more pastiches in magazines like *Le Chat Noir*. We also think of Corbière in reading Henri Second's 'Amour platonique', in which an unduly innocent young man ('. . . pauvre innocent/Brisant à peine ma coquille') picks up a refined-looking girl, pledging love and respect to her, only to have her answer, '. . . Je veux bien./Mais, mon petit, ça ne fait rien,/Tu me devras cent sous quand même' (15 July 1882). The self-mockery, the biting final line, and the parody of a romantic situation recall the Breton poet. Henri Second again deals ironically with a prostitute in 'Sonnet à l'ail et au patchouli: une prostituée'. Street-walkers are a standard fixture of the naturalist street scenes which we discussed in chapter 1, and they are also frequent butts of ridicule; what sets this poem apart as to ironic language is passages like the Corbièresque pun on *boutons* ('buttons'–'pimples') in the final tercet:

> Tous les boutons de son corsage
> Par les doigts du vice arrachés
> Ont émigré sur son visage.   [10 June 1882]

Not even death is spared the poets' humour: in 'Croquis funèbre' Adolphe Vautier takes a wry view of a funeral; in the second stanza it is the mourners' waxy, corpse-like attitudes which would amuse the deceased; in the third, pedantic language mocks the simple act of wiping the eyes:

> Dans l'église de noir tendue,
> Le prêtre, un étique aumônier,
> Murmurait l'oremus dernier
> D'une messe à peine entendue.
>
> Tous les assistants avaient pris
> Des airs de figure de cire,
> Dont le défunt devait bien rire,
> S'il est un monde des esprits.
>
> L'un, saisi d'amitié subite,
> Penchait un front tout attristé,

L'autre, d'un mouchoir humecté,
S'imprégnait doucement l'orbite;

Tandis qu'auprès du bénitier,
Larmoyaient d'antiques parentes
En supputant tout bas les rentes
Que bientôt aurait l'héritier,

Et qu'au dehors, le nez humide,
Narguant le soleil de juillet,
Le noir croque-mort sommeillait
A l'ombre du corbillard vide!   [19 August 1882]

With lesser skill but with similar irony Louis Marsolleau treats the
same subject in 'Sonnet' (8 April 1882). Another kind of humour is
represented by Emile Goudeau's 'Sonnet Extrême Orient;' extravagant
language, puns, and a fanciful anecdote are suddenly and humorously
reduced to scale when we learn that the poem serves merely to explain
how two porcelain vases got broken:

Ka-ka-Dor mandarin militaire, et Ku-Ku,
Auteur d'un million et quelques hémistiches,
Causent en Javanais sur le bord des potiches,
Monosyllabiquant d'un air très vaincu.

Vers l'an cent mille et trois ces magots ont vécu
A Nangasaka qui vend des cheveux postiches,
C'étaient d'honnêtes gens qui portaient des fétiches
Sérieux, mais, hélas! chacun d'eux fut koku.

Comment leur supposer des âmes frénétiques!
Et quel sujet poussa ces poussahs lymphatiques
A se mettre en colère un soir? je ne sais pas.

Mais un duel s'ensuivit — ô rages insensées
Puisqu'ils se sont ouvert le ventre avec fracas
Voilà pourquoi vos deux potiches sont cassées.   [15 April 1882]

There was a series of pseudo-scientific poems by a 'K. Lomel'; as with
Laforgue, a flippant treatment of a serious subject is mingled with
nonsense refrains of popular songs; and the spelling (in lines 2 and 4)
imitates spoken French:

L'azote est un gaz bien malsain
Dans l'quel on n' peut pas vivre,
Il se trouve dans l'air le plus sain,
C'est pas lui qui enivre,

Il n'a pas la moindre action,
La faridondaine, la faridondon,
Il empêche même la vie
  Biribi
A la façon de Barbari mon ami. [10 June 1882]

Parisians, more so perhaps than other poets, have always written light, mocking verse, and in a youthful poem Verlaine made fun of a burial;[5] the similarities with Corbière (who was probably completely unknown to readers of *Le Chat Noir*)[6] are most likely due not to his influence but to a common tradition on which all poets drew. Yet we do notice foreshadowings of decadent verse. Referring back to 'Ballade des assassins', the substitution of the artificial for the natural in 'La gélatine de vos seins' is decadent. The neologism *merdauculatif* and the abundance of slang terms reveal the same interest in language *per se* as Gautier and Bourget discussed in their essays. Indeed, what all these poems have in common is fanciful use of the resources of language and a resulting contrast between poetic form and anti-literary diction. In the line 'Gaupes, gouges, vadrouilles, filles,' the alliteration and assonances are representative of the verbal music of decadent poets. Homonyms like *poussa–poussahs* in 'Sonnet Extrême-Orient' will be common in decadent verse. Overdoing the alliterations and assonances they had detected in *Les Fleurs du mal*, minor decadents accumulated such effects to the point of absurdity, as in the final lines of Félix Decori's 'La Sultane':

Et maintenant, un mot échappé de sa bouche
Ferait à ses genoux rouler le corps sanglant
Du fou qui toucherait le bout de sa boubouche. [17 June 1882]

The mocking treatments of prostitutes and funerals, as well as the naturalist treatments of urban scenes we described in chapter 1, show a decadent preoccupation with modernity. These tendencies seem slight, yet they are in contrast with poems treating Parnassian and even Romantic themes in altogether pedestrian fashion.

Poems by Maurice Rollinat ('L'Etang' and 'Rondeau du guillotiné', 6 May; 'Les Serpents', 18 November 1882; 'Ballade des nuages', 6 January 1883) recall that *Les Névroses* are an intensification and an exaggeration of the morbid aspects of Baudelaire. What is interesting is how a study of Rollinat's poetry by Léon Bloy[7] brings out the connection between this sort of *bas-romantisme* and the decadent sensibility. When Bloy describes music and poetry in Rollinat's verse as being so inseparably joined as to form 'une nouvelle espèce d'art androgyne et miraculeux, à la fois terrestre et angélique', when he speaks of 'les nerfs enroulés autour de l'âme par cette mélodie tortionnaire—comme les entrailles du martyre de Rubens autour de son cabestan', and when he writes, 'Porté comme je l'étais par ma sensation sur le rebord crépusculaire de la vie normale' (2 September 1882), we recognise such typically decadent concepts as transposition of the arts, comparison of life to art instead of vice versa, painfully sensitive nervous acuity, artistic experience so intense as to be beyond the pale of normality, and, most important, the thesis that *sensation* is henceforth to be the language of art. (The term *art androgyne*, in fact, suggests the hermaphroditic characters of decadent novels.) Bloy's conclusion—'il sera démontré surabondamment que ce poète-musicien, bien loin d'imiter qui que ce fût, était, au contraire, le plus solitaire, le plus hermétique et le plus inaccessible des originaux' (16 September 1882)—anticipates the reasoning of much decadent criticism, which argues that poetry excels only when it is too individualistic in conception and expression to be understood by the average reader.[8]

On 2 September 1882, we meet a thoroughly decadent subject in Jean Lorrain's portrait of a lesbian; again we are reminded of Corbière when the girl's vice becomes apparent only in a final quip: 'Le paradis n'a plus de pommes,/Monsieur, je n'aime pas les hommes.' The very title, 'Modernité', suggests that Lorrain regards this vice as peculiarly contemporary.

Finally, we reach poems which complete the decadent concept by specifically comparing Paris to Rome. Emile Goudeau's collection of verse *Les Fleurs du bitume* (out of print when *Le Chat Noir* began publication) is an extended handling of this metaphor; two of the poems appear in *Le Chat Noir*. 'Les Affranchies' (4 February 1882) compares the expensively kept *lionnes* who drive their carriages up and down the Champs Elysées to ancient Roman freedwomen ('affranchies de la vertue'). Paris is called 'Lutèce', and additional Latinisms adroitly transform Paris of the Second Empire into imperial Rome:

Les voyez-vous passer, les belles affranchies?
Sur les chemins sablés et les routes blanchies,
Que l'esclave arroseur humecte à longs jets d'eau,
Leurs chars à huit ressorts volent, et le badaud
Lutécien s'écrie: oh! la belle païenne!
Elles suivent au trot la voie Elyséenne,
Derrière elles laissant le vieux palais des rois,

Et le Forum couvert où l'on fit tant de lois;
Elles montent lançant des oeillades de Parthe,
Jusqu'à l'Arc triomphal de César Bonaparte.
O Romains de Paris, regardez-les de loin
. . .
C'est ainsi qu'elles vont au bois Boulonien
Respirer le printemps. La porte Maillotine,
Large, s'ouvre devant leur foule libertine;
. . . .
Parfois, croisant leur char, quelque pubère équestre
Leur envoie un salut amical de la dextre;
Tandis qu'un sénateur, un consulaire, un vieux
Tribun, en tapinois les dévore des yeux.
Oh! Vénus a donné le charme à ses prêtresses!

'Les Grecs' (28 January 1882) describes in similar language an evening spent by a young student ('l'éphèbe') in a Latin Quarter gambling den. In the same vein, Paul Marrot contrasts the former royal glories of Paris under Louis XIV with naturalist Paris of the 1880's in 'L'Enseigne' (16 December 1882).[9] These two poems can be contrasted with Hugo's 'A Virgile', cited in the previous chapter, which is not decadent in spirit or intent, while Goudeau and Marrot compare the two cities with reference to debauchery and to the collapse of a former stable regime.

The decadent sensibility, as expressed in language, theme, and the essential Roman-decadence motif, appears sharply and dramatically focused in a single image in Jean Lorrain's 'Bathylle', which appeared on 1 July 1882:

Au fond d'un bouge obscur, où boivent des marins,
Bathylle, le beau Thrace aux bras sveltes et pâles,
Danse au bruit de la flûte et des gais tambourins.
Ses pieds fins et nerveux, font claquer sur les dalles

Leurs talons teints de pourpre, où sonnent des crotales
Et, tandis qu'il effeuille en fuyant brins à brins
Des roses, comme un lys entr'ouvrant ses pétales,
Sa tunique s'écarte aux rondeurs de ses reins.

Sa tunique s'écarte et la blancheur sereine
De son ventre apparaît sous sa toison d'ébène.
Bathylle alors s'arrête et, d'un oeil inhumain

Fixant les matelots rouges de convoitise,
Il partage à chacun son bouquet de cythise
Et tend à leurs baisers la paume de sa main.

Here we have a picture of classical debauchery at its perverted worst (or best?); Flaubert said that one should look for decadence in the night-spots of ancient Subure; he mentioned tambourines, and *crotales* were rattles used in the cult of Cybele. Homosexuality and Bathylle's theatrical make-up embody the idea of artificiality. The vocabulary is rich: foreign names (Bathylle, Thrace), musical instruments (*tambourins, flûte, crotales*), and names of flowers (*roses, lys, cythise*)—vocabulary items whose occurrence will become epidemic in decadent verse. The ubiquity of the homosexual Greek boy attests the extent to which he was thought to epitomise the spirit of decadence: three other poets composed poems on this subject, and Lorrain himself did a portrait of a nineteenth-century pervert as well; at least nine versions of this theme were published and republished during the decade 1880–90.[10]

These poems place Paul Verlaine's role in the decadent movement in a rather new light. Traditionally, his sonnet 'Langueur', which did not appear in *Le Chat Noir* until 26 May 1883, has been regarded as the departure point of the decadent movement in poetry. On the contrary, the appearance of 'Bathylle' eleven months before, and expressions of a decadent sensibility throughout the first sixteen months of the *Chat Noir's* existence, indicate that decadence had already found fully articulate expression in verse. Verlaine therefore appears not as the founder of a new school, but rather as an outstanding figure chosen to represent a movement which was already in active existence.[11]

The irony of the situation is that for sixteen years Verlaine had been writing verse which often crystallised decadent tendencies, but he was still obscure, known chiefly to a few friends of his own generation. The verse of Stéphane Mallarmé would soon appeal to young poets of *Le Chat Noir* and similar magazines; but although he had been teaching in Paris since 1871 and had begun his Tuesday evening receptions in the Rue de Rome in 1880, he too was still known only to a few friends, and even they knew him personally better than they did his rather slight output of verse. In October of 1882, when Joris-Karl Huysmans was collecting material for his novel *A Rebours*, he was obliged to write to Mallarmé for copies of 'Mort de la pénultième', 'qui a paru dans une revue dont je ne retrouve pas le nom',[12] of 'Hérodiade', and for a complete text of 'L'Après-midi d'un faune', of which he had seen only quotations. Consequently, it would appear that a problem confronting French poets in 1882 was simply that of making contact with other poets of similar tastes and goals. Many of these writers were provincials, newly arrived in Paris, who first of all looked for lodgings and employment. The solution to their problem lay in the socialising function of reviews like *Le Chat Noir* and in poetic schools like the *Hydropathes*.

Emile Goudeau, the author of *Les Fleurs du bitume*, was a *Périgourdin* who quit his native province and came to Paris in 1873, bringing with him a collection of manuscript poems.[13] Like so many before him, he found a job in a government Ministry, and, once settled in a position that would support him, he began to read his poems aloud to his friends in cafés. It was soon realised that a more formal organisation was desirable; so on 5 October 1878 he met with his friends Abram, Georges Lorin, Rives, and Maurice Rollinat to found a literary circle, which they decided to call the Hydropaths. The name seemed appropriate for several reasons: Goudeau was fond of a waltz tune, the *Hydropathenvaltz*, his name lent itself to the pun *goût d'eau*, his friends and he preferred wine to water, and *hydropathe* lent itself to a pun, *hydro-patte*. These considerations illustrate the *côté fumiste*, the high-spirited fun and jokes, which were fully as typical of these groups as more serious literary purposes. The group, swollen by now to sixty-five persons, held the first of its Friday evening meetings on 11 October 1878, in the second-floor banquet room of a café at the corner of the Rue Cujas and Boulevard Saint-Michel. Growing numbers forced them to move from café to café in quest of larger quarters until finally, 300 to 350 strong, the Hydropaths settled at the Café de l'Avenir, 1 Place Saint-Michel.

The site could hardly have been better chosen from the standpoint of historical associations with decadence. Within a few hundred yards to the east and to the south are the pavings of the ancient Roman road to Orléans, the ruins of Roman baths next to the Musée de Cluny, the Librairie Vanier on Quai Saint-Michel, where one can still buy books of Verlaine's poetry, and the Hôtel des Etrangers on the Rue Racine, where Rimbaud was lodged by his friends in 1871. Farther away on the Ile Saint-Louis is the Hôtel Pimodan, where Baudelaire onced lived and which Gautier described in his Notice'.

Three months after the formation of the club, its newspaper began to appear, *L'Hydropathe*: each issue was illustrated with a full-page cartoon portrait of one of the club members, and there were poems and prose as well. The *Hydropathe* published thirty-two issues, from 22 January 1879, to 12 May 1880; it was succeeded by *Tout Paris* (eight pages in lieu of four!), which published only five issues (23 May to 26 June 1882). Then the venture collapsed, apparently for lack of funds.

Meanwhile, the weekly gatherings were growing immoderately

large, noisy, and unruly; it was difficult to maintain order, much less to accomplish the original purpose of reading poems and discussing literature. There were complaints from the neighbours, difficulties with the police, objections from the manager of the café. After a particularly boisterous meeting—it appears that a dissident literary faction intentionally disrupted it—the Hydropaths discontinued their meetings in May or June of 1880 Nevertheless, there must have been some continuing contact among members of the group, for as late as 4 February 1882 there was a notice in *Le Chat Noir* of postponement of a scheduled meeting of the Hydropaths

The next group to be formed was called the *Hirsutes*, or 'hairy ones'.[14] In September of 1881 Maurice Petit, organist and pianist, and a former member of the Hydropaths, conceived the idea of forming a literary circle of his own. Circulars were passed around the Latin Quarter, and in October or November of 1881 the 'constituent meeting' was held in the Café du Commerce. Emile Goudeau attended; Léo Trézenik was one of the two vice-presidents. The Hirsutes never had a publication of their own, and in their meetings they encountered the same difficulties as the Hydropaths: too much noise and planned disturbances by former Hydropaths and by groups of students; the near-sighted Maurice Petit was not well qualified for presiding over such raucous assemblies, and the organisation finally collapsed in April of 1883. By this time the need for such organisations was largely met by the literary magazines.

These played the same role as the cafés and literary circles. *Le Chat Noir* was both a newspaper and a literary café, and like other periodicals, it published announcements for other cafés and literary groups. In *La Nouvelle Gauche* we read,

> On annonce pour le lundi, 11 Décembre, à la salle des Capucines, une conférence de notre confrère Mallat du *Courrier du Soi* sur le 'Nervosisme [*sic*] dans la littérature'.
>
> Il passera en revue les dernières poésies de MM. Crésy, Haraucourt, Lorin, Marrot, Rollinat, Léo Trézenik.   [8–15 December 1882]

Editorial offices were the scenes of informal discussions, for each magazine normally announced its 'hours' when members of the *rédaction* were available to contributors and readers. The offices of *La Nouvelle Rive Gauche*, 63 bis, Rue du Cardinal Lemoine, were open to the public on Thursdays and Fridays from two to six in the afternoon; much later *La Revue Blanche* 'received' in Thursday afternoons. Jean Ajalbert describes the editorial offices of *Lutèce* several years later:

Les collaborateurs vont cueillir la 'feuille' au sortir des presses, le vendredi
soir. On rencontre à l'imprimerie Verlaine, Moréas, Caze, de Régnier,
Grenet, Dancourt, G. Lorin, J. Vidal, P. Adam, R. Darzens, E. Mikaël [*sic*],
Reynaud [*sic*], Norès, Cohl, Henri Mangis, le critique théâtral . . . et les
heures passent à médire les absents,—tout le monde debout, nul ne re-
marquant qu'il n'y a que deux chaises dans la salle de rédaction.[15]

The significance of these semi-social gatherings was that a new poet was
launched by word of mouth and by favourable critical studies as much
as by having his poems published in magazines. As in any other human
venture, the proper contacts could be most useful. Among those
mentioned by Ajalbert, Jean Moréas was an *habitué* of the cafés and the
perennial spokesman for successive schools of poetry; Ernest Raynaud
was one of the historians of French symbolism (*La Mêlée symboliste*,
Renaissance du livre, 1920; *En Marge de la mêlée symboliste*, Mercure de
France, 1936). Both helped Verlaine acquire readers, although Moréas,
coming earlier, was more timely with his aid. After leaving the offices
of *Lutèce*, Ajalbert tells us, the *collaborateurs* met on Saturdays at the
Café de l'Ecole de médecine, which was but one of a number frequented
by writers. Another was the François Ier, Verlaine's favourite, where,
in the days of his glory, journalists, foreign visitors, and young writers
could locate him.[16] It was a small world, and there is a constant overlapping of names among the patrons of the various cafés and the
contributors to periodicals. Even a very short list of contributors to
those magazines which published Verlaine's poems illustrates this point.
Jean Moréas contributed to *Le Chat Noir*, *Lutèce*, *La Revue Indépendante*,
and *La Vogue*; Edmond Haraucourt to *Lutèce*, *La Revue Contemporaine*,
and *Le Chat Noir*; Laurent Tailhade to *Lutèce*, *La Revue Indépendante*,
and *Le Décadent*; Jean Lorrain to *Le Décadent*, *Le Chat Noir*, *La Nouvelle
Revue*, and *Le Scapin*; Huysmans to *Le Chat Noir* and *La Revue Indépendante*; Léo Trézenik and Charles Morice contributed to *Le Chat Noir*
in addition to their work on *Lutèce*. Since these men also contributed
reviews and critical articles, each was able to advance the others'
reputations. In this way a friendship here, an autographed copy of a
recueil there, could lead to a favourable review which, it was hoped,
would cause increased sales and eventually an established literary
reputation.

The period was suitable for the flowering of small literary reviews.
Since 1870, under the Third Republic, the press enjoyed fairly complete
freedom of expression, and economic conditions favoured the founding
of new periodicals.[17] Even a rather slight capital was sufficient for a

few friends to get together, found a magazine, hire a printer, and distribute copies to bookshops and news-stands. Léon Vanier, who became the publisher of most of the decadent poets whom we shall discuss, sold individual copies and also complete sets of *Lutèce*, *Le Décadent*, and *La Revue Indépendante*. According to announcements in their pages, these magazines were available at most downtown news-stands although the department stores stopped carrying *La Nouvelle Rive Gauche* in their book departments after it published a series of articles denouncing working conditions in the stores. If funds were scarce, other expedients were available: Trézenik and Georges Rall printed *Lutèce* themselves on a hand press, as did Anatole Baju of *Le Décadent*, and the latter required contributors to set their own articles in type, Even so, there was an unfortunate tendency for magazines to cease publication after a few issues, or a few years, for lack of funds. Formats varied: *Le Décadent* and *Le Scapin* were small pamphlets; *La Basoche* was slightly over five by nine inches and always had at least thirty-six pages; *Lutèce* varied its format several times in the course of its existence; *Le Chat Noir* was more nearly newspaper format, and so was *Le Symboliste* at twelve and a half inches by nineteen. Circulation figures varied, but they seem rather high: in 1884 *La Revue Indépendante* started out at 2,100 copies, in 1889 *La Revue Blanche* at 1,500; between 1886 and 1889 the two series of *Le Décadent* usually printed 4,500 copies, but the issue containing an open letter from Verlaine (1–15 January 1888) came out in 10,000 copies. The first issue of Maurice Barrès' *Les Taches d'Encre* ran through a printing of more than 2,000 copies. In the early years of the movement *Lutèce*, *La Revue Indépendante*, and *La Basoche* prided themselves on their literary neutrality, promising to print anything worthy; with the schisms of 1886, partisan magazines like *Le Décadent* and *Le Symboliste* maintained a fierce and narrow orthodoxy. This very year of schism illustrates how easily a new periodical could be founded, for in 1886 five new magazines began publication: *Le Décadent* on 10 April, *La Vogue* the next day, the second series of *Le Scapin* on 1 September, *La Décadence* on 1 October and *Le Symboliste* on 7 October.

The role of the *grande presse*, those newspapers and magazines of large circulation which were addressed to the general public, was important, too. At a time when the annual Salon and Salon des refusés art expositions attracted large crowds on Sunday afternoon and were reviewed in most newspapers, it is not surprising that the activities of obscure writers were considered newsworthy as well as scandalous or silly. Even today Paris newspapers devote more coverage to cultural events than their American or English counterparts: in weekly publications like *Le Figaro Littéraire, Arts et Spectacles,* or *Les Nouvelles Littéraires,* every film, art exhibit, play, and new book is at least listed, and a colourful or controversial personality easily rates a feature article. In the 1880's major critics like Anatole France in *Le Temps,* Jules Lemaitre in *La Revue Bleue,* or Ferdinand Brunetière in *La Revue des Deux Mondes* wrote essays condemning, or attempting to explain, current poetry, or else simply reviewing recent books, and such articles would set off a series of outraged replies in little magazines. Thanks to such coverage, the general public at least heard about the new poetic school and its poets. Thus the effect of Anatole France's review of a *Petit Glossaire* of esoteric vocabulary used in decadent writing[18] was at least to inform readers of *Le Temps* that the decadent–symbolist movement existed. Jean Moréas' manifesto on symbolism appeared in *Le Figaro's* literary supplement, rather than in an obscure poetry review, because the editors felt that the subject was newsworthy and asked him to write it for them:

> Depuis deux ans, la presse parisienne s'est beaucoup occupée d'une école de poètes et de prosateurs dits 'décadents' . . . M. Jean Moréas, un des plus en vue parmi ces révolutionnaires de lettres a formulé, sur notre demande, pour les lecteurs du *Supplement,* les principes fondamentaux de la nouvelle manifestation d'art.[19]

Those who read *Le Temps* and not *Le Figaro* learned of it a week later when Anatole France wrote a scornful rebuttal in his regular column (*Le Temps,* 26 September 1886). When Charles Morice wrote to France for his prediction of what literature would be in the future, France chose to reply in his column again (*Le Temps,* 5 August 1888). Sensing a good story, Jules Huret of *L'Echo de Paris* interviewed various literary figures, both great and small—whence his *Enquête sur l'évolution littèraire* (Charpentier, 1891), which is still a valuable source of first-hand statements by writers of the period. Not all of this publicity was favourable or even intelligently conceived: Verlaine's admission to Tenon Charity Hospital in 1886 inspired substantially more articles than his new edition of *Sagesse.*[20] Nevertheless, it was all publicity, publicity of the sort that creates reputations and sells books, and even adverse publicity was preferable to the silence with which the press first greeted decadent poetry and impressionist painting.

Notes

1 To summarise references to the first issues: No. 1, 9 November 1882; No. 2, 17 November 1882; No. 3, 24 November–1 December 1882; No. 4, 1–8 December 1882; No. 5, 8–15 December 1882.

2 *Cf.* Henri Khébir, 'Chanson du quartier', *Nouvelle Rive Gauche*, 8–15 December 1882.

3 20 May 1882. See also Florent Fulbert, 'Ballade du *Chat Noir*', 14 January 1882; Lefebvre, 'Ballade des escholiers', 21 January 1882; Edmond Haraucourt, 'Ballade des pucelaiges morts', 22 July 1882, and 'Ballade des malséans pucelaiges', 5 August 1882.

4 10 June 1882. 'Lisette, quand tu as fui la plaine, mon bonheur s'est envolé, et mes pleurs, en double fontaine, ont coulé sur ta fuite. Le jour en coupant la canne, je songe à l'amour que j'ai pour toi. Et la nuit, quand je dors, dans ma cabane, un rêve me met dans tes bras.'

5 'L'Enterrement', *Oeuvres poétiques complètes*, Y.-G. Le Dantec and Jacques Borel, eds. (Gallimard, 1962), p. 125.

6 Léo Trézenik of *La Nouvelle Rive Gauche*, a Breton himself, did know Corbière's verse; it was he who got Verlaine interested in him in 1883, whence the essay in *Les Poètes maudits*. To how many other poets did Trézenik communicate his enthusiaism for his compatriot?

7 'Maurice Rollinat', *Chat Noir*, 2, 9, and 16 September 1882.

8 *Cf.* the definition given by Ernest Raynaud: 'Tout artiste qui écrit, en dehors de la préoccupation du public, avec l'idée bien arrêtée de ne rien sacrifier de son art en vue d'applaudissements, mérite d'être étiqueté tel [décadent] . . .' Chronique littéraire', *Décadent*, 15–31 January 1888.

9 See chapter II, note 16.

10 See chapter VI, note 49.

11 See our article 'Decadent poetry in *Le Chat Noir* before Verlaine's "Langueur" ', *Modern Language Quarterly*, XXX (4 December 1969), 535–544.

12 Quoted by Henri Mondor, *Vie de Mallarmé* (Gallimard, 1941), p. 420.

13 For Goudeau and the Hydropaths, see Noël Richard, *A l'Aube du symbolisme* (Nizet, 1961), chapters II and III, pp. 18–35.

14 For the Hirsutes, see Richard, pp. 36–9, and Léo Trézenik, 'Les Hirsutes: leur histoire depuis Pharamon–Maurice–Petit jusqu'à nos jours', *Lutèce*, serially but intermittently, 1–8 June to 3–10 August 1883.

15 'Lutèce', *Basoche*, II, 2 February 1886), 105. *Lutèce*, of course, was originally *La Nouvelle Rive Gauche*. See also Richard, p. 95.

16 For studies of the various literary cafés of the period, see Ernest Raynaud, 'Le Symbolisme et les cafés littéraires', *Mercure de France*, CCLXVIII, 911 (1 June 1936), 282–93, and Howard Sutton, 'Some literary cafés of the late nineteenth century', *Kentucky Foreign Language Quarterly*, X, 2 (1963), 114–122.

17 See Jacques Lethève, *Impressionnistes et symbolistes devant la presse* (Colin, 1959), p. 11.

18 See 'La Vie littéraire: la langue décadente', *Le Temps*, 28 October 1888; this is a review of Jacques Plowert (Paul Adam), *Petit Glossaire pour servir à l'intelligence des auteurs décadents et symbolistes* (Vanier, 1888).

19 'Le Symbolisme', *Supplément littéraire du Figaro*, 18 September 1886.

20 See Charles Donos, *Verlaine intime* (Vanier, 1898), p. 130, and Lethève, *Impressionnistes et symbolistes*, p. 10.

Chapter IV

1882–84: from 'Art poétique' to *A Rebours*

Verlaine returned to Paris no later than July of 1882, ten years almost to the day after leaving the city with Rimbaud. At one of his several teaching posts, the Collège de Notre-Dame at Rethel, he had formed a deep and presumably homosexual attachment for one of his pupils, Lucien Létinois; when Verlaine was dismissed from Rethel for his drinking he took Lucien with him to England. Upon their return to France, Verlaine bought a farm at Juniville; he was to work it in co-operation with Lucien and the latter's parents, who were peasants. Verlaine, to be sure, was no farmer, and when the venture collapsed in a dismal failure he sold the farm in January of 1882. He and Lucien then went to Paris, where Lucien took up a post as monitor in a private school, the Institution Esnault, at Boulogne-sur-Seine, south-west of Paris; and Verlaine, to be near him, rented a room over a café at 5 Rue de Parchamps. When Lucien left for a better-paying job in industry at Ivry, Verlaine replaced him for a while at the school. Verlaine there-fore spent the summer of 1882 at Boulogne; in the evening he would take a horse tram into the Latin Quarter and make the rounds of the literary cafés. The poems 'L'Aube à l'envers' and 'Nouvelles Variations sur le Point du Jour' refer to his sojourn. By December he was living with his mother at 17 Rue de la Roquette in Paris.

In October Verlaine asked Edmond Lepelletier, the most faithful of his schoolmates, to help him get back his old job as clerk in the City Hall. There was some official correspondence on the matter, but with Verlaine's compromising role in the Commune, his prison record in Belgium, and with the resignation of Charles Floquet, the Prefect of the Seine who was favourably disposed to his candidacy, nothing came of it. Verlaine therefore decided to earn his living by his pen, since his private means, although not yet exhausted, were seriously depleted. It was a rash decision, for he had never been successful as a writer, and now there were factors actually working against him. His first three collections of verse had not sold well, and his two most recent, *Romances sans paroles* and *Sagesse*, had literally been placed in storage by their publishers, although the *service de presse*, or distribution of reviewers' copies, had resulted in reviews of both books. The editors of the third edition of *Le Parnasse contemporain* in 1875 had deliberately rejected his poems for personal reasons, and many editors and reviewers still refused even to mention Verlaine's name on account of the scandal of his conduct with Rimbaud.

Lepelletier, who was then editor-in-chief of *Le Réveil*, turned his column 'Paris-vivant' over to Verlaine; the some eighteen prose pieces he wrote for it would later be collected as *Mémoires d'un veuf*. Two anecdotes reveal the extent to which he had been forgotten by the world of letters. Henri Bauër, another contributor, noticed the eccentrically dressed individual entering and leaving the office of *Le Réveil* and asked about him; Lepelletier explained that he was a good poet who was no longer remembered, handing Bauër a copy of *Sagesse*; when he returned the book after reading it, Bauër agreed that he was indeed a true poet. Even a year later, as Verlaine's name was beginning to appear in print again, Jean Moréas and Maurice Barrès had difficulty getting a copy of *Sagesse* at the Palmé bookshop. The sales assistant had never heard of it, and it took the manager a week to find a copy in the basement. Through Lepelletier's influence again, Verlaine was able to publish some poems in *Paris Moderne*, a magazine recently established by a Léon Vanier, who sold both books and fishing tackle in his shop on the Quai Saint-Michel. 'Le Squelette' and 'Et nous voilà très doux à la bêtise humaine' appeared in the issue of 25 July 1882, and 'Pierrot', 'Art poétique', and 'A Léon Valade' in the 10 November issue. They were Verlaine's first appearance in a periodical in ten years!

Fortunately the long arm of coincidence was reaching out to help him. Among those who read these poems was Charles Morice, of *La Nouvelle Rive Gauche*.We have seen how this magazine was devoted to new developments in literature and how it also seemed to need copy; so, under the pseudonym 'Karl Mohr', Morice discussed Verlaine's 'Art poétique' in the fourth issue, 1–8 December 1882:

Boileau–Verlaine

Paris Moderne a publié récemment une curieuse poésie de M. Paul Verlaine, intitulée 'Art poétique.' Le titre est effrayant,—mais il n'y a que trente-six vers.

    Cette pièce a ceci de très intéressant, qu'elle indique avec assez de précision où en sont les novateurs à outrance, ce qu'ils pensent faire de l'art et quelle est leur audace:

        'Si l'on n'y veille, elle ira jusqu'où?'

La doctrine poétique de M. Verlaine se résume en ces deux mots: Musique et Nuance:

> 'Pas la Couleur, rien que la Nuance!'

Puis voici les préceptes secondaires: choisir de préférence l'Impair; joindre l'Indécis au Précis; fuir la Pointe, l'Esprit, le Rire et l'Eloquence; assagir la Rime ...

> 'Et tout le reste est littérature.'

Trouvez-vous que cela manque de clarté? c'est que *rien n'est plus cher* à M. Verlaine que:

> 'La chanson grise,'

et qu'il ne va point

> 'Choisir ses mots sans quelque méprise,'

C'est précepte et exemple tout à la fois.

Mais en prose qu'est-ce que cela veut dire?

Que signifie cette haine de l'Eloquence et du Rire? Qu'est-ce que ce musicien qui attaque la rime? Comme si la rime n'était pas dans les vers la grande harmonie! On a souvent essayé de s'en passer, toujours il a fallu revenir; mais on ne s'était pas encore avisé de rimer contre la rime:

> Oh! qui dira les torts de la rime?
> Quel enfant sourd ou quel nègre fou
> Nous a forgé ce bijou d'un sou
> Qui sonne faux et creux sous la lime?

Le fond du système, c'est l'obscurité voulue! *Des beaux yeux derrière des voiles.*

Il déplaît à M. Verlaine d'être intelligible au commun peuple.

Cela n'est pas très neuf. Sans remonter à Lycrophon, il y a a eu sous François Ier un poète d'infiniment de talent, nommè Maurice Scève, qui écrivit, dans un style absolument dédaigneux de toute clarté, un poème de 458 dixains. Le livre est mort avec l'auteur.

Balzac, dans une de ses nouvelles, raconte l'histoire d'un peintre qui, perdu dans d'abstruses méditations sur la philosophie de son art, fit un tableau dont lui seul distinguait le sujet: le vulgaire, et même des gens du métier, n'y voyaient qu'une masse confuse de couleurs empâtées. Dans un coin de la toile, un pied se détachait, un pied de femme parfait, un chef-d'oeuvre.

C'est à peu près le cas de M. Verlaine. Cet art qu'il rêve. *soluble dans l'air, gris, indécis et précis,* il ne l'a que trop réalisé, et lui seul peut comprendre ce qu'il a voulu faire. J'espère donc qu'il n'aura pas de disciples et que cette poésie n'est pas celle de l'avenir. Une seule chose lui reste, malgré lui peut-être: c'est l'harmonie. Ecoutez plutôt:

> 'C'est des beaux yeux derrière des voiles,
> C'est le grand jour tremblant de midi,

> C'est, par un ciel d'automne attiédi,
> Le bleu fouillis des claires étoiles!'

Mais il ne faut pas lui demander davantage, et nous devons nous féliciter de ne pas l'entendre, quisqu'il ne veut pas être entendu.

Karl Mohr

We have seen that Morice's own verse was quite traditional, and his reaction to 'Art poétique' reflects the same conservatism. Verlaine was grateful for the attention, but he was also disturbed that Mohr had failed to understand his intentions. 'Art poétique' had been composed eight years before, when, under Rimbaud's inspiration, Verlaine was experimenting with metric liberties which he no longer believed appropriate. To clarify his position, Verlaine wrote Mohr a tactful and persuasive reply which the magazine generously published two weeks later in the issue of 15–22 December:

Monsieur Karl Mohr,

Je lis à l'instant l'article que vous me consacrez sous le titre 'Boileau–Verlaine' dans votre avant-dernier numéro.

Je vous remercie de la dernière partie de l'avant-dernier paragraphe, et de la citation qui l'appuie,—cela, bien cordialement.

Mais permettez-moi, tout en vous félicitant de si bien défendre les vrais droits de la vraie Poésie française, clarté, bonne rime et souci de l'Harmonie, de défendre à mon tour, en fort peu de mots, l'apparent paradoxe sous lequel j'ai prétendu réagir un peu contre l'abus, quelque fois dérisoire, de la Rime trop riche.

D'abord, vous observerez que le poème en question est *bien* rimé. Je m'honore trop d'avoir été le plus humble de ces Parnassiens tant discutés aujourd'hui pour jamais renier la nécessité de la Rime dans le Vers français, où elle supplée de son mieux au défaut du Nombre grec, latin, allemand et même anglais.

Mais puisque vous m'affublez de la perruque, très décorative du reste, de cet excellent versificateur, Boileau, *'je dis que je veux'* n'être pas opprimé par les à-peu-près et les calembours, exquis dans les *Odes Funambulesques*, mais dont mon cher maître Théodore de Banville se prive volontiers dans ses merveilleuses oeuvres purement lyriques.

Tout les exemples sont là d'ailleurs, partant des plus hauts cieux poétiques. Je ne veux me prévaloir que de Baudelaire qui préféra toujours la Rime rare à la Rime riche.

Puis, pourquoi pas la Nuance et la Musique?

Pourquoi le Rire en poésie puisqu'on peut rire en prose et dans la vie?

Pourquoi l'Eloquence, dont la place serait à la Chambre?

Pourquoi la Pointe, puisqu'elle est dans tous le journaux du matin?

J'aime ces trois manifestations de l'âme, de l'esprit et du coeur, parbleu!

Je les admets, même en vers. Nul plus sincère admirateur que moi de Musset dans *Mardoche*, d'Hugo dans les *Châtiments* et d'Heine dans *Atta-Troll*. Mais, laissez-moi rêver si ça me plaît, pleurer quand j'en ai envie, chanter lorsque l'idée m'en prend.

Nous sommes d'accord au fond, car je résume ainsi le débat: rimes irréprochables, français correct, et surtout de bons vers, n'importe à quelle sauce.

Excusez-moi auprès de vos lecteurs, si vous deviez insérer cette rectification tout intime, de l'improviste d'icelle,—et veuillez agréer, Monsieur Karl Mohr, avec mes meilleures sympathies, le salut d'un vétéran (un peu taquiné) à votre vaillante escouade.

> Bien à vous,
> Paul Verlaine

Morice's article is typical of the off hand, mocking reception a poet could expect to meet with even from an enlightened reader, and Verlaine's reply illustrates his very real dexterity in handling a potentially useful critic. This chance encounter was the turning point in Verlaine's literary career and even in the development of French poetry. Thanks to the comparative restraint of Morice's article and to Verlaine's diplomacy, it was possible for the two men to meet and reconcile their differences, subsequently forming a friendship that would last for the rest of their lives.[1] Completely won over by Verlaine's personality, Morice became his staunchest advocate, defending his poetry in the pages of *La Nouvelle Rive Gauche*, in his books, *Paul Verlaine* (1888, the first book-length study of Verlaine) and *La Litterature de tout à l'heure* (1889), and even long after Verlaine's death. Ernest Raynaud describes how in 1918 Morice carefully discussed with him plans for a Verlaine memorial ceremony at Metz, disregarding the fact that the poet's birthplace was still in German hands, and oblivious even to a German shell that fell in the nearby Rue Denfert-Rochereau.[2]

The effects of their friendship became apparent almost immediately, as Verlaine's poems began appearing regularly in *La Nouvelle Rive Gauche*. The issue of 5–12 January 1883 contained 'A Horatio' and 'Le Clown'; that of 26 January–2 February, 'Kaléidoscope'; 23 February–2 March, 'Le Sonnet' ('Sonnet à la louange de Laure et de Pétrarque'); 'Amoureuse du diable' was printed in the issue of 23–30 March; at the end of June, 'Un Crucifix' (22–9 June); on 13–20 July, 'Le petit coin, le petit nid que j'ai trouvés'. In May of 1883 appeared the first of the prose selections ('Le Cheval de retour', 11–18 May), which, together with those from *Le Réveil*, would be published as *Les Mémoires d'un veuf*.

Two months after Morice's review of 'Art poétique', *La Nouvelle Rive Gauche* published a sympathetic and perceptive study, 'Les Vivants et les morts: Paul Verlaine', signed with the pen name 'Jean Mario'.[3] The author begins by pointing out the injustice of Fame, which has passed over Verlaine's five volumes of verse, even though they contain some masterpieces. If 'le gros public bourgeois et notaire' does not even suspect his existence, men of letters esteem him and some of the young hail him as a master. Verlaine is one of Baudelaire's immediate disciples, although he has not adopted the masters' 'pharmacie de poisons et ses violences superflues'. Even without having read Baudelaire, however, Verlaine would have composed the same kind of verse anyway, for he has understood nature better than Baudelaire and has had the good sense to seek to renovate poetry by translating nature's nearly untranslatable harmonies.

'Mario' continues his exposition of Verlaine's unique treatment of nature:

> C'est l'aspect le plus intéressant de ce talent curieux et sincère. Il cherche le nouveau, je ne sais quel art qui serait vaguement des vers, de la peinture, de la musique, mais qui ne serait précisément ni de la musique, ni de la peinture, ni des vers,—quelque chose comme un concert fait avec des couleurs, comme un tableau fait avec des notes,—une confusion voulue des genres, une Dixième Muse. Evidemment les gens sages, classiques et de bon goût affirmeront que, cette Dixième Muse, ni Verlaine ni personne ne la trouvera. Du moins il rencontre en route, dans son effort vers elle, des effects inattendus, des combinaisons nouvelles. Seulement, cela n'est guère à la portée de la foule. Que dirait-elle de ceci?
>
> [Quotes 'Il pleure dans mon coeur' *in toto*.]
>
> Cela s'appelle une *Romance sans paroles*, un titre fou, ne'est-ce pas?—et très justifié. Mais cette folie est adorable, ce mélange d'insaisissable et de précis est dans la nature; c'est une sensation morale et physique que tous nous avons éprouvée souvent et qui voulait, pour s'exprimer, cette infinie délicatesse, cette perfection de demi-teinte et de demi-ton.[4]

The danger of this quest for such unusual and specious effects is that 'on arrive fatalement au gongorisme, à l'affection pure, à l'obscurité absolue. Il y a pis: à force de ténuité, l'idée disparaît. Cela reste harmonieux, mais cela ne veut plus rien dire.' Having praised the third 'Ariette oubliée', 'Mario' quotes the second one, calling it,

> Des vers adorablement vides pour la plupart, et s'ils nous rappellent à nous quelque très vague et très ancienne rêverie, comme d'une vie antérieure, nous ne sommes guère que deux ou trois à nous comprendre.

'Mario' finds that Verlaine's life is a reflection of the tenuousness and the contradictions of his art; in spite of his sensitivity and his aspirations, his life has become a bizarre and tormented existence. After resuming Verlaine's past and projected publications, 'Mario' concludes by expressing the hope that the public will atone for its past neglect by recognizing this poet of indisputable, if somewhat strange, talent.

The significance of this brief (two newspaper columns of about a hundred lines each) article is that it is the first of a number of sympathetic analyses of his verse, and it emphasises the same aspects of his poetry as will subsequent articles. For the first time Verlaine criticism becomes part of the history of the decadent movement in poetry, as his friends and admirers plead for his poetry before the public. If 'Jean Mario' is Morice, then his complete reversal of opinion since the 'Boileau–Verlaine' article must have been the fruit of many hours of discussion over café tables and in the Verlaines' rooms; if, as is more likely, Léo Trézenik is the author, then we applaud the acumen and foresight of this critic, today forgotten, who was the first to recognise the worth and publish the verse of Corbière and Laforgue. The statement 'Plusieurs parmi les jeunes le saluent comme un maître' is tantalising: does it mean that a number of young poets have begun to imitate Verlaine's verse, or simply that several of the magazine's staff admire his poetry? While already in the issue of 2–9 February 1883 Gaston Sénéchal dedicates a poem to him,[5] it will be another year before Verlaine's influence on younger poets is indicated by the appearance of poems imitating his techniques. Also, like all the other critics whom we shall discuss, 'Jean Mario' obviously had read all Verlaine's work, including *Fêtes galantes*, which were out of print. Despite the very limited distribution of Verlaine's first six collections of verse, they apparently were available. Verlaine had author's copies of his own works, which he lent to friends. *Poèmes saturniens* and *La Bonne Chanson* were still in stock at Lemerre, the original publisher, from whom Léon Vanier bought up the remaining copies in 1884; *Sagesse* could be purchased from Victor Palmé, Rue des Saints-Pères, by insisting on having a copy disinterred from storage, as Barrès and Moréas did in 1883. There must have been a second-hand market, for Francis Vielé-Griffin relates that in 1886 he succeeded in buying for 75 centimes the last available copy of *Fêtes galantes*,[6] which were not reissued by Vanier until 1887. By the end of 1884 Vanier's advertisements listed all Verlaine's works except *Fêtes galantes*. Furthermore, current magazines occasionally republished early poems of Verlaine (e.g. on 1 October

1886 *La Decadence* published 'L'Allée' and *Le Scapin,* 'Les Ingénus' and 'Colloque sentimental').

Starting with the issue of 24–31 August 1883, and continuing intermittently through the rest of the year, *Lutèce,* as *La Nouvelle Rive Gauche* was now called, began the serial publication of 'Les Poètes maudits': first Corbière, then Rimbaud and Mallarmé. For Verlaine even to have heard of the Breton poet is typical of the benefits he gained from his renewed personal contacts with the literary milieu. Trézenik, himself a Breton, and Charles Morice spent a whole night in January or February of 1883 in Verlaine's rooms, reading aloud to him *Les Amours jaunes.*[7] Corbière's unconventional verse was a revelation for Verlaine—the mere fact that he treated Corbière before his beloved Rimbaud or his old friend Mallarmé suggests its impact on him. The readers of *Lutèce* must have liked Corbière, for the following October (26 October–2 November 1883), in response to many requests, *Lutèce* reprinted another of his poems, 'Décourageux'.

The other magazine to publish Verlaine's poetry in 1883 (apart from *Paris Moderne,* which published only two minor poems, 'Ecrit sur l'album de Mme N. de V.' and 'A Ernest Delahaye') was Rodolphe Salis' *Le Chat Noir,* which in the issues of 26 May 14 July and 18 August printed eight of the nine poems grouped in *Jadis et naguère* under the title 'Vers à la manière de plusieurs'. The poem omitted was 'Le Poète et la muse', a frank treatment of the Rimbaud relationship; doubtlessly Verlaine wished to avoid recalling the scandal which still menaced his livelihood. Among these poems was the sonnet 'Langueur', which expressed Verlaine's conception of the Roman decadence: 'Je suis l'Empire à la fin de la décadence.'[8] The frankly imitative intent of 'Vers à la manière de plusieurs' coincided with the parodies, imitations, and language experiments of *Le Chat Noir.*

The year 1883, therefore, saw a complete transformation of Verlaine's literary fortunes. He published sixteen poems, some of the *Mémoires d'un veuf,* and the first (and more important) series of *Les Poètes maudits* in various magazines. The first critical study of his poetry appeared, and by the end of the year he had a circle of useful friends, whose visits to him and his mother in their rooms at 17 Rue de la Roquette have been affectionately recalled in memoirs of the period. It seems impossible to underestimate the role of friendship, or 'connections', in Verlaine's rehabilitation. Lepelletier first got his poems published in *Paris Moderne,* Morice noticed 'Art poétique' and drew attention to it, and Trézenik wrote his admiring article; if it were not for these three men, Verlaine might conceivably still be a long-forgotten Parnassian awaiting rehabilitation. Of the friends that Verlaine made during 1883, two, Léon Vanier and Jean Moréas, deserve special attention.

Léon Vanier had the bookshop on the Quai Saint-Michel and had just (in 1881) founded *Paris Moderne*. He had been trying since 1876 to get into book publishing with small pamphlets, and it was his willingness to publish small editions of a hundred copies or so, either on luxury paper or on ordinary material, which got him involved with the new poetic school.[9] One of his first successes was Joris-Karl Huysmans' *Esquisses parisiennes*; Vanier then went on to publish Verlaine's *Poètes maudits*, Moréas' *Les Syrtes* and *Les Cantilènes*, Charles Vignier's *Centon*, *Les Déliquescences d'Adoré Floupette*, and finally the work of most of the decadents, so that he became known as 'le Lemerre des décadents', after Alphonse Lemerre, who published the *Parnasse contemporain* and the works of most Parnassians. We can trace the increasing scale of Vanier's operations in the pages of *Lutèce*. The first issue (*Nouvelle Rive Gauche*, 9–16 November 1882) had advertisements for the 'Plaquettes humoristiques de la collection Vanier' (e.g. *La Chanson du colonel*, *Le Général Fricassier*, *La Pêche à la ligne*) at a franc apiece, as well as for his books of poetry, Trézenik's *Les Gouailleuses*, for instance, was already in its second edition. In the following spring (4–11 May 1883), along with the 'Plaquettes humoristiques', Vanier advertises *Le Vers rongeur* by Benjamin Brillouin, *Les Hommes et les choses* by Charles Morice, and, 'pour paraître prochainement, *Choses de jadis et de naguère*, poésies de Paul Verlaine'. He also handled back issues and complete collections of *La Nouvelle Rive Gauche–Lutèce*. Finally, by the end of 1884 (21–8 December 1884), we find the 'Extrait du catalogue de Léon Vanier', which was to become ubiquitous, appearing in each issue of *Lutèce*, *La Revue Indépendante*, *Le Décadent*, and other reviews. In this announcement Vanier has taken over the sale of all Verlaine's works, from *Poèmes saturniens*, published by Lemerre in 1866, *Fêtes galantes* (listed in the catalogue as out of print), through *Romances sans paroles* and *Sagesse* (he simply took over the unsold copies), to his own recent editions, *Poètes maudits* and *Jadis et naguère*. Vanier was only four years younger than Verlaine, and he survived him by just a few months in 1896. The two men became warm personal friends in spite of the commercial aspects of their relationship and in spite of numerous quarrels. It was Vanier's practice, perhaps misguided, of paying a few francs apiece for individual poems that helped Verlaine stay alive during the most difficult years of his life, before he began receiving subsidies from his friends and from the Ministry of Education.

Jean Moréas, or Papadiamantopoulos, was a young Athenian with a passionate love of French letters and a solid knowledge of the classics, both French and ancient. After studying in Germany, Switzerland, and Italy, Moréas settled in Paris in 1882, at approximately the same time as Verlaine. From then until his death in 1910 he was a fixture of the Parisian literary scene, with his aristocratic bearing and dress, his acute consciousness of his Greek classical heritage, and his love of café conversation. Besides his own verse, he wrote statements explaining the aims of the successive schools of poetry: 'Les Décadents' in 1885 and 'Le Symbolisme' in 1886. In 1891 he led a revolt against symbolism by founding the *Ecole romane*, whose purpose was to restore to French poetry the simplicity of its classical heritage. Again, despite occasional quarrels and doctrinal estrangements, he and Verlaine were devoted friends. In the period 1883–85 he helped Verlaine by bringing up his name and advocating his poetry in café discussions with other young writers.[10]

So far we have discussed Verlaine's activities in Paris, where he dealt directly with men who could further his career. Now we must treat another prolonged and scandalous absence from Paris, the last before he settled permanently in the city two years later. In April of 1883, in the midst of his activities, Verlaine learned that Lucien Létinois was extremely ill, and on 7 April the youth died of typhoid. The loss affected Verlaine even more deeply than is suggested by the poignancy of the poems in *Amour* composed in his memory ('Lucien Létinois,' pp. 443–63). As he usually did upon undergoing a severe emotional shock, Verlaine departed for a long absence—not immediately, but the following summer. At the end of July 1883 Madame Verlaine *mère* purchased the Létinois' farm at Coulomnes, and in September she and her son left Paris and settled on it. It does seem incredible that Verlaine should abandon Paris just at the moment when he had successfully re-established contact with the world of letters, just as it seems equally incredible for him to embark on another ill-advised farming venture; the only explanation seems to be his tendency to respond to emotional stress by literally fleeing from it.[11] His absence lasted from July 1883 to June 1885.

L'Anglais de Coulomnes, the name given to him by the local people, sums up all that is despicable in this phase of his life: it refers to Verlaine's plaid macfarlane (a sort of overcoat with a short cape over the shoulders and sleeves; this garment, with his cane and broad-brimmed hat, became Verlaine's distinctive uniform during his last years) and evokes his outrageous behaviour. Far from doing the labour necessary to operate his farm, he spent his time drinking in local taverns, struck up relationships of a questionable nature with vagabonds, and imported boys from Paris. As his perverted tastes became known, he was apparently sought out by penniless vagrants who preyed on his willingness to treat them to drinks and pay for their favours. Verlaine's style of living soon became a scandal and caused the local people to despise him. 'Poème saturnien' describes one of his escapades of this period.

His humiliating fall was accentuated by a second prison experience. On 24 March 1885, at Vouziers, he was sentenced to a month's imprisonment for threats of violence against his mother—threats he made while in a drunken rage and for which some neighbours had him prosecuted. There was some delay in beginning to serve his sentence, so that he did not emerge from the local jail until 13 May. The several days at the end of May and beginning of June 1885 were spent in penniless vagabondage; while France was officially mourning the death of Victor Hugo, Verlaine was roaming the countryside in a drunken stupor. During that year, on 9 February, his wife Mathilde Mauté divorced him. When his mother died in January of 1886 Mathilde obtained a court order sealing his apartment until he satisfied her unpaid alimony judgement. Verlaine was honest enough to hand over to the bailiff executing the order the last of his securities, which his mother had hidden in a mattress. This act, together with the expenses of his debauches at Coulomnes and the disadvantageous sale of the farm, effectively ruined him financially. Henceforth, with no means of support except petty remittances from publishers, he was to live in genuine poverty, a poverty which precluded any hope of returning to correct, self-respecting, bourgeois life.

An important difference between this absence and the earlier one of 1872–82 was that now Verlaine was in close contact with literary affairs and made frequent trips to Paris. On 28 November 1883, for instance, he was in Paris, missed Charles Morice at his room, and wrote him a letter fixing a rendezvous for the next day.[12] Furthermore, there is an extensive correspondence from this period with people like Lepelletier, Morice, and Léon Vanier, attending to all manner of literary errands— the portraits to go with *Les Poètes maudits*, his failure to receive issues of

Lutèce or of *Le Chat Noir* at Coulomnes, copy he submitted to editors, and so on.[13] Bearing in mind, then, that Verlaine was again absent from Paris and again leading the sordid, scandalous life that belied his claims to social rehabilitation and to practicing Catholicism, we return to literary events of 1884.

In 1884 Verlaine published thirteen poems in *La Revue Critique*, two in *La Libre Revue*, and the series 'Les Amies' in *La Revue Indépendante*. In *Lutèce* he published 'Luxures', 'Vendanges', 'L'Impénitence finale', and 'La Dernière Fête galante'. He was no longer dependent on personal connections, or on one or two forward-looking editors, to place his poems in magazines. With the publication of poems composed during his association with Rimbaud in 1872–73 ('Luxures', 'Vendanges', and 'Vers pour être calomnié') and of early poems which had first appeared in *Le Hanneton* in 1867 ('Circonspection', 'Allégorie', 'Sappho'), readers could see examples of his earlier verse.

A major event for both Verlaine and decadence early in 1884 was Vanier's publication of *Les Poètes maudits* in an edition of 253 copies. In announcing its appearance, *Lutèce* (29 March–5 April 1884) carried on its front page the portraits of Mallarmé, Corbière, and Rimbaud from the book. *Les Poètes maudits* enjoyed a *succès d'estime* and sold well, the first of Verlaine's books to do so, and this fact encouraged Vanier to continue investing in books by Verlaine. The significance of *Les Poètes maudits* was that, besides advancing Verlaine's fortunes, too,[14] it revealed three almost completely unknown poets to a public which was now ready for their poetry. Verlaine's idea of including complete poems with his own commentary was particularly felicitous, for his criticism was less than profound, and the texts of the poems were able to speak for themselves. While Corbière's reputation remained obscured, those of Rimbaud and of Mallarmé can be said to begin with the publication of *Les Poètes maudits*.

The introduction of Rimbaud to French readers was one of the most portentous effects of *Les Poètes maudits*. Both Rimbaud and Mallarmé were even less well known than Verlaine at the beginning of 1884, but while Mallarmé's influence was growing apace with Verlaine's, Rimbaud had disappeared permanently from France, and there were no copies of his work extant; so, when Verlaine quoted such poems as 'Les Voyelles' and 'Le Bateau ivre', he was really recalling from oblivion a poet who would shortly become one of the most important influences on French symbolism. Verlaine ended his article with a call for copies of Rimbaud's poems, which would be published by *La Vogue* in 1885–

1886. As for Mallarmé, he and Verlaine had corresponded ever since 22 November 1866, when he had graciously acknowledged a complimentary copy of *Poèmes saturniens*.[15] Probably they had met sometime after 1868 at the home of Nina de Villars, whose *soirées* gathered many of the Parnassians. On 16 August 1882, immediately after his return to Paris, Verlaine wrote to Mallarmé, outlining his scheme for a series of critical sketches and requesting a photograph and permission to write about him.[16] Later, Verlaine's son Georges was in Mallarmé's English class at the Collège Rollin, and in 1886 Verlaine wrote for news about Georges and to see if a visit could be arranged.

It should still be remembered that *Lutèce* was a magazine with a small circulation and a highly specialised public, so that when we speak of the effects of Verlaine's book—all 250-odd copies!—we are talking about the narrow, elite public which, the decadents claimed, was alone capable of appreciating their poetry. So far as the general public was concerned, Verlaine was still suffering from the editorial boycott prompted by the Rimbaud scandal, and perhaps this fact explains the paucity of reviews in general periodicals. *Les Petites Nouvelles*, for example, was one of several periodicals which refused to review *Les Poètes maudits* on the grounds that it was impossible to print Verlaine's name.[17] On the other hand, the limited audience which did read *Lutèce* or *Les Poètes maudits* included those who, either by their verse or by their acceptance of new poetic idioms, would soon create a substantially different kind of poetry in France, and on this audience Verlaine's book did make an impression. Mallarmé, according to his biographer, noticed a different mood about him when he went out in public and an increased attendance at his Tuesday evening receptions.[18] On a practical level, since the *Lutèce* article had contained some gross misprints of his poems, Mallarmé complained to Verlaine, who allowed him to check the proofs of the book, thus assuring an accurate text.[19] As Laurent Tailhade stated later, 'Ces poètes, Corbière, Rimbaud, Mallarmé, avec, pour compléter le brelan, Verlaine lui-même, furent les inspirateurs et maîtres des générations nouvelles . . . Leur influence épanouie en traînée de poudre, éclata comme un feu d'artifice et, du soir au matin, métamorphosa la chose littéraire.'[20] Letters to *Lutèce*, while facetious, still make it clear that readers held Verlaine responsible for the extravagances—or, more charitably, innovations—of those who followed in the footsteps of Corbière, Mallarmé, and Rimbaud. Referring to two of Jules Laforgue's *Complaintes*, Edmond Haraucourt writes:

Quelles éstranges machines vous avez publiées dans votre numéro d'aujourd'hui! Je parle des vers . . . Cet animal de Verlaine, en publiant ses
Poètes maudits aura fait plus de fous que Gagne et *Unitéide*. Si ça continue, il
suffira dans six ans: 1, de n'avoir rien à dire; 2, de le dire en mauvais vers et
en vers faux; 3, d'écrire comme un Javanais: pour être un poète de génie.

Et vous savez, vous les engueuleurs de tous, que vous aurez votre part de
responsabilité.[21]

It is precisely Verlaine's achievement to have created an atmosphere
hospitable to such poetry.

Nevertheless, Haraucourt's remarks on the incomprehensibility of
Verlaine's poetry were echoed by Léon Bloy, reviewing *Les Poètes
maudits* in *Le Chat Noir*, where he called Verlaine 'l'archi-ténébreux
poète catholique de *Sagesse*, livre hermétique et à jamais inscrutable'; he
also complained of the obscurity of Mallarmé and of Rimbaud: 'Les
deux autres, à la bonne heure! Arthur Rimbaud and Stéphane Mallarmé
sont des poètes immobiles et solidement assis dans la même pagode
d'imbécillité parfaite où le lecteur exaspéré peut toujours leur décrocher
sûrement sa malédiction.'[22] Bloy had words of praise only for Tristan
Corbière, whom, he said, he was surprised to find in this trilogy, for
Corbière was a true poet. (Like Morice, Bloy later changed his mind
and supported Verlaine's poetry.)

In May of 1884, two months after *Les Poètes maudits*, another book
was published which was to have a substantial and beneficial effect on
the fortunes of Verlaine and the decadents: Joris-Karl Huysmans'
novel *A Rebours*. It had to do with decadence and it discussed extensively
the poetry of Baudelaire, Verlaine, Corbière, and Mallarmé. Huysmans
was one of the *groupe de Médan*, who were well known, so that the
success of *A Rebours* and the discussion surrounding it brought decadence
and its followers to the attention of the general public—readers of
daily newspapers, large-circulation magazines, and best-selling novels—
who otherwise would never have heard of such esoteric writers. Such
unawareness on the part of the general public was a greater ob-
stacle for Verlaine and the decadents than the hostility of traditional
critics.

A Rebours marked a turning-point in Huysmans' artistic development, too, His previous novels, *Marthe*, *Les Soeurs Vatard*, 'Sac au dos'
in *Les Soirées de Médan*, and *En Ménage*, had been conventional
naturalist treatments of real-life situations, with a beginning, an end,
and a narrative plot. While Huysmans did apply naturalist techniques
of research, description, and minuteness of detail to *A Rebours*, he also

dropped linear plot narration in order to concentrate on the development of his protagonist. Des Esseintes' childhood and youth are disposed of in a 'Notice' of nine and a half pages; the sixteen chapters are each devoted to an aspect of his decadent tastes; what links the chapters together are rough indications of the passage of time and the progressive deterioration of his health, until, in the last chapter, he is obliged to renounce his isolation and return to Paris. So a typical chapter opens with an account of his illness, then deals with aesthetic experiences suggested by his symptoms.

Jean Floressas des Esseintes is the last descendent of an old, aristocratic line. Since both parents died while he was young, he had a lonely childhood and was educated in Jesuit boarding schools. Upon reaching majority, he took up a pleasure-loving, debauched life at Paris, but he soon grew tired of human society, and his health, already undermined by the hereditary ills of very old families, gave cause for alarm. He therefore determined to leave the world and retire into isolation at a house he had bought at Fontenay-aux-Roses, in what is now the *banlieue sud* of Paris. His life there is the epitome of decadence: tired and bored, disgusted with humanity and with the age into which he was born, des Esseintes devotes himself to the indulgence of his refined tastes, sleeping by day and living at night. An old serving couple from his ancestral château silently attend to his needs. He surrounds himself with works of art, with customised furnishings, with evocations of other existences. The dining room of his house is a ship's cabin fitted inside the original room. Where a porthole coincides with one of the original windows an aquarium has been arranged between the two panes of glass; but the fish are mechanical, and injections of colouring into the water tint the transmitted glass according to the time of day and the season. The room is decorated with maps, advertisements for steamship lines, and nautical paraphernalia. The only book in the room is a custom-made copy of Edgar Poe's *Adventures d'Arthur Gordon Pym*. In such a manner, this chapter presents the notions of artificiality, escape from the world, aesthetic refinement, and Baudelairean *correspondances* (e.g. the décor of the room, the subject of Poe's tale, des Esseintes' taste for Poe, and the aroma of pitch which is injected into the room before he enters it correspond to each other). The bedroom resembles a monk's cell, liturgical items (e.g. a former baptismal fount now serving as a washstand, *Les Fleurs du mal* so printed on parchment and bound as to resemble an altar missal) decorate the house, and among des Esseintes' favourite writers are the Church Fathers and contemporary Catholic writers; by such means the theme of Roman Catholicism is kept present. Des Esseintes disdains the crowd to the extent of preferring to read a musical score at home rather than submit to the promiscuity of a concert hall For him, bread and wine have become so adulterated by modern commercial techniques of preparation that one can no longer be sure of making a valid Communion. Similar variations on decadent motifs abound in the novel, and all the major tenets of decadence are presented. As one reviewer observed, the novel 'peut surprendre quand on le confronte avec les oeuvres antérieures de M. Huysmans';[23] but for readers chiefly interested in the phenomenon of decadence, des Esseintes' practices must have been the confirmation of their own tastes.

Almost as interesting as the incarnation of the decadent ideal in des Esseintes is Huysmans' connection with decadence. Like many novelists of the period, Huysmans also wrote art and literary criticism, and as his aesthetic attitudes matured his own tastes tended to resemble those of des Esseintes. Doing criticism brought him into contact with the names and works of many minor figures of whom he might otherwise have been unaware; moreover he came to realise that the *avant-garde* was a cause common to all the arts, so that by supporting experimental efforts in painting he was actually fighting for greater freedom of literary expression for himself.[24] Like his mentor, Zola, who got him a post as art critic for *Le Voltaire* and defended him against irate editors who found his first article too advanced for their taste, Huysmans upheld the new impressionist painting, which was still too unconventional for public acceptance. His article on the 1881 *exposition* was one of the first to express appreciation of the painting of Paul Gauguin.[25] In 1876 Huysmans reviewed the third edition of *Le Parnasse contemporain* for the *Republique des lettres*;[26] this was the edition from which Verlaine was excluded, but the fact that Huysmans read selections by the several dozen poets who did contribute illustrates how journalism familiarised him with very obscure writers whose work might one day become celebrated. As early as 22 October 1882, in a letter to Mallarmé, he shows that he knew the work of Verlaine, Corbière, and Mallarmé.[27]

We turn now to Huysmans' views on decadent literature, as expressed in the choice of books for his protagonist's library. Chapter III, devoted to Latin authors, interests us chiefly for its categorical denunciation of Golden Age authors; in chapter XII, on Catholic writers of the nineteenth century (significantly, des Esseintes has few

books to bridge the gap between late Latin and nineteenth century
France), we note mainly des Esseintes' unbounded admiration for
Barbey d'Aurévilly, treated chiefly as a Catholic polemicist, and for
Baudelaire. Generally, he esteems Baudelaire for having penetrated
more deeply than previous writers—Balzac, for example—into
psychology:

> Baudelaire était allé plus loin; il était descendu jusqu'au fond de l'iné-
> puisable mine, s'était engagé à travers des galeries abandonnées ou inconnues,
> avait abouti à ces districts de l'âme où se ramifient les végétations mon-
> strueuses de la pensée. [28]

Attention is drawn to the maturity of the emotions Baudelaire depicts:
'Il avait révélé la psychologie morbide de l'esprit qui a atteint l'octobre
de ses sensations . . .' (p. 183); 'il avait suivi toutes les phases de ce
lamentable automne . . .' (p. 184). Baudelaire had explored the 'douleur
de vivre' caused by satiety, disillussionment, and scorn. A final paragraph on Baudelaire spells out what will become a litany in decadent
criticism: Baudelaire's language permits him to express the ineffable,
to fix the ephemeral states characteristic of tired souls:

> Et plus des Esseintes relisait Baudelaire, plus il reconnaissait un indicible
> charme à cet écrivain qui, dans un temps où le vers ne servait plus qu'à
> peindre l'aspect extérieur des êtres et des choses, était parvenu à exprimer
> l'exprimable, grâce à une langue musculeuse et charnue qui, plus que toute
> autre, possédait cette marveilleuse puissance de fixer avec une étrange santé
> d'expressions, les états morbides les plus fuyants, les plus tremblés, des
> esprits épuisés et des âmes tristes.   [p. 185]

It is in chapter xv that contemporary lay writers are discussed. Des
Esseintes is rearranging his library: appropriately enough, by the time
he gets to modern writers he is so prostrated by the physical symptoms
of his neurosis that he cannot handle his books; the old servant shows
them to him one by one, and des Esseintes tells him where to place
them on the shelves. For him, literary schools are unimportant; what
matters is the intellectual processes of a writers, and a work mut have a
quality of strangeness which detaches him from reality and permits
him to indulge in daydreams, suggested by what he is reading, but
guided by his own phantasy. Because of his increasing horror of modern
life, it is this insubstantiality that he seeks more and more from his
reading; hence he prefers, for instance, Flaubert's *Tentation de Saint
Antoine* to his *Education sentimentale*. Des Esseintes' three favourite
authors are Flaubert, Edmond de Goncourt, and Zola: 'avec Baudelaire,

ces trois maîtres étaient, dans la littérature française, ceux qui avaient le mieux pétri l'esprit de des Esseintes . . .' (p. 228). It is at first surprising to find Zola in this catalogue of ethereal, suggestive authors, until we remember the close, father–son relationship between the master of Médan and his disciples; it would have been an unforgiveable affront to omit him from a discussion of contemporary writers. As it was, Zola took Huysmans to task for deviating in *A Rebours* from the narrow path of naturalist orthodoxy. As for Edmond de Goncourt, while in des Esseintes' judgement the eighteenth century in France was the 'société agonisante' which corresponded to the 'paganisme mourant' of ancient Rome, it had not produced a writer to express its feelings; only de Goncourt, in the nineteenth century, was capable of making the soul of that century live again. A revealing paragraph on *La Faustin* expresses the decadent admiration for de Goncourt, while suggesting in passing why the decadents esteemed him more highly than they did Flaubert:

> Ce livre d'Edmond de Goncourt était l'un des volumes les plus caressés par des Esseintes; et, en effet, cette suggestion au rêve qu'il réclamait, débordait de cette oeuvre où sous la ligne écrite, perçait une autre ligne visible à l'esprit seul, indiquée par un qualificatif qui ouvrait des échappées de passion, par une réticence qui laissait deviner des infinis d'âme qu'aucun idiome n'eût pu combler; puis, ce n'était plus la langue de Flaubert, cette langue d'une inimitable magnificence, c'était un style perspicace et morbide, nerveux et retors, diligent à noter l'impalpable impression qui frappe les sens et détermine la sensation, un style expert à moduler les nuances compliquées d'une époque qui était par elle-même singulièrement complexe. En somme, c'était le verbe indispensable aux civilisations décrépites qui, pour l'expression de leurs besoins, exigent, à quelque âge qu'elles se produisent, des acceptions, des tournures, des fontes nouvelles et de phrases et de mots.   [p. 226]

Next come some minor authors, including our poets, Verlaine, Corbière, and Mallarmé. Des Esseintes has come to like these authors of 'livres qui le délassaient de la perfection des écrivains de plus vaste encolure, par leurs défauts mêmes . . .' (p. 228). Huysmans enlarges on the thesis that, at least in a decadent period, minor authors are more interesting than the masters:

> L'imperfection même lui plaisait, pourvu qu'elle ne fût ni parasite, ni servile, et peut-être y avait-il une dose de vérité dans sa théorie que l'écrivain subalterne de la décadence, que l'écrivain encore personnel mais incomplet, alambique un baume plus irritant, plus apéritif, plus acide, que l'artiste de la

même époque, qui est vraiment grand, vraiment parfait. A son avis, c'était parmi leurs turbulentes ébauches que l'on apercevait les exaltations de la sensibilité les plus suraiguës, les caprices de la psychologie les plus morbides, les dépravations les plus outrées de la langue sommée dans ses derniers refus de contenir, d'enrober les sels effervescents des sensations et des idées.

[pp. 228–29]

These writers are rendered dearer to him by 'le mépris dans lequel les tenait un public incapable de les comprendre' (p. 229).

Paul Verlaine is the first of these writers; in *Poèmes saturniens* des Esseintes recognises 'des pastiches de Leconte de Lisle et des exercices de rhétorique romantique' and the influence of Baudelaire ('un talent déjà profondément imbibé de Baudelaire'), as well as the appearance of the poet's true personality in poems like 'Mon Rêve familier'. In examining Verlaine's work, Huysmans first discusses form:

Muni de rimes obtenues par des temps de verbes, quelquefois même par de longs adverbes précédés d'un monosyllabe d'où ils tombaient comme du rebord d'une pierre, en une cascade pesante d'eau, son vers, coupé par d'invraisemblables césures, devenait souvent singulièrement abstrus, avec ses ellipses audacieuses et ses étranges incorrections qui n'étaient point cependant sans grâce.   [p. 229]

After a paragraph on Verlaine's efforts to rejuvenate the fixed forms he turns to his ability to suggest uncertain and fugitive moods:

Mais sa personnalité résidait surtout en ceci: qu'il avait pu exprimer de vagues et délicieuses confidences, à mi-voix, au crépuscule. Seul il avait pu laisser deviner certains au-delà troublants d'âme, des chuchotements si bas de pensées, des aveux si murmurés, si interrompus, que l'oreille qui les percevait, demeurait hésitante, coulant à l'âme des langueurs avivées par le mystère de ce souffle plus deviné que senti. Tout l'accent de Verlaine était dans ces adorables vers des *Fêtes galantes*:

> Le soir tombait, un soir équivoque d'automne,
> Les belles se pendant rêveuses à nos bras,
> Dirent alors des mots si spécieux tout bas,
> Que notre âme depuis ce temps tremble et s'étonne.   [p. 230]

A quotation from 'Art poétique' indicates des Esseintes' enjoyment of Verlaine's handling of nuances. The virtue of *Sagesse* is that, in so far as it permits the reader to dream before suggested scenes, it possesses the very quality which des Esseintes seeks in imaginative literature:

Des Esseintes relisait souvent ce livre de *Sagesse* et se suggérait devant ses
poèmes des rêveries clandestines, des fictions d'un amour occulte pour une
Madone byzantine qui se muait, à un certain moment, en une Cydalise
égarée dans notre siècle, et si mystérieuse et si troublante, qu'on ne pouvait
savoir si elle aspirait à des dépravations tellement monstrueuses qu'elles
deviendraient, aussitôt accomplies, irrésistibles; ou bien, si elle s'élançait,
elle-même, dans le rêve, dans un rêve immaculé, où l'adoration de l'âme
flotterait autour d'elle, à l'état continuellement inavoué, continuellement
pur.   [p. 231]

Huysmans' analysis of Verlaine's poetry, then, is accurate and sensitive,
so that we can consider these two and a half pages from the novel as
the second critical essay to deal with Verlaine.

Des Esseintes' admiration of Verlaine, Corbière, and Mallarmé is an
exception, for he is not usually responsive to poetry, and his favourite
author is Villiers de l'Isle-Adam. Of chief interest in the remaining
portion of the chapter is the discussion of Mallarmé, which emphasises
how he has succeeded in capturing the decadence of contemporary
French literature, since a literature wears out just as a civilisation does.
While the decomposition of Latin required a long period of transition,
that of French occurred all at once. 'Le style tacheté et superbe des de
Goncourt et le style faisandé de Verlaine et de Mallarmé se coudoyaient
à Paris, vivant en même temps, à la même époque, au même siècle'
(p. 246).

A Rebours was published sixteen years after Gautier's 'Notice' to
Les Fleurs du mal and concurrently with Bourget's *Essais* and *Nouveaux
Essais de psychologie contemporaine*. Thus it was the third exposition of
the decadent syndrome, and also perhaps the most telling in that, while
Huysmans contributed little new to the notion of decadence, in des
Esseintes he portrayed, alive and in the round, attitudes that previously
had been expressed merely as notions of literary criticism. Gautier
mentioned Baudelaire's satanism and his awareness of evil, but Huysmans illustrates that the decadent is a lapsed Catholic steeped in the lore
and especially in the art of the Church. When des Esseintes scorns
public taste and esteems Verlaine, Corbière, and Mallarmé all the more
for their being neglected by the public, he romanticises a conception of
the poet which had been gaining ground in France since Leconte de
Lisle: Verlaine's poets are *maudits* because of public neglect, and both
decadent and symbolist criticism were contemptuously indifferent to
public response.

As for Verlaine, Huysmans was the first to call him a decadent in the sense that his writing, like Baudelaire's or the Goncourts', resembled Latin literature of the decadence. It was inevitable for this characterisation to be applied to Verlaine: the idea was in the air, Baudelaire had been repeatedly described in such terms, and someone would have discovered Verlaine's essay on Baudelaire in *L'Art* in 1865, in which he underlined Baudelaire's decadent treatment of 'l'homme physique moderne, tel que l'ont fait les raffinements d'une civilisation excessive, l'homme moderne, avec ses sens aiguisés et vibrants . . . '[29] Yet the fact is that neither Léo Trézenik nor Léon Bloy called Verlaine decadent, while Huysmans and every critic writing after *A Rebours* did so.

Verlaine appears in reviews of *A Rebours* as an epitome of decadence. *Lutèce* (18–25 May 1884) revealed its bias by devoting most of its review of *A Rebours* to quoting those passages in the novel having to do with Verlaine. Paul Margueritte, writing in *Le Croquis* for June 1884, describes the novel as 'le *Manuel du parfait névrosé* à l'usage non des gens à la graisse et au rire irritants, mais des douleureux et des subtils, des Verlaine, Mallarmé, Rollinat, Huysmans et *tutti quanti*'.[30] With reference to des Esseintes' tastes in literature, Jules Lemaitre writes sarcastically, 'Il n'aime pas les livres "dont les sujets délimités se relèguent dans la vie moderne." . . . Poë lui plait, et Villiers de l'Isle-Adam. Mais rien ne vaut Verlaine, ni surtout Stéphane Mallarmé!'[31] In *La Revue Independante* Emile Hennequin credits Huysmans with having discovered the influence of philosophical pessimism on artistic taste; it is because of his pessimism that des Esseintes prefers, among other writers, 'quelques poètes réellement décadents comme Paul Verlaine dont certains volumes ont les subtilitieés métriques des derniers hymnographes byzantins'.[32] The fact that Verlaine is so characterised only *after A Rebours* casts doubt on the traditional view that it was his sonnet 'Langueur' which crystallised the decadent movement.[33]

Three reviews of *A Rebours*—or, rather, three discussions of Huysmans and naturalism prompted by the novel—attract our attention. In *La Revue des Deux Mondes* for 1 August 1884 Ferdinand Brunetière discusses 'les petits naturalistes' with special reference to Maupassant and Huysmans, whose latest novels he has just read.[34] Brunetière does not like naturalism. What is interesting is that he seems completely to have missed the point of *A Rebours*; for him, it is unsatisfactory for the same reasons as other naturalist novels; nowhere does he refer to the decadence presented by the novel. He even notes Huysmans' pessimism, but calls it an additional point of contact between naturalism

and vaudeville! As for Jules Lemaitre, in *La Revue Contemporaine* for
25 April 1885, he disapproves of naturalism too, but with more
preceptiveness. His essay examines all Huysmans' work to date, shows
how the hero of each novel represents the author, and how *A Rebours*
is the culmination of his previous work. He makes fun of him ('Des
Esseintes, mon ami, vous êtes un nigaud. Par quoi voudriez-vous que
Virgile terminât ses hexamètres sinin pat un dactyle et un spondée?'),[35]
but he does realise the intent of the novel, concluding:

> Tout compte fait, M. Huysmans, en dépit des outrances puériles et des
> incohérences, a décrit une situation d'esprit exceptionnelle et bizarre, mais
> où nous entrons encore sans trop de peine et qui est, je crois, celle d'un
> certain nombre de jeunes gens. Il reste dans la mémoire, son des Esseintes si
> bien pourri, faisandé et tacheté,—et qui devrait s'appeler des Helminthes:
> type quasi fantistique du décadent qui s'applique à être décadent, qui se
> décompose et se liquéfie avec une complaisance vaniteuse et se conjouit
> d'être pareil à un cadavre aux nuances changeantes et très fines qui se vide
> avec lenteur.   [p. 333]

Albeit sarcastically, he concedes that Huysmans' style resembles late
Latin: 'Et de même que les écrivains latins du Ve siècle, tant aimés de
des Esseintes, hésitaient sur la syntaxe et même sur les conjugaisons,
M. Huysmans n'est pas très sûr de ses passés définis' (p. 334). Still more
significantly, in the quotation above ('celle d'un certain nombre de
jeunes gens') and in his concluding paragraph, he recognises that
decadence prevails among young people, whom he calls 'des sauvages
à la fin d'une vieille civilisation avec des nerfs très délicats' (p. 334).

The interest of Emile Hennequin's article on Huysmans in the *Revue
Indépendante* (like that of his study of Edmond de Goncourt the previous
May) is that, without calling him decadent or mentioning declining
civilisation, he still describes Huysmans in purely decadent terms. Thus
when he praises him for knowing Paris, its streets, it suburbs, and its
changing aspects better than other novelists, and for giving freer reign
to his imagination in *A Rebours* by substituting the artificial for the
natural, the compliment is more applicable to Huysmans' decadence
than to his naturalism! To describe his enlarged vocabulary, Hennequin
uses almost the same words as Gautier describing Baudelaire's style,
or Bourget the Goncourts':

> Attentif aux conversations qu'il a entendu bruire autour de lui, renseigné
> par ses observations sur les termes techniques des métiers, il a retenu et su
> employer tout un vocabulaire populacier, populaire, bourgeois et artiste,
> amasser et déverser un trésor de mots d'argot et d'atelier qui lui permet de

noter des sensations et des émotions dans la langue même des personnes qui la ressentent, lui fournit le mot exact ou pittoresque qui illumine une phrase du charme de la bonne trouvaille.[36]

He shows Huysmans' style, with its borrowings from various levels of language, to be marvellously suited to the rendering of sense impressions and nervous tensions, like the Goncourts.' He also puts his finger on the decadent psychology of Huysmans' characters, attributing their lack of human charity, fear of the future, and recondite artistic tastes to their exclusive dependence on sensory perception:

A measure que M. Huysmans rend ses personnages plus nerveux, c'est-à-dire plus soumis et plus directement sensibles aux impressions externes, il est forcé d'atténuer leur force de volonté, de les décrire plus incapables de tirer de leurs sensations de forts et persistants mobiles d'agir.   [p. 209]

In the same issue as Hennequin's review *La Revue Indépendante* published a substantial article on Verlaine by Louis Desprez, 'Les Derniers Romantiques: Paul Verlaine', in which he proposes to analyse the decomposition of the Romantic tradition. He characterises the 'derniers romantiques' in terms more applicable to the decadents:

. . . ces esprits sont tous caractérisés par la haine des télégraphes et des chemins de fer, par un subjectivisme dédaigneux du fait, et, conséquemment, par des fugues continues dans l'antiquité païenne, dans le moyen âge catholique, et même dans les lunes d'Edgar Poë. Au demeurant, tous des Renés, tous des aristocrates rococos qui refusent de prendre la pioche et de nous aider dans la besogne du siècle. . . .[37]

Desprez recognises Leconte de Lisle's influence on the young Verlaine, but he sees Baudelaire as a more durable influence:

M. Paul Verlaine a, comme Baudelaire, l'amour des heures crépusculaires et des terminaisons liturgiques; il mêle, comme Baudelaire, la religiosité à la recherche voluptueuse; comme Baudelaire, il a recours à des comparaisons quintessentiées, il amalgame les sons aux couleurs et se noie dans d'étranges rêveries. Poésie aux tons 'cuivreux et roux' dont le 'Nocturne parisien' peut laisser une idée très complète; dégoût spleenétique d'un pessimiste byzantin pour la vie bourdonnante et banale.   [p. 219]

After quoting from *Poémes saturniens*, he observes, 'M. Paul Verlaine . . . a essentiellement une vision de peintre' (pp. 221–2); in *Fêtes galantes* he recognises that 'Dans la fuite calme des eaux et dans l'or éteint du soleil, il y a de la tristesse. C'est l'heure où le carnaval finit en tendresse mélancolique' (p. 222), that the protagonists from the *commedia dell'arte* are stiff and artificial. *La Bonne Chanson* seems 'beaucoup moins verlainienne, beaucoup moins suggestive, et partant, beaucoup moins intéressante dans l'étude de cet esprit' (pp. 223–4). *Romances sans paroles* inaugurates 'une nouvelle période poétique, la plus originale et la plus féconde' (p. 225). Referring to *Poètes maudits*, Desprez finds that it is Mallarmé who has exercised the strongest influence on Verlaine's language and rhythms, and he quotes from 'Bise marine'. He describes Verlaine's rhythms as follows:

> Pourtant M. Verlaine a des rythmes bien à lui dans cette dernière période poétique. Rythmes subtils où le poète se grise d'assonances et emploie, presque exclusivement, soit des rimes masculines, soit des rimes féminines, selon qu'il prétend traduire quelque idée vibrante, ou qu'il veut endormir son ennui dans la douceur des finales traînées. Et puis une bien plus grande liberté de césure que dans la plupart des poètes parnassiens eux-mêmes; et, grâce à cette liberté, des effets inattendus.   [pp. 226–7]

Desprez attaches slight importance to Verlaine's conversion to Catholicism, dismissing it as an 'évolution très fréquente dans ces esprits byzantins où il y a du saint Antoine' (p. 227), and, in spite of frequent quotations from *Sagesse*, he also denigrates Verlaine's religious verse:

> Les grandioses envolées se transforment en rêves mystiquement tendres. Le saturnien ébauche des bergeries évangéliques; des moutons bêlant sous la houlette du bon Pasteur (Livre III–XII). De temps en temps quelque intermède pour lancer l'anathème au peuple souverain ou pour bénir les jésuites expulsés. Je dois avouer au bon moine qu'il a bien tort de regarder ainsi par la lucarne de sa cellule. D'assez pauvres inspirations que celles-là: le vers s'y aplatit.   [p. 299]

It is Verlaine's pictorial poems that Desprez esteems in *Sagesse*, and he quotes with enthusiastic praise 'Beauté des femmes, leur faiblesse, et ces mains pâles' and 'Les chères mains qui furent miennes.' In conclusion he calls Verlaine

> . . . ce poète inégal, à l'accent si personnel et si artiste, qui monte si haut et tombe si bas, s'effondre si souvent dans l'étrangeté et le gâchis: somme toute, une des expressions curieuses de ce temps, et, par suite, un maître pour un petit groupe d'intelligences distinguées—mais subtiles.   [p. 234]

Desprez, himself a minor novelist of the Médan group and one who had only limited critical experience, seems to owe as much to Huysmans as to his own critical insights. Verlaine's debt to Baudelaire and the Parnassians, his metrics in *Romances sans parole*, and, of course, his decadence, were already indicated in *A Rebours*, and Desprez' procedure of quoting and discussing favourite poems did not lend itself to penetrating analysis. On the other hand, he emphasises the painterly quality of Verlaine's verse, a point which Huysmans omitted, and in calling attention to it Desprez reveals his own decadent sensibility.

Léo Trézenik makes the point that Verlaine's growing prestige places French poetry in a different light from before. In reviewing Catulle Mendès' *Histoire du Parnasse contemporain* he criticises Mendès for neglecting Verlaine. Now that he is regarded as a leader of the younger poets, he, like Mallarmé, emerges in retrospect as one of the most important of the Parnasians. [38]

Maurice Barrès published a long essay on 'La Sensation en littérature: la folie de Baudelaire' in the November and December 1884 issues of *Les Taches d'encre*. Since this magazine, which Barrès wrote and published himself, lasted only a few issues, its chief contribution to the decadent movement is this essay. Barrès' outlook can be called decadent for the way he presents Baudelaire and his followers as being peculiarly equipped to handle sensations and as speaking to modern man:

> Parmi ceux qui se partagent le domaine mental, c'est-à-dire qui représentent la sensibilité et l'intelligence d'aujourd'hui, en même temps qu'ils modèlent les sensations, les sentiments et les idées de demain, Baudelaire et ses amis s'imposent comme les interprètes de la sensation.[39]

Do we not hear echoes of Gautier and Bourget in the following statement, with its implications of hypersensivity and of the uniqueness of modern man?

> Les sensations de Baudelaire et des siens sont d'ordre rare toujours et les plus excessives où puisse atteindre la machine humaine se travaillant elle-même. Tous les esprits vraiment de cette époque se sont rencontrées à quelque heure à sentir de façon analogue.   [p. 14]

In the first half of his essay he explains Baudelaire's uses of sensation. Poetry based on physical sensation is necessarily subjective and intuitive: 'La logique des filliations, le soulignage du critique n'y peuvent mais [*sic*]. Vous sentez ou vous ne sentez pas. C'est nous qui faisons la beauté de Baudelaire' (p. 13). Baudelaire deals especially with the lower senses of touch and smell, singling them out by his choice of epithets. Barrès develops the handling of *correspondances*, or 'sensations associées', of which Rimbaud's 'Les Voyelles' is an example. The result of such practices is for Baudelairian poets to express themselves by analogy, not by logical contructions:

> Et ici nous touchons au suprême effet de ce procédé; par l'analogie, nous atteignons à supprimer toute composition dans l'oeuvre d'art et à rendre les sensations bout à bout ou mêlées telles qu'elles se présentent au poète, juxta-posées par les associations les plus bizarres, selon le tempérament individuel, les habitudes, etc. La raison n'a plus que faire ici. Seuls, les sensualistes de tempérament analogue peuvent se comprendre les uns les autres.
>
> [pp. 16–17]

For them, the *résonnances* of a word are as closely tied to its nuances of meaning as form is to content.

Barrès, a Catholic himself, now turns to Baudelaire's mysticism. With Baudelaire, love is a sensual experience to be analysed with scientific finesse, and as such it leads to remorse, to sadism, and also to mysticism. The section 'Au bout du fossé' describes Baudelaire's suffering as, constantly urged on by his own appetites and by his artistic inspiration, he cannot desist from analysing the very amorous-ness which fills him with disgust and remorse. Christian mysticism is the escape from this self-created hell. But for Barrès the Catholic, this mysticism often is as much literary affectation as authentic religious faith:

> Gardons-nous peut-être de les saluer trop vite chrétiens, ces poètes. La liturgie, les anges, les satans, tout le pieux appareil, ne sont qu'une mise en scène pour l'artiste qui juge que le pittoresque vaut bien une messe. Leur religion n'a pas surgi soudaine par la grâce d'un élan de foi, c'est la tristesse qui développa dans l'intimité de leur âme des germes pieux héréditaires.
>
> [p. 19]

'Les sublimes poètes' deals with the poets who continue to work in the Baudelairian tradition: Mallarmé, Verlaine, Rollinat. In an eloquent paragraph describing the pleasures of reading Baudelaire, Barrès evokes the modern city such as the decadents knew it:

> Plaisir amer et des plus doux que de se répéter tel vers de Baudelaire au matin de la nuit parisienne, dans l'ombre coupée de fiacres plus rares et de gaz pâlissant, le long des boulevards désertés, alors qu'un écoeurement de nerfs surmenés, un souvenir des heures insipides, des camaraderies douteuses de la lutte si mesquine et si vaine, vous envahit toujours pareil et traînant une ardeur inassouvie, quelque irritation qui salit. —Des ombres rôdeuses chuchotent d'amour et d'argent; et le dégoût pâteux de cette vie, de son passé et de ses lendemains nous emplit et se fond dans une nostalgie des pays bleus et gris où l'âme voltigerait par dessus le corps au milieu des harmonies.[40]

Baudelaire's influence was evident in the first *Parnasse contemporain* of 1865; alongside the 'groupe plastique de Leconte de Lisle' were the sensualists, 'quétant la nuance, les vibrations lointaines; leurs nerfs, toujours tendus, perçoivent ce qui échappe à nos bonnes santés . . .' (p. 23). Barrès discusses Mallarmé's poetry, its infrequent appearances in print, its subtlety, its classic simplicity (already Barrès calls it 'cette poésie symbolique', p. 26), contrasting it with the robustness of Hugo, Leconte de Lisle, or Balzac.

Next he turns to Verlaine:

> Plus facile est le domaine de M. Paul Verlaine. Il connaît les souffrances communes; il écrit d'exquises élégies, des romances chastes et sentimentales, là où il est bon, c'est le poète du tact; de l'infinie nuance. Le grand succès près des lettrés ne peut manquer de lui venir. . . . Dans les *Fêtes galantes*, dans la *Bonne Chanson*, dans les *Romances sans paroles*, nous sommes bien loin de Baudelaire. Ce sont des plaintes qui meurent avec une tristesse incomparable, des murmures d'amour tristes à faire pleurer. C'est le dernier degré de l'énervement dans une race épuisée. C'est de l'art, parfois le plus exquis que nous sachions.   [p. 27]

He calls *Sagesse* 'un livre de désolation qui mérite de demeurer comme le terme suprême du mysticisme baudelairien' (p. 28); its verses are 'd'une grâce mélancolique qui se contourne sur des fonds gris, sur des teintes impressionnistes et que traversent des soupirs de dévotes jeunes . . .' (p. 28). In spite of his admiration for certain poems, Barrès' esteem for *Sagesse* is not unmitigated, for elsewhere he observes, ' . . . *Sagesse* pour ses inégalités pourrait parfois faire sourire des âmes simples' (p. 39).

Rimbaud, 'l'étrange jeune homme qu'il [Verlaine] nous fit connaître' (p. 30), is discussed in a single paragraph.

The last poet to be considered is Maurice Rollinat, author of *Les Névroses*, whom Barrès correctly places in Baudelaire's genealogical tree. We might question so much attention paid to the untalented and now forgotten Rollinat, but, as Barrès points out, his interest is psychological and not aesthetic, and he does conform to the pattern of the sensual poet. Reading *Les Névroses* introduced Baudelaire to more than one person who did not meet him through Mallarmé or Verlaine. Nevertheless, Barrès writes, Rollinat's poetry fails to move us because his poetic gifts are not equal to his excitement or to the intensity of his emotion.

(Barrès' critical values seem distorted: he passes rapidly over Rimbaud and ignores Corbière, whom he must have read in *Les Poètes maudits,* to devote five pages to Rollinat; among the novelists in 'Les Décadents,' he lumps together Catulle Mendès, Pierre Loti, Francis Poictevin, the Goncourts, and Huysmans!)

Barrès acknowledges that these poets do not have a large public, that their *oeuvre* is slim, yet 'le flot qui les porte avance chaque jour', it is their effort which is important, and they are a reaction against the materialism of current literature. For these reasons they deserve our attention.

From the four essays we have considered (omitting Léon Bloy's article in *Le Chat Noir,* which does not discuss Verlaine's verse) there emerges a common impression of Verlaine. All call him a disciple of Baudelaire, comment on the originality of his versification and on his painter's vision, praise his handling of nuances, and mention with reservations his Catholic inspiration in *Sagesse.* All agree that he has a small following of younger poets and admirers. Finally, all seek to define Verlaine's ability to express the ineffable, to evoke in his verse experiences, too delicate for words, which we recognise from having felt them ourselves: '. . . une sensation morale et physique que tous nous avons éprouvée souvent . . .';[41] '. . . il avait pu exprimer de vagues et délicieuses confidences, à mi-voix, au crépuscule';[42] 'Ce sont des plaintes qui meurent avec une tendresse incomparable . . .'[43] Thus, besides his technical prowess and the decadence of his verse, Verlaine is represented as a poet of mystery, dream, and intimate, inter-personal communication.

Notes

1 Morice's statement concerning 'Art poétique' six years later in his book, *Paul Verlaine* (Vanier, 1888), is interesting: 'Ici une explication. M. Paul Verlaine m'a dédié 'Art poétique' et il me devait bien ce grand honneur puisque, à une époque où j'étais trop loin de moi-même pour pouvoir comprendre ce poète, je l'attaquai à propos de cette pièce même, dans un petit journal de lettres. Mais l'étonnement est le commencement de l'admiration car on ne s'étonne que du Nouveau. Mon attaque d'ailleurs, pour irréfléchie qu'elle fût, n'avait point perdu le respect et Paul Verlaine put me faire une résponse qui me donna le désir de le connaître. Comme je *devais* l'aimer et comme j'étais de bonne foi, ma conversion fut prompte et entière. Elle fut d'ailleurs, ma faute, une heureuse et bienfaisante faute, car cet accident donna l'occasion à Paul Verlaine de connaître la jeune génération qu'il devait ensuite si heureusement influencer.' (Page 62, n. 1.)

2 See Ernest Raynaud, *La Mêlée symboliste,* three volumes. (Renaissance du livre, 1920), III, pp. 147–9

3 Is 'Jean Mario' Morice, Trézenik, or Georges Rall? All three wrote under the various pen names of this magazine, but none, to our knowledge, ever claimed authorship of this crucial article, not even Morice in his *Paul Verlaine*. Noël Richard suggests Trézenik as the most probable author in his *A l'Aube du symbolisme* (Nizet, 1961), p. 79.

4 *Nouvelle Rive Gauche*, 9–16 February 1883.

5 'Moyen Age' (A Paul Verlaine), *Nouvelle Rive Gauche*, 2–9 February 1883.

6 See 'Autour d'une tombe', *Mercure de France*, XVII, 74 (February 1896), 155.

7 See Noël Richard, *A l'Aube du symbolisme* (Nizet, 1961), pp. 105–7.

8 *Oeuvres poétiques complètes*, Y.-G. Le Dantec and Jacques Borel, eds. (Gallimard, 1962), p. 370. Hereafter poems by Verlaine will be identified in the text by page reference to this edition.

9 See Verlaine's sketch of Vanier in *Les Hommes d'aujourd'hui*, *Oeuvres complètes*, II (Club du meilleur livre, 1960), pp. 643–8. Robert Caze describes him enthusiastically as follows: 'Et ce n'est pas tout. Après le journal [*Lutèce*], l'éditeur! Trézenik, Rall et leurs amis dénichent dans leur voisinage un brave garçon très bibliophile qui ne demande qu'à les éditer. Il s'appelle Léon Vanier, et il a une manie, une toquade, toute spéciale. Les autres éditeurs sont partisans des éditions multiples, des tirages répétés. Vanier, lui, est l'ami des volumes tirés à petit nombre. Il y a chez lui telle plaquette, *Amour du chic*, par exemple, qui n'a pas plus de cent exemplaires. Les poètes, les amateurs et les bibliophiles sont, on le comprend, les clients ordinaires de Vanier. Il a du reste, des idées géniales et amusantes. C'est lui qui a réhabilité le papier à chandelle et le papier à beurre sur lesquels il a fait imprimer de très étonnants volumes.' 'Les Jeunes Poètes', *Le Voltaire*, August 1885, reprinted in *Lutèce*, 23–30 August 1885.

10 For a picture of Moréas' continuing activity twenty years later, see Cecily Mackworth, *Guillaume Apollinaire and the Cubist Life* (New York: Horizon, 1963).

11 For discussions of Verlaine's flights, see François Porché, *Verlaine tel qu'il fut* (Flammarion, 1933), pp. 330–6, and Antoine Adam, *Le Vrai Verlaine* (Droz, 1936), pp. 22–4.

12 See 'Lettre XI' in Georges Zayed, *Paul Verlaine; lettres à Charles Morice* (Minard, 1964), pp. 40–1

13 For example, here is a portion of a letter to Lepelletier, dated at Reims, 8 October 1883: 'Ecris-m'y souvent, en attendant. Dis à Enne que j'attends toujours *La Vie simple* [Francis Enne, *La Vie simple* (Charpentier, 1882), a collection of short stories] et si tu peux, fais-moi faire le service du *Réveil* (comme *collaborateur* . . . et ami). Je publie en ce moment une série d'articles dans *Lutèce* sur les *Poètes maudits* (Corbière, Rimbaud, Mallarmé). Tâche de faire réclame à ce petit travail,—et envoie-moi le numéro où elle aurait paru.' *Oeuvres complètes*, I, p. 1175.

14 Verlaine already had at least a small number of admirers, to judge from a letter to him from Mallarmé, 7 April 1884: 'Beaucoup de jeunes gens ont

pour vous le culte dû; j'en suis heureux, les soirs où je les vois.' Quoted by Henri Mondor, *L'Amitié de Verlaine et Mallarmé*, Gallimard, 1939, p. 79.

15 See Mondor, *ibid.*, p. 18.

16 See *ibid.*, p. 59.

17 See Mostrailles, 'Têtes de pipes: Verlaine', *Lutèce*, 5–12 July 1885.

18 See Henri Mondor, *Vie de Mallarmé* (Nouvelle Revue française, 1941), p. 424. On the other hand, *Les Poètes maudits* obviously failed to reach all those who would in time become involved with decadence and symbolism. Writing of the period 1883–1834, René Ghil states: '. . . Nous [Ephraïm Mikhaël, Stuart Merrill, André Fontainas, and others] discutions, en admiration, des grands Maîtres du Romantisme et du Parnasse,—mais nous ignorions Verlaine, et de Mallarmé savions seulement qu'à 'Fontanes', tout près de nous, enseignait l'anglais (tous, nous avions été en classe d'allemand), un poète peu connu et assez étrange. . . .' *Les Dates et les oeuvres*, Crès, 1923, p. 2.

19 'Publiez-vous ces pages en plaquette comme vous comptiez le faire? . . . Ceci encore: si vous donnez suite à ce projet, faites passer sous mes yeux les épreuves de mes vers, dont plusieurs ont été très malmenés à l'imprimerie, au point de ne plus présenter de sens. Or on triompherait trop facilement.' Letter from Mallarmé to Verlaine, 13 January 1884, quoted by Mondor, *L'Amitié de V. et M.*, pp. 68–9.

20 Quoted by Mondor, *Vie de Mallarmé*, pp. 429–30.

21 'Où ils vont', *Lutèce*, 15–22 March 1885. 'Gagne' refers to Paul Gagne, author of *L'Unéitide ou la femme messie* and famous for his colourfully extravagant actions.

   Three months previously *Le Petit Nord* of Lille had expressed surprise on learning Verlaine's position:

   'Mais le premier ténor, le chef, l'étoile, le Sirius de cette nouvelle pléïade, c'est Verlaine, le grand Verlaine, le dieu Verlaine, auprès duquel Hugo n'est que poussière et Baudelaire crottin de bique.

   'Connaissez-vous Verlaine? Non. Ni moi non plus. Et cependant, hélas! il n'est plus jeune, ce Verlaine.' 'Chronique lutécienne', *Lutèce*, 7–14 December 1884.

   A year and a half later another letter to *Lutèce* still marvels at the extent of Verlaine's influence: 'Alors que vous publiiez la première série des *Poètes maudits*, pouvait-on prévoir que Verlaine, Raimbaud [*sic*], Corbière et Mallarmé feraient tant d'enfants que cela? Ah! vous aurez de rudes comptes à rendre là-haut, redoutables fumistes que vous êtes! Et comme vous les avez lâchés gentiment'. 'Coup de botte', *Lutèce*, 26 September–3 October 1886.

22 'On demande des malédictions', *Chat Noir*, 3 May 1884.

23 Emile Hennequin, 'J.-K. Huysmans', *Revue Indépendante*, 1, 3 (July 1884), 200.

24 *Cf.* Helen Trudgian: 'Cette façon d'identifier sa propre cause avec celle du

mouvement artistique contemporain, constitue une véritable originalité dans la critique d'art. Elle fait que les tâtonnements de la jeune école sont enregistrés par Huysmans dans les *Salons* avec une minutie qu'on chercherait vainement ailleurs. Ni Duranty, ni Duret, ni Gustave Geffroy, ni Philippe Burty, n'apporteront au récit de ces années une comparable précision.' *L'Evolution des idées esthétiques de J.-K. Huysmans*, Conard, 1934, p. 101.

25 See Jacques Lethève, *Impressionnistes et symbolistes devant la presse* (Colin, 1959), pp. 136-7.

26 'Le Salon de la poésie', 20 April 1876. See Trudgian, p. 50.

27 See Mondor, *Vie de Mallarmé*, p. 420.

28 *A Rebours* (Fasquelle, 1955), p. 183. Further quotations from *A Rebours* will be identified in the text by page number.

29 'Charles Baudelaire', *Oeuvres complètes*, I, p. 54.

30 Quoted by Lethève, p. 170.

31 'J.-K. Huysmans', *Les Contemporains*, first series, twenty-third edition. (Société française d'imprimerie et de librairie, n.d.), p. 329. The article originally appeared in *La Revue Contemporaine*, I, 4 (25 April 1885), 544-59.

32 Hennequin, 'J.-K. Huysmans', p. 213.

33 See also chapter III, note 11.

34 Vol. 64, pp. 693-704, especially pp. 698-700.

35 *Les Contemporains*, p. 327. Further references will be given in the text.

36 'J.-K. Huysmans', p. 202. Further references will be given in the text.

37 I, 3 (July 1884), 219. Further references will be given in the text.

38 Léo Trézenik, 'Chronique lutécienne: les Parnassiens', *Lutèce*, 2-9 November 1884.

39 I, 1 (5 November 1884), 4. Further references will be given in the text.

40 I, 2 (5 December 1884), 22. Further references will be given in the text.

41 'Jean Mario', *art. cit.*

42 Huysmans, p. 230.

43 Barrès, I, 2, p. 27.

Chapter V

1884–85: Verlaine's influence
and *Les Déliquescences d'Adoré Floupette*

As Verlaine receives favourable treatment in critical articles, verse appearing in magazines reveals his influence on younger poets. The earliest instance we have been able to find is Guy-Valvor's (Georges André Vayssière) 'Raquettes et volants', which appeared in *Lutèce* on 7–14 September 1883. Guy-Valvor describes two girls playing badminton: oblivious to love, they are unaware that one day they will be the rackets and their lovers, 'les pauvres coeurs torturés', the shuttlecocks they hit back and forth. It is obvious that his poem copies Verlaine's 'La Chanson des ingénues':[1] both contrast the frivolity of young girls with their amorous maturity when they have grown into women, both use similar language and identical form. While in Verlaine's poem it is the girls who feel their hearts beat harder, '. . ./ A des pensers clandestins, / En nous sachant les amantes / Futures des libertins', in Guy-Valvor's it is the poet–observer who is so moved: 'Sous l'enfant trouvant la femme, / Mon coeur se sentait frémir / A voir ces jeunes coquettes, / . . . / Se renvoyer le volant.' One stanza of 'Raquettes et volants' could serve as a summary of Verlaine's poem, as well:

> Mais elles, insouciantes,
> De l'amour encor lointain,
> Avec leurs grâces riantes
> Eblouissaient le jardin.

In both the girls wear white, airy dresses and shepherdess hats, in both they have blue eyes. The stanza

> Quand les blanches mousselines
> S'envolaient en plis bouffants,
> Les brises semblaient câlines
> Ravir les belles enfants!

recalls Verlaine's lines 'Et nos robes—si légères— / Sont d'une extrême blancheur', and the third line, with *câlines* seemingly out of place ('Les

brises *câlines* semblaient . . .') recalls the difficult *vont charmant* construction which opens 'Clair de lune' (p. 107). Turns of a phrase suggest
Verlaine's very language: '[le volant] . . . / Par leurs prodiges d'adresse
/ Contrarié sans pitié', to choose from many possible examples, echoes
the *préciosité* of much of the language of *Fêtes galantes*.[2] Guy-Valvor
need not have gone to Verlaine for the eighteenth century theme
(although his equating an historical period with a subject for erotic
revery is Verlainean), which was popular during the 1880's quite
independently of *Fêtes galantes*. As for the heptasyllabic line, Guy-
Valvor's other poems are in alexandrines or other *vers pair* rhythms,
and *vers impairs* in fact begin to appear only as such imitations of
Verlaine become prevalent. Apparently 'Art poétique' introduced a
metre which Verlaine himself probably took from Baudelaire.

A year later Georges Khnopff has a dozen poems entitled 'XVIIIe
siècle' in *La Jeune Belgique*,[3] a magazine which otherwise did not usually
reflect decadent trends. In one ('III', pp. 436–7) Pierrot, with his flask
of claret and his *pâté*, the word group *ce faquin d'Arlequin*, and the
presence of Cassandre suggest Verlaine's 'Pantomime'; the line 'La
brise ride les bassins' recalls 'Et le vent doux ride l'humble bassin' of 'A
la promenade' (p. 109). Another poem ('IX', p. 439) has numerous
verbal similarities of this order, most of which echo 'Clair de lune'—
a further indication that Khnopff probably imitated Verlaine is the
mingling of gaiety with melancholy, and the sad hearts hidden by
carnaval masks, which characterise *Fêtes galantes*:

> La belle Colombine . . .
> . . . songe
> Que toute joie, au loin, n'est que mensonge
> Et que tous ces railleurs élégants et fantasques
> Déguisant leur ennui sous le blanc de leurs masques
> Et le satin brodé de leurs basquines roses
> Raffinent la tristesse adorable des choses.   [p. 439]

It should be borne in mind that devices which remind us of Verlaine's
verse were often in fact clichés of the period which he himself got from
Victor Hugo, the Parnassians, or Baudelaire. This is true of the verbal
music and the metric variations which became more and more common
in poetry during the season 1883–84. The increasing popularity of the
impressionist style must have been due to the Goncourts' prose rather
than to Verlaine. Traits which are peculiar to Verlaine, and thus
exclude his predecessors as possible sources, are echoes of his diction,

his distinctive mood of dream and melancholy, his vagueness, and his taste for pale, muted colours. Such distinctions can be made in Emile Michelet's 'In votis':

> Ce serait par un soir doux et calme d'été,
> A l'heure où les lueurs et les rumeurs dernières
> S'éteignaient mollement dans la sérénité.
> . . .
> Elle aurait dix-huit ans et des mines câlines,
> Et me raconterait des riens, niaise un peu,
> D'une voix douce comme un chœur de mandolines,
> Blonde et blanche dans son peignoir de satin bleu.
>
> [*Lutèce*, 15–22 March 1884]

Although the opening line is an obvious echo of 'Donc, ce sera par un clair jour d'été' in *La Bonne Chanson* (p. 153), the various assonances and alliterations of the second line were in common use before Verlaine's poems began appearing in *La Nouvelle Rive Gauche*. In the last stanza, to the contrary, the conditional tense, the inversion of *niaise* and *un peu*, the simile based on aural *correspondances*, and the pairing of colours which are close to each other in hue or value ('Blonde et blanche') are most likely derived from Verlaine. Equally reminiscent of him is Charles Vignier's 'Dans le [*sic*] rose':

> Errants au pays falots
> Mes rêves, berceuses yoles,
> Ont arboré pour falots
> Deux yeux bleus, deux lucioles.   [*Lutèce*, 27 April–4 May 1884]

As with Guy-Valvor's poem, the *vers impair* of seven syllables can be attributed only to Verlaine, and the vocables *falots* and *berceuses* are also typical of his verse. Additional poems by Vignier ('Paysage' and 'Vision', *Lutèce*, 18–25 May 1884; 'Retour de Cythère' and 'Tristesses', 1–7 September 1884) bear out the judgement of reviewers who commented on the Verlainean tenor of his collection of verse *Le Centon* in 1887.

A facetious, but revealing, commentary on the extent of Verlaine's influence is made by a parody which appeared in *Lutèce* in the fall of 1884:

> Las! la fleur qui fleure, effleure
> L'ultime heure, la meilleure,
> Et pleure;—oh! combien subtils
> Les sanglots en les pistils.[4]

Jean Laurent's poem does not seem too different from some of Vignier's serious verse; apparently, in the year since Guy-Valvor's poem appeared, certain of Verlaine's mannerisms had become platitudes of minor decadent verse! An accompanying letter has an epigraph from Verlaine consisting simply of two lines of suspension points, thus suggesting that a few poems were so honoured *ad nauseam*, and perhaps poking fun at the ineffableness of Verlaine's verse:

> Monsieur le Directeur,
>   La très niaise humanitairerie musagète se meurt. D'aucuns pionniers, humbles mais fiers, installent audacieusement la poésie enfin vraie, celle du transcendantalement intime vertige (Obliquitas somnorum). Il faut les suivre, sinon les imiter. (Interroga virtutem tuam.) J'ai travaillé dans ce sens. Je vous envoie une de mes meilleures oeuvres. Son insertion dans *Lutèce* sera l'irréfragable sanction de mon enrôlement définitif. J'ose attendre.
>   Salut dans l'art,
>
>   Jean-Charles Laurent

As in this letter, the decadents' sometimes pompous literary theories and their Latinate prose style were common targets for parody. More interesting is the reference to *d'aucuns pionniers*, which implies that Verlaine and others had been accepted as guides.

At the end of 1884 and the beginning of 1885 the Belgian periodical *La Basoche* published two poems showing Verlaine's influence: 'Lune d'avril', by Adolphe Ribaux:

> La lune de printemps, sur les amandiers roses,
> Sur le vert chèvrefeuille et les pruniers en fleur,
> Glisse, comme un baiser, sa laiteuse pâleur,
> Et dans l'air musical flotte l'âme des choses.   [1, 2 December 1884, p. 82]

and 'Sur la plage', by Jacques Madeleine:

> Blanches ailes des barques frêles,
> Vois ces taches d'un ton plus clair
> Sur le vert sombre de la mer:
> Sont-ce des voiles ou des ailes?   [11, 3 January 1885, p. 120]

This highly impressionistic first stanza (dated, appropriately enough, at Etretat on the Channel coast) could have been imitated from Verlaine, or it could be cognate with Verlaine's landscapes. The date of the poem, the polish of its impressionism, and perhaps the interrogation in the fourth line, argue for Verlaine as the source. Almost certainly derived from Verlaine are the dream-like quality of the tercets and their apostrophe to an unreal, inaccessible woman. They duplicate the tone of love poems like 'En Sourdine' (p. 120) and 'Circonspection' (p. 329):

> Rêveuse qui les suit des yeux,
> Veux-tu regarder tous les deux
> La même voile, au loin qui tremble?
>
> La seule extase sans rancoeurs,
> Le plus délicat des bonheurs,
> C'est encor, de rêver ensemble.

Verlaine's influence is also apparent in the verse of his friend Jean Moréas, some of whose poems appeared in *Lutèce* ('Rythme boîteux' and 'Les Bonnes Souvenances', 29 June–6 July 1884; 'Remembrances', 10–17 August 1884), and whose first collection, *Les Syrtes*, came out at the end of the year. Reviewing the volume in *La Revue Contemporaine*, Gabriel Sarrazin praised it ('Ceci est un exquis volume de vers, et qui nous a complètement séduit'),[5] but with major reservations. Some poems, he says, are resonant and meaningless, others repeat, perhaps unintentionally, some of Baudelaire's mystic poems: 'Bref, *Les Syrtes* ne dégagent pas une pensée poétique vraiment originale, et en outre, l'art—si remarquable—de l'auteur va se perdre et s'enliser parfois dans le byzantisme [synonym for decadence].' Then—at least, implicitly— he compares Moréas to Verlaine: 'Son vers est le plus musical de l'heure actuelle et la suavité de sa mélodie métrique dépasse celle de M. Verlaine lui-même. . . . Puis la plastique de M. Moréas rivalise sa musique; en lui, comme en M. Verlaine, fusionnent avec science un peintre et un lyrique. . . .' In *La Basoche* a reviewer states bluntly: 'Jean Moréas est de ceux qui prennent pour devise les vers de Paul Verlaine: "Car nous voulons la nuance encore, / Pas la couleur, rien que la nuance",'[6] thus indicating not only Moréas' debt to Verlaine but also the importance which 'Art poétique' was beginning to have for the younger generation.

At the end of 1884 Léon Vanier published *Jadis et naguère* in an edition of 500 copies printed by Léo Trézenik, presumably on the same hand press he used for *Lutèce*. This was Verlaine's first collection of verse since his return to Paris, and it contained poems from all stages of his career, as well as 'Art poétique'; it could therefore serve as an anthology for those who were just now beginning to read his poetry. In his review for *La Revue Contemporaine* Sarrazin is distinctly un- charitable; while granting 'l'adorable et musicale suavité' of some

poems he states '. . . peut-être l'oeuvre entière de M. Verlaine relè-
verait-elle plus de la psychologe que de l'esthétique. . . . Pour le moment'
nous nous contenterons de recommander à ceux qui se croient obligés
d'aimer qu'on dépasse les limites permises de l'énervement et de la
déliquescence de la pensée certaines pièces à cet égard très réussies,
dans *Jadis et naguère*, et de vrais modèles du genre: 'Sonnet boîteux', 'A
Albert Mérat', 'Langueur', 'Madrigal', etc.'[7] It is significant that
Sarrazin devotes most of his remarks to the decadence of Verlaine's
poems.

What distinguishes the year 1885 from the preceding one is a
growing awareness, both in little magazines and in the *grande presse*,
of the existence of a decadent school of poetry, with Verlaine and
Mallarmé at its head. Thus in an article by Paul Grandet in *Le Cri du
Peuple* (quoted in *Lutèce*) we notice the matter-of-fact way in which
Grandet describes Verlaine as the leader of the new poetry:

> De la poésie! mais cela n'est pas de la poésie, s'écrieront ceux pour qui M.
> Paul Verlaine est un grand homme et aux yeux desquels M. Laurent Tailhade
> (???!) est assez près d'égaler Victor Hugo. Sans doute, ce n'est pas de la
> poésie telle qu'ils la comprennent; assemblage de mots sans signification
> précise; petit jeu de patience à l'usage des fils de famille; idées: néant; rimes
> riches. . . .[8]

Writing in *Les Débats*, Paul Bourget observes that French literature is
becoming increasingly like that of northern Europe, and that the
place to look for the works of promising new poets is in the newspapers
and magazines where they publish. Neither realism, nor pictorial
verse, nor even Victor Hugo influence these young writers any longer;
the only modern writer whom they revere as a master is Baudelaire,
and then it is not the etcher of *Tableaux parisiens* but the mystic poet
whom they esteem. He goes on to describe the influence of Verlaine:

> De tous les poètes de talent qui firent partie du groupe du *Parnasse*, un seul
> paraît avoir fait école parmi cette jeunesse, M. Paul Verlaine. Cet écrivain
> étrange, et dont le grand public ignore jusqu'au nom, a essayé de réproduire
> avec ses vers les nuances qui font le domaine propre de la musique, tout
> l'indéterminé de la sensation et du sentiment. Parfois il a échoué dans cette
> tentative presque impossible, parfois il a réussi à composer des poèmes d'une
> originalité délicieuse, comme celui-ci tiré de ses *Fêtes galantes*, et qui fait tenir
> en deux strophes tout un infini de rêveries: [quotes 'Le Faune', p. 115].
>   Inégal et heurté, parfois exquis et parfois insaisissable, M. Paul Verlaine
> a une popularité de cénacle qui est un des signes les plus particuliers de cette
> époque. Il est aimé les par mêmes jeunes gens qui, du premier jour se sont

reconnus dans les romans traduits de ce douleureux Dostoïewski! . . . de ces jeunes gens qui se passionnent pour la peinture de M. Gustave Moreau, pour les dessins de M. Odilon Redon, pour tout ce qui est suggestion, demi-teinte, recherche de l'au-delà, clair-obscur d'âme. Après la débauche de réalisme à laquelle se sont livrés les écrivains de 1870, voici venir l'inévitable réaction; après l'idolâtrie de la vie, le culte du rêve. *A Rebours*, ce roman de M. Huysmans, où se trouvaient analysées les sensations d'un homme uniquement épris d'artifice, n'est pas loin d'être un livre de stricte exactitude. . .[9]

Bourget states Verlaine's ascendancy over younger writers in stronger terms than 'Jean Mario' did two years previously; for Bourget, Verlaine has 'fait école parmi cette jeunesse' and he enjoys 'une popularité de cénacle'. While heretofore decadence was seen as characterising a few obscure but worthy authors, for Bourget, as for subsequent observers, it is a widespread style among the young generation. Finally Bourget describes decadence not as a curious literary style but in aesthetic terms: dark introspection, Dostoievskian intricacy, and highly imaginative paintings. Although Bourget acknowledges the public's ignorance of Verlaine, he gives the impression of Verlaine presiding over substantial numbers of literate youth, a youth imbued with a coherent *esthétique*. The picture is not yet that of a school of poets, but it is closer to it than previous treatments of Verlaine as an unjustly neglected author only now beginning to receive his due.

Beside an edited version of Bourget's article in the 19–26 April issue of *Lutèce* appeared Trézenik's regular 'Chronique lutécienne' column, devoted to 'Les Décadents de l'allitérature': 'Ils ont longtemps porté les cheveux longs "à la Musset". Aujourd'hui les ciseaux de la décadence ont passé par là. Ils s'enorgueillissent d'une tête rase et se vantent d'un menton glabre "à la Baudelaire".'[10] After indicating Verlaine's influence on the decadents, he predicts that they will go on to new excesses: already Verlaine is insufficiently obscure, and the day is not far off when Mallarmé will be too clear and Poictevin too bourgeois. Trézenik's article is a practical, facetious counterpart of Bourget's; with the good-humoured mockery which was his trademark, he shows what decadent literature will be like when Bourget's aesthetics have been put into practice by the minor writers who, by and large, composed the decadent movement.

The publication in *Lutèce* of two of Jules Laforgue's *Complaintes* in March (8–15 March) and in June the first instalment of the second series of Verlaine's 'Poètes maudits', on Marceline Desbordes-Valmore (7–14 June), was illustrative of a new tone. Laforgue, who was to die

prematurely of tuberculosis after composing a few slim volumes of
ironic, pungently moribund verse, was an epitome of decadence;
thanks to T. S. Eliot's and Ezra Pound's adoption in English of his
techniques, he is also a principal link between decadence and contemporary poetry. When we see four of Verlaine's 'Limbes' literally beside
Laforgue's 'Complainte de mon Sacré-Coeur', as we do in the issue of
19–26 July 1885, we can appreciate how much poetic sensibility had
changed in less than three years.

During the spring of 1885 *Lutèce* published facetious comments
under the rubric 'Lettre d'un bourgeois', which purported to show
the reactions of the typical conservative bourgeois to the new poetry,
although, in a double-edged sort of way, the letters also indicated
weakness of decadent verse. With reference to Mallarmé's 'Prose pour
des Esseintes', recently published in *La Revue Indépendante*, one such
letter complains that the writer is sick of 'Des Esseintisme' and its
quest for the unusual at any cost (1–8 March 1885), and another observes,
'Et bien, en vérité, toute cette école actuelle, tous ces bons petits jeunes
qui ne font qu'éclore à la littérature, sont des—oh! je vous en prie, M.
Mostrailles, accordez-moi d'imprimer ce mot, qui rend si bien ma
pensée—sont des emmerdeurs.'[11] The same writer protests that the
decadents' philosophical pessimism is a German import unworthy of
young Frenchmen.

The outstanding event of 1885, which brought the various confused
notions of the new poetry into sharp focus, was the publication in May
and June of *Les Déliquescences* of Adoré Floupette.[12] This was simply a
collection of silly poems parodying the decadent manner, but even
parody illustrated the decadent style, and, as with *A Rebours* the previous
year, the furor attracted the attention of the general public and of the
grande presse. Of course, it also brought fame to Etienne Arsenal and
Bleucoton, as Mallarmé and Verlaine were dubbed in the book.

Like several other documents the importance of which in the history
of decadence outweighs their intrinsic literary worth, *Les Déliquescences*
appeared first in *Lutèce*. On 1–8 February there were two poems,
obvious parodies of Mallarmé's style, over the signature of Etienne
Arsenal: 'Le Petunia sauveur' and 'Cantique avant de se coucher'. The
issue of 19–26 published under the title of 'Les Déliquescences' three
'Fragments d'une symphonie en vert mineur': 'Andante', 'Scherzo',
and 'Pizzicati'. The issue of 3–10 May carried four more poems:
'Platonisme', 'Pour être conspué', 'Madrigal', and 'Rhythme claudicant''.
On 2 May these poems, and ten more, were published in a small

brochure on luxury paper, one of Vanier's limited editions for bibliophiles.[13] In keeping with the parody, the title page gave 'Lion Vanné'
as the publisher and Byzantium as the place of publication. This edition
was so promptly bought up that a second one of 1,500 copies, aug-
mented with a preface by Marius Tapora, pharmacist second-class, was
published the following month. (The preface appeared in *Lutèce* for
14–12 June.) Even this edition was sold out in a fortnight, and copies
soon became collector's items. 'Adoré Floupette' was the pseudonym
of two *Lutece* contributors, Henri Beauclair and Gabriel Vicaire, both
very minor poets who continued to publish conventional verse long
after the *Déliquescences* affair. Ironically, the poems of *Les Déliquescences*
are their best-known work, and, just as ironically, what began as
another joke for the amusement of staff and readers mushroomed into
the publication which brought more notoriety to the decadents than
their serious literary efforts.

The 'Préface' describes the life of Adoré Floupette, his literary
evolution from romantic to decadent, and how Tapora finds him in
Paris. The two men go to a café, the *Panier fleuri*, where a decadent
meeting is taking place, and where Floupette gets wonderfully drunk.
In the course of the evening Bleucoton–Verlaine is positively identified
by an allusion to one of his poems. The next day Floupette and Tapora
visit Floupette's mentor, M. Poulard des Roses; Floupette recites
Mallarmé's 'La Mort de la pénultième', and Tapora, too, decides to
become a decadent. With much effort and goodwill he succeeds in
understanding some of the decadent poets, but not all: if Bleucoton is
comprehensible, Arsenal continues to elude him.

After the introduction, or 'Liminaire', which continues the satirical
tone of the 'Préface', there follow the eighteen poems, some of them
nonsense, others parodies of individual styles, and all of them exaggera-
tions of decadent vocabulary and versification: 'Les Enervées de
Jumiège', 'Platonisme', 'Pour etre conspué', 'Suavitas', 'Avant d'entrer',
'Idylle symbolique'; four poems comprising the movements of
'Symphonie en vert mineur: variations sur un thème vert pomme',
'Madrigal', 'Rhythme claudicant', 'Pour avoir péché', 'Le Sonnet
libertin', 'Catique avant de se coucher', 'Remords', 'Bal décadent',
and 'Décadent'.

The response from the philistine press was so prompt and voluminous
that suddenly articles on Verlaine and the new poets were no longer a
rarity. We shall, therefore, comment only on a few of the more
representative ones. Gabriel Mermeix, writing in *Le XIXe Siecle* on 17

May, seems, to the merriment of the decadents, to have taken the whole thing seriously. In *Gil Blas* ('Le Décadent', 17 May 1885), Paul Arène merely questions the decadents' originality, pointing out that young poets have always sought novel effects. The *Revue Contemporaine* describes the decadent school, recognises the *Déliquescences* as a timely parody, and suggests that the parody hurts the minor followers more than it does the two leaders, Verlaine and Mallarmé.[14] Before undertaking to discuss 'Les Poètes impressionnistes et Adoré Floupette' the *Bibliothèque Universelle et Revue Suisse* felt obliged to explain, 'La langue des vers change si vite en France, à notre époque, qu'il suffit de la délaisser pendant quelques mois pour n'y plus rien comprendre du tout.'[15] It then approaches *Les Déliquescences* by way of Banville, Maurice Vaucaire (*Arc-en-ciel*, Lemerre 1885, in verse; prolific author of comedies and novels), and Mallarmé, after whom 'il n'y a plus qu'à tirer l'échelle' (p. 389). Sutter Laumann ('*Les Déliquescences*', *La Justice* 19 July 1885) ridicules the *Déliquescences*, and he seems to have originated the theory that decadent poetry could be composed simply by choosing words at random, in a dictionary or a hat, and arranging them according to the number of syllables. In *Le Figaro* (22 September 1885) Labruyère draws a humorous portrait of the typical decadent. Paul Armon, after some delay, discusses 'Les Poètes maudits', or decadents, in *La France Libre* for 3 October 1885.

In June appeared two articles which addressed themselves to the general question of philosophical pessimism among the youth of the country, rather than specifically to *Les Déliquescences*. Both seek to determine the causes and to describe the effects of the mood which prevailed among the young generation.

In *La Revue Bleue* for 6 June 1885 Dionys Ordinaire treats the question in a light, sarcastic, and mocking tone; while correctly identifying the phenomenon of pessimism, he refuses to take it seriously: 'Il souffle d'Allemagne, depuis quelques années, sur notre jeunesse française, un vent aigre et malsain qui nous apporte une épidémie nouvelle, inconnue à notre vieille Gaule: celle du pessimisme.'[16] He proceeds to describe, always in bantering terms, the effects of this malady and to discuss its Teutonic origin. The disease is all the more redoubtable in that the French, *outranciers* by nature, tend to overdo new ideas. Thus Teutonic pessimism has taken root in France, even among young men who have not read the German philosophers. These youths reject all the gifts of Mother Nature and long for death and even for complete annihilation of being. Such is the case of a few young writers who act like wits and wish to shock the bourgeoisie. Every school has its antecedents, and those of the pessimists are ' . . . les moroses comme Stendhal, comme Mérimée, comme Flaubert, l'écrivain le plus surfait de notre siécle' (p. 707), and the ' . . . poètes désespérés: Musset, le chantre de l'hystérisme; Baudelaire, l'esprit le plus gâté, le plus méchamment raffiné de notre temps, un solide écrivain toutefois; Richepin, l'auteur des *Blasphèmes*' (p. 708). Their psychologist is Bourget, and although Ordinaire dislikes him, he correctly describes his style: 'Ce style est métaphorique, plaqué de couleurs, précieux jusqu'à l'obscurité, plein de soleils couchants et de clairs de lune, imité, assez habilement d'ailleurs, de Taine, de Flaubert, des Goncourt, de ceux qu'on appelle coloristes parce qu'ils confondent la plume et le pinceau' (p. 708). Ordinaire compares Bourget's *L'Irréparable* to *Les Liaisons dangereuses* for its crass immorality, a comparison which he feels Bourget and his followers would welcome, since they are the decadents (and here is Ordinaire's first use of the term) of their century, as Crébillon *fils* and Laclos were of theirs. Expanding on this notion, he states:

> Ce mot de *décadent* sonne dans les pages de M. Bourget avec une fanfare si éclatante qu'il a piqué ma curiosité. Je me suis informé, et c'est ainsi que j'ai appris, non sans stupeur, que la maladie du pessimisme n'a pas atteint seulement quelques excentriques, mais qu'elle fait rage et infecte une notable partie de notre jeunesse. [p. 709]

Ordinaire ridicules the decadents for their unwarranted despair and contrasts them with the generous youth of previous times. As for himself, he sees cause only for optimism in the challenges that lie ahead, concluding:

> Pour moi, quand tous les autres motifs d'exister me manqueraient, quand je me sentirais menacé de choir en désespérance, je regarderais, si j'étais jeune comme vous, du côté de l'Allemagne, par la trouée des Vosges, et ce n'est pas Shopenhauer [*sic*] que je verrais. [p. 710]

(This patriotic note is less gratuitous than might be supposed: it was common to trace the pessimism of the younger generation to the defeat of 1870 and profess astonishment that such a Teutonic philosophy should have taken root in France. Fifteen and seventeen years after the defeat, anti-Prussian sentiment was again rising. Articles and cartoons in *Le Chat Noir* were so virulently anti-Prussian that French authorities seized the 13 January 1883 issue at the request of the German ambassador.)

The following week the same magazine published an article by the distinguished critic, Jules Lemaitre: 'La Jeunesse sous le Second Empire et sous la Troisième République'. A propos of a new edition of *Poésies de Jacques Richard*, a minor poet who flaunted his hostility to the Second Empire, Lemaitre dwells at length on the enthusiasm and generosity of the generation which was finishing its studies around 1860. At the same time, however, another literature was growing up, '... celle de la seconde moitié du siècle, une littérature d'observation morose et de recherche plastique ... qui est devenue l'expression la plus exacte de notre tristesse et de notre détraquement. Flaubert écrivait son premier roman et Taine ses premiers livres de critique. Les Goncourt suivaient. . . .'[17] In contrast to that enthusiastic generation, today's youth is profoundly pessimistic, at least that portion of it which is engaged in creative writing. Perhaps this pessimism is justifiable, considering both the defeat of 1870 and recent political events: both the empire and the republic have failed them. Lemaitre now examines the literary expression of this pessimism, developing a point he first made in his article on J.-K. Huysmans a few months before: as literature shifts its emphasis from content to style it inevitably becomes sordid and amoral. His thesis is of real interest to us, because he does go to the heart of the decadent aesthetic:

> Et à mesure que, par une philosophie superbe et courte, les romanciers s'enfermaient dans la réalité fatale et brutale, ils attribuaient au style plus d'importance qu'on n'avait jamais fait. D'ordinaire, ce qui intéresse dans l'oeuvre d'art, c'est à la fois l'object exprimé et l'expression de cet object; mais, quand l'objet est vil, on est bien sûr que ce qu'on aime dans l'oeuvre d'art, c'est l'art tout seul. Voilà pourquoi le 'naturalisme,' loin d'être, comme quelques-uns le croient, un art grossier, est un art aristocratique, un art de mandarins égoistes, le comble de l'art. Et l'on voit aussi comment le naturalisme, et la poésie parnassienne, et l'impressionnisme s'appellent et s'engendrent. Quand on renonce à ce qui avait été presque le tout de la littérature classique et de la littérature romanesque, à la peinture de la vie morale et à l'idéalisation de l'homme, que reste-t-il que la sensation, l'impression pittoresque et sensuelle? L'art nouveau se réduit peut-être à cette recherche inventive de la sensation rare. Mais cette recherche implique ou amène une indifférence absolue à l'égard de tout, morale, raison, science. De plus, la sensation toute seule est un abîme de tristesse; le désir qui l'appelle et qu'à son tour elle provoque est de sa nature inassouvissable.
>
> [pp. 742–3]

The decadents themselves would have agreed with his characterisation of them: 'Ils sont ravis de se sentir décadents; ils se complaisent dans

leur névrose et savourent leur déliquescence; et leur âme jouit profondément d'être pareille à un cadavre aux nuances changeantes et très fines
qui se vide lentement' (p. 743). In conclusion he asks whether, in the
final analysis, pessimism is an organic sickness of society or simply a
literary style, and he replies that only time will tell.

Finally we come to Paul Bourde's article in *Le Temps* for 6 August
1885, in which he surveys the decadent phenomenon with stinging
sarcasm:

> D'après les oeuvres de l'école, et Floupette nous venant en aide, voici
> comment nous nous représentons le parfait décadent. Le trait caractéristique
> de sa physionomie morale est une aversion déclarée pour la foule considérée
> comme souverainement stupide et plate. Le poète s'isole pour chercher le
> précieux, le rare, l'exquis, Sitôt qu'un sentiment est à la veille d'être partagé
> par un certain nombre de ses semblables, il s'empresse de s'en défaire, à
> la façon des jolies femmes qui abandonnent une toilette dès qu'on la
> copie.

He mentions the decadents' Parnassian origins, he calls Verlaine and
Mallarmé the two columns of the school, and he lists Moréas, Laurent
Tailhade, Charles Vignier, and Charles Morice as members. He
discusses their aversion to the natural, their religious attitudes, metric
innovations, vocabulary, use of *correspondances* and analogy, and so on.
In conclusion Bourde points out that decadence offers nothing new,
since it is just a continuation and exaggeration of ideas already put
forth by the Jeunes-France of Romanticism: 'Le romantisme épuisé a
donné cette dernière petite fleur, une fleur de fin de saison, maladive et
bizarre. C'est sûrement une décadence, mais seulement celle d'une
école qui se meurt.'

Jean Moréas' rebuttal in *Le XIXe Siècle* for 11 August was 'Les
Décadents', the first of his manifestoes defining the successive goals of
current poetry.[18] He begins by quoting Vigny to the effect that 'les
esprits paresseux et routiniers' find anything new ridiculous and bar-
barous, and he counters with his own sarcasm Bourde's attacks on the
personal life of the decadents. He adduces the examples of Baudelaire
and Poe to justify the decadent cult of art for art's sake and their use of
symbolism and suggestion, Littré in defence of their neologisms. He
concludes with another quotation from Vigny, urging the poet to
remain well ahead of his public.

To the glee of the decadents, Bourde's name lent itself to a pun, since
bourde in French means lie, 'poor excuse; frivolous tale'. L.-G. Mostrailles
(Léo Trézenik) in *Lutèce* replies in an article entitled 'Bourde's bourdes'.[19]

using the English possessive to emphasise the double meaning. With delightful wit Trézenik merely contests the passage in which Bourde '... accuse la rédaction de *Lutèce*... de se "pâmer" sur les élucubrations de M. Mallarmé', citing several articles in *Lutèce* which had criticised Mallarmé's obscurity, and he demands a retraction from the editor of *Le Temps*; Bourde's reply was to quote Verlaine's laudatory remarks on Mallarmé in his 'Poètes maudits' article.[20]

In his regular 'Chronique lutécienne' Trézenik congratulates himself on having obtained from the *grande presse* more publicity than it would ever have deigned to bestow on a more serious literary effort, confesses that the whole thing was not a parody but a joke made up by Beauclair and Vicaire, and accuses the whole press, particularly Mermeix and Bourde, of having fallen for it. Finally, he explains that *décadent* is a misnomer:

> Il n'y a pas plus *décadence* aujourd'hui qu'il n'y eut décadence alors qu'à l'Art classique s'essaya à succéder le romantisme, alors qu'Hugo détrona Ponsard, alors qu'on acclama, en 1830, les *Burgraves* [sic] au détriment de *Lucrèce*. Il y a une simple transformation. Il y a une tendance de la jeune littérature à faire *neuf*, et pour cela à faire *autre*. Les étiquettes ne signifient si bien rien que les prétendus décadents ont déjà été affublés de l'épithète de *néo-romantiques*, parce que 'romantisme,' au fond, au temps de sa gloire et de son audace, ne voulait que dire *changement*. Et c'est encore faire du romantisme, aujourd'hui, mais du *néo-romantisme* que de s'essayer à sortir, littérairement, de la routine et de l'ornière.[21]

In basing their appeal on the examples of established writers of the past and on the naturalness of constant, evolutionary change in literature, Moréas and Trézenik display good common sense and reduce the polemic to its just proportions; indeed, most decadent criticism is more sensible and down-to-earth than either the attacks of conservative critics or the practices of decadent writing which stirred up controversy in the first place!

The last article we shall consider was published outside France. From May to November Vittorio Pica published a series of articles in *La Gazzetta Letteraria* of Turin, entitled 'I moderni bizantini'—Francis Poictevin, Huysmans, and Verlaine.[22] The first article, on Poictevin, observes the flowering in France of *opere bizantine*, whose roots are to be found in the strange and pessimistic works of Edgar Poe and of Arthur Schopenhauer, and which, too refined for the general public, are intended for 'un pubblico ristretto di artisti et di iniziati, capaci d'intenderne et gustarne le squisite bellezze' (2 May 1885, p. 137). The essay on Huysmans is devoted largely to *A Rebours* and its analysis of Des Esseintes' literary and ecclesiastical tastes. The Verlaine article is remarkable: consisting of twenty newspaper-size columns, it made an unusually complete and intelligent study of his verse. A résumé would simply repeat what is now generally known, but we should mention Pica's detailed history of the *Parnasse*, his mention of *Amour* and *Les Poetes maudits*, and his references to the articles of 'Jean Mario' and Desprez. Pica emphasises decadence in Verlaine's poetry ('Langueur' is quoted in its entirety) and discusses the liberating influence of his metrics on French versification. Three years later Félix Fénéon translated the article for *La Cravache*.[23] Even in France Pica's insights would have been precocious for the period; his familiarity with current French literature must have been due to his contacts with Paris, for in the spring of 1885 he was foreign correspondent for *La Revue Contemporaine*. Otherwise, 'I moderni bizantini' anticipates by five years or more the spread of Verlaine's fame and that of decadence beyond the borders of France and Belgium.

Léo Trézenik came closer to the truth than anyone else when he observed that their joke had obtained for the decadents more publicity from large-circulation periodicals than their serious writing ever had. The decadents did not childishly seek publicity for its own sake; rather, reviewers in the *grande presse* had consistently overlooked their verse, so that when the clamour surrounding *A Rebours* and *Les Déliquescences* brought their names and discussions of their verse—even hostile ones!— before the literate public, they made the most of the opportunity. Obviously people can only buy books that they have heard about, and now they were hearing about Verlaine, Mallarmé, Moréas, and the others. If the poetry esteemed by des Esseintes and parodied by Beauclair and Vicaire had really been inconsequential or a hoax, it would have gone no further; but because some poetry of real worth did exist behind the façade parodied by *Les Déliquescences* and ridiculed by a Bourde, sensitive readers who had first looked at it out of curiosity came to appreciate it for its real value. In this way, the nonsense and buffoonery of *Les Déliquescences* served a worthy purpose.

Les Déliquescences did not create a school of poetry where none had existed before, any more than *Les Poètes maudits* transformed minor poetasters into major poets; what the parody did achieve was to indicate the existence of a group of poets with common ideals and to name specific individuals among them. In their café discussions and social gatherings the decadents were probably more aware of comprising a 'school' than they had been two or three years previously. Lethève states that the press campaign against *Les Déliquescences* obliged the poets to group together and to define their goals.[24] Perhaps the fact that Jean Moréas was moved to compose his first manifesto by press treatments of *Les Déliquescences*, and not by those of *A Rebours* the previous spring, indicates that their sense of community had increased during the intervening year.

As for Verlaine, his position after *Les Déliquescences* can be appreciated in terms of his publications. Although he would never succeed in living from his pen, by the end of 1885 his poems were appearing frequently in magazines, and, what is more, henceforth Vanier would publish his earlier works, as well as his current ones, at his own expense, not Verlaine's! In 1886 *Fêtes galantes* was reissued in an edition of 600 copies, in 1887 *Romances sans paroles*; the new volumes *Amour* (1888, 651 copies) and *Parallèlement* (1889, 600 copies) were followed in 1889 by a second edition of *Sagesse* in 1,100 copies; in 1891 Vanier brought out the first *Choix de poésies* in an edition of 1,500 copies. During the 1890's Verlain published at least one new volume of verse each year, in addition to placing poems in magazines.

Notes

1 *Oeuvres poétiques complètes*, Y.-G. Le Dantec and Jacques Borel, eds. (Gallimard, 1962), p. 75. Further references to poems by Verlaine will be identified in the text by title and page number in this edition.

2 For the text of the poem and additional information on Guy-Valvor, see our article 'Paul Verlaine and Guy-Valvor', *Romance Notes*, XI, 1 (autumn, 1969), 41–5.

3 III (1883–84), 435–40.

4 Jean-Charles Laurent, 'Les Fleurs blêmes', 28 September–5 October 1884. Laurent was actually Louis Marsolleau, a contributor to *Le Chat Noir*. See Noël Richard, *A L'Aube du symbolisme* (Nizet, 1961), pp. 171–2.

5 'Poésie: *Les Syrtes*', I, 2 (25 February 1885), 290.

6 'Chronique de l'art et du livre: les nouveaux-nés', I, 4 (February 1885), 169–70.

7 'Poésie: *Jadis et naguère*', I, 1 (25 January 1885), 131–2.

8 'Paul Verlaine et J.-B. Clément', 15–22 March 1885.

9 Quoted in 'La Poésie contemporaine', *Lutèce*, 19–26 April 1885.

10 *Ibid.*

11 5–12 July 1885. See also 'Lettre d'un bourgeois' in the issue of 10–17 May.

12 Since few copies of the *Déliquescences* are available, it is useful to note where, besides *Lutèce*, extracts can be found. André Barre, *Le Symbolisme* (Jouve,

1912), gives the 'Liminaire' (pp. 149–50), followed by a description of all eighteen poems, with a few brief quotations (pp. 150–54). Richard, *A l'Aube du symbolisme*, quotes the 'Préface' *in toto* (pp. 281–315). G. L. van Roosbroeck, *The Legend of the Decadents* (New York: Columbia University Press, 1927), gives the complete texts of 'Les Décadents', 'Platonisme', 'Scherzo', and 'Remords', as well as brief passages from other poems. Adolphe Van Bever and Paul Léautaud, *Poétes d'aujourd'hui* (Mercure de France, 1947), III, pp. 396–9, give the texts of 'Les Enervés de Jumiège', 'Platonisme', 'Suavitas', and 'Idylle symbolique'. Finally, Albert Schinz, *Nineteenth Century French Readings* (New York: Holt, 1939), II, pp. 777–9, gives the texts of 'Cantique avant de se coucher', 'Décadents', and 'Scherzo'.

13 Here are the two original editions of *Les Déliquescences*: (*a*) 2 May 1885, 110 copies. This contains only the 'Liminaire' and the eighteen poems, and was printed by Trézenik on the press of *Lutèce*. Ten copies only carried the names of Vicaire and Beauclair on the cover. (*b*) 20 June, 1,500 copies. 'La Vie d'Adoré Floupette' by Marius Tapora is found on pages v–xlvii, 'Liminaire' and 'Déliquescences' occupy pages 49–80. This edition is incorrectly listed in *Journal de la librairie* (1885, second series, p. 492) as having appeared on 1 August; the first edition is not listed at all. In this edition Léon Vanier is correctly identified in the *achevé d'imprimer*, although elsewhere (i.e. on the title and first pages) he is still called Lion Vanné.

There have been two reprints: (*c*) Crès edition, 15 May 1911, 635 copies. No. 1 of the collection 'Les Maîtres du livre', (*d*) Jonquières edition, 20 April 1923, 825 copies. See Richard, *A L'Aube du symbolisme*, pp. 174, 188 and 281.

14 'Poésie: *Les Déliquescences*', II, 2 (25 June 1885), 266–7.

15 'Chronique parisienne': 'Les Poètes impressionnistes et Adoré Floupette', XXVII, 80 (August 1885), 388.

16 'La Jeune Génération', *Revue Politique et Littéraire* (*Revue Bleue*), XXXV, 23 (6 June 1885), 706. Further references to this article will be given in the text by page number.

17 *Ibid.*, XXXV, 24 (13 June 1885), 740. Further references to this article will be given in the text by page number.

18 Also in *Les Premières Armes du symbolisme* (Vanier, 1889), pp. 25–30.

19 *Lutèce*, 16–23 August 1885.

20 Bourde's confusion is understandable. Even today Guy Michaud lists *Lutèce* for November 1883 as the first publication of 'Don du poème' and 'Sainte', without indicating that they appeared as quotations in Verlaine's 'Poètes maudits' article (*Mallarmé*, Hâtier-Boivin, 1953, p. 187). These were, as a matter of fact, the only poems of Mallarmé to appear in *Lutèce*. Trézenik's hostility to Mallarmé's verse seems all the more incongruous in view of his efforts to promote Verlaine's, Corbière's, and Laforgue's.

21 16–23 August 1885.

22 *Gazzetta Letteraria, Artistica e Scientifica*, IX, 18, 30, 46, 47, 48 (2 May, 25 July, 14, 21 and 28 November 1885), 137–9, 233–5, 361–2, 369–71, 378–9.
23 *La Cravache Parisienne*, 3 November 1888. See Jacques Lethève, *Impressionnistes et symbolistes devant la presse* (Colin, 1959), p. 282, n. 38.
24 See *ibid.*, p. 179.

Chapter VI
The poetry of decadence

Undoubtedly the *Déliquescences* owed some of their success to the fact
that decadent verse, with its already overdrawn effects, was particularly
apt for the exaggeration of parody. It is such minor but purposeful
heightening of Mallarmé's manner which still makes us smile today
when we read 'Pour avoir péché':

> Mon coeur est un Corylopsis du Japon, rose
> Et pailleté d'or fauve,—à l'instar des serpents.
> Sa rancoeur détergeant un relent de Chlorose,
> Fait, dans l'Ether baveux, bramer les Oegypans.
>
> Mon âme Vespérale erre et tintinnabule,
> Par delà le cuivré des grands envoûtements;
> Comme un crotale, pris aux lacs du Vestibule,
> Ses hullulements fous poignent les Nécromans.
>
> Les Encres, les Carmins, flèches, vrillent la cible,
> Qu'importe si je suis le Damné qui jouit?
> Car un Pétunia me fait immarcessible!
> Lys! Digitale! Orchis! Moutarde de Louit![1]

How easily Verlaine's repetitions, qualifiers, and extreme simplicity
become funny in the 'Scherzo' of 'Symphonie en vert mineur':

> Si l'âcre désir s'en alla,
> C'est que la porte était ouverte.
> Ah! verte, verte, combien verte,
> Etait mon âme, ce jour-là!
>
> C'était,—on eût dit,—une absinthe,
> Prise,—il semblait,—en un café,
> Par un Mage très échauffé,
> En l'Honneur de la Vierge sainte.
>
> C'était un vert glougloutement
> Dans un fossé de Normandie,
> C'était les yeux verts d'Abadie
> Qu'on a traité si durement.

C'était la voix verte d'un orgue,
Agonisant sur le pavé;
Un petit enfant conservé
Dans de l'eau très verte, à la Morgue.

Ah! comme vite s'en alla,
Par la porte, à peine entr'ouverte,
Mon âme effroyablement verte,
Dans l'azur vert de ce jour-là!   [pp. 65–6]

In the same way, 'Platonisme' caricatures the liturgical imagery, far-
fetched respect for Woman, and disdain for the commonplace which
were common attitudes in decadent verse:

La chair de la Femme, argile extatique,
Nos doigts polluants la vont-ils toucher?
Non, non, le Désir n'ose effaroucher
La Vierge Dormante au fond du Tryptique.

La chair de la Femme est comme un Cantique
Qui s'enroule autour d'un divin clocher,
C'est comme un bouton de fleur de pêcher
Eclos au Jardin de la nuit Mystique.

Combien je vous plains, mâles épaissis,
Rongés d'Hébétude et bleus de soucis,
Dont l'âme se vautre en de viles proses!

O sommeil de la Belle au Bois Dormant,
Je veux t'adorer dans la Paix des roses,
Mon angelot d'or, angéliquement.   [p. 58]

Thus, in spite of their humorous intention, the *Déliquescences* can in
fact serve as an introduction to decadent poetry, for they share with
serious verse the same themes and the same characteristics of closely-
spaced assonances and alliterations, interior rhymes, esoteric vocabulary,
names of flowers and musical instruments, and abundance of colour.

Although these traits occur in the work of Verlaine or Mallarmé, too,
generally speaking it is the minor poets who are more interesting and
'decadent' for the way in which they overdo them. Des Esseintes
preferred minor writers because their incompleteness emphasises the
specific traits of a literature in its decline,[2] and Léo Trézenik complained
that the decadents exaggerate the faults of their leaders.[3] We saw in
our first chapter how minor poets, who lacked their mentors' nice
sense of proportion, misapplied Baudelaire's, Verlaine's, and Mallarmé's
use of alliteration, internal rhyme, and assonance; by 1885 such over-

done verbal music was a distinctive feature of decadent verse. Jean Lorrain wrote, '. . . Et dans Paris caverne / Bout le boniment fou des poètes forains,'[4] Laurent Tailhade, 'Pleurent dans le roucoulement des tourterelles,'[5] and Gustave Kahn, 'Désir devenu doux d'avoir tant attendu'.[6] Such heavy-handed repetitions of sounds become even more noticeable when they are continued for several lines, as in a stanza by Stuart Merrill:

La blême lune allume en la mare qui luit,
Miroir des gloires d'or, un émoi d'incendie.
Tout dort. Seul, à mi mort, un rossignol de nuit
Module en mal d'amour sa molle mélodie.[7]

The effect is one of incantation, as if the poet intended to lull the reader by the very music of his language. The repetition of the same sounds leads to homonymity between syllables, as in the *pâle–opâle–appâlie* below:

O Lune pâle qui délie,
Liliale en le soir berceur,
Ta lueur d'opâle appâlie
A la douceur d'une alme soeur.   [Tailhade, 'Sonnet', P.E, p. 92]

In another poem, homonyms of *rose* and of *l'heure* lead to a confusion comparable to that of nonsense verse:

Roses roses, où les rosées
Roulent leurs gouttes d'argyrose,
Roses, on les dirait rosées
Par les fards de l'aurore rose!

. . .

Puis l'heure fuit. Eternel leurre
Qui promet l'heur à notre rêve!
O douleur en le coeur qui pleure,
En le coeur qui pleure sans trêve![8]

The decadents were aware of these effects, for we observe deliberate efforts at punning in Moréas' 'Dans du Sèvres les mets exquis dont tu te sèvres'[9] or in Gustave Kahn's 'Les masques de la mascarade' ('Chansons, VIII', p. 302). One is reminded of Verlaine's '. . . masques et bergamasques' in 'Clair de lune',[10] where masks and an Italian dance are linked by a common vocable. By such devices the poet draws our attention away from the meaning of words, so that he can use their sounds as musical notes.[11]

Such word play also reflects the decadents' preoccupation with words for their own sake. As a characteristic of decadent language, esoteric vocabulary attracted as much hostile criticism as the obscurity of their poetry or their allegedly depraved morals. The opulence of their vocabulary is the foreseeable outcome of a constant enlarging of the lexicon of poetry that had been going on ever since Victor Hugo boasted, 'Je mis un bonnet rouge au vieux dictionnaire.'[12] Both Gautier, in his 'Notice' to *Les Fleurs du mal*, and Huysmans, in *A Rebours*, indicated enlargement of vocabulary as a feature of decadent style. Mallarmé used the Greek word *ptyx* because he needed a rhyme for *Styx*,[13] and Jacques Plowert (Paul Adam) sought to counter complaints against the decadents' over-rich, and hence *abscons* (<*absconditus*, 'hidden'), vocabulary by compiling a *Petit Glossaire pour servir a l'intelligence des auteurs décadents et symbolistes*.[14] Since decadence was defined in terms of the florid diction of late Latin and of the need for a different language to express new and subtler sensations, the decadents proceeded to create neologisms along the lines of recognised word-formation procedures in Greek and Latin. The suffix *-ance* attenuates the original meaning of a noun. Thus, '*Lueur*, c'est l'effet d'une flamme, *Luisance* sera un reflet de flamme dans un panneau verni, dans le nacre humide de l'oeil, dans le froncis d'une sombre et soyeuse étoffe, etc., la syllabe *ance* produisant l'illusion sonore des dernières vibrations d'une corde harmonique au moment où elle va cesser de bruire'.[15] The creation of *mestesse* from *moestitia* is justified by the fact that it does not have quite the same meaning as *tristesse* or *mélancolie*; furthermore, the advantage of such words is 'créer un abîme plus profond entre les gens intelligents et les philistins, en rendant à ces derniers plus difficile, sinon presque impossible la lecture de ce que les premiers produisent'.[16] Latin reformations of this sort are frequent: *plangorer, clangorer, alme, orer, refulger, rutilescent, amène, soëve, éplorer, déplorer, incandescent*, and *marcescent*. Other terms were resuscitated from Old French: *emmy, ouïr, sainct* (with the *c*), *oint, antan*; 'Un peu de deuil *seyait* aux modes musicaux' (Kahn, 'Mélopées, I', p. 60). Argot and the vocabulary of colloquial French appear in descriptions of a working class environment. Even among terms chosen from standard French the decadents preferred words of low frequency count,[17] neologisms like the verb *crépusculer*, or common terms used in a rare sense, as *veuf*, meaning 'deprived of': '. . . veufs de tout encens, / Les zinnias ont l'air d'être en tôle vernie.'[18] Finally, there are foreign words, particularly from English, either gallicised or used in their original form; derivatives of *remember* are favoured because of their sonority: 'Je songeais alors à quelque fresque, / Remembrée avec des blancheurs d'ailes!' ('Pour être conspué', *Les Déliquescences*, p. 59). Like the Romantics before them, the decadents use foreign expressions to create an exotic atmosphere: 'La printanière blondeur / De sa gorgerette a l'odeur / Amène de l'Iris powder' (Tailhade, 'Stances pour le nouvel an', *P.E.*, p. 64). In 'Griserie de gin' Robert Caze states (in a reminiscence perhaps of des Esseintes' abortive voyage to England?), 'Je suis à Londres sans bouger de chez moi, . . .' and amplifies his statement in the final stanza:

> —Encore un coup de gin odorant et sans prix!—
> Voici le home; thé sur la table de laque,
> Bon feu—j'entends ton rire, et ta pantoufle claque,
> Mary, miss à l'accent canaille de Paris.[19]

Corbière's use of Italian in his Naples poems, Mallarmé's '. . . *Steamer* balançant ta mâture' in 'Brise marine', and Laforgue's quotations from Shakespeare are but typical examples of a widespread practice. The decadents' fondness for English appears in titles like 'Nevermore' and 'La Vieille Femme de Berkeley' of Moréas; 'Miss Miser', 'Little boy', 'Jockey', and 'Darling' of Jean Lorrain; 'Senescent moon', 'Prospero's island', and 'Vers pour Miss Lilian' of Laurent Tailhade.

The original title of Etienne Arsenal's 'Pour avoir péché', 'Le Petunia sauveur', indicates the ubiquity of names of flowers in decadent poetry. For Edmond Rodrigue, the chrysanthemum, 'Fleur des derniers beaux jours qui vont partir, . . .' images the passage of time and the approaching death of evening or winter.[20] A very common scene in decadent landscapes, which reminds us of Verlaine's 'Crépuscule du soir mystique' or 'Promenade sentimentale', or of Mallarmé's prose poem 'Le Nénuphar blanc', is a swamp at sunset, with water-lilies (again we note the sonority of *nénufar*), rushes, and gladioli. Flowers are not necessarily used as symbols, although the beflowered swamp or garden often is a suggestion of the poet's mood; rather, as with Verlaine's '. . . mainte floraison / —Dahlia, lys, tulipe et renoncule—' ('Crépuscule du soir mystique', p. 70), the decadent poet's verbal luxuriance leads him to enumerate flowers for their own sake, or else for that of adding specific details to a general impression. Laurent Tailhade's description of 'Prospero's island' is lusher and more particularised for the mention (within a space of three pages!) of *nénufar, tubéreuse, menthe, fleur du saule, rose*, and *prêle*.[21] Similar botanical exuberance is found in a poem by Moréas:

Parmi les marronniers, parmi les
Lilas blancs, les lilas violets,
La villa de houblon s'enguirlande,
De houblon et de lierre rampant.
La glycine, des vases bleus pend;
Des glaïeuls, des tilleuls de Hollande.   ['Parmi les marronniers', p. 37]

After Baudelaire's 'Correspondances' it is inevitable that the perfumes of all these flowers should blend with the sound of distant music and with moonlight. The various instruments imply moods: bassoons, cellos, and violins weep; oboes, mandolines, and fifes laugh ('Sous les blancs cérisiers et sous les lilas rose / C'est l'heure de courir au rire des hautbois', Merrill, 'Eté', p. 9]. Pianos express the decadent's disillusionment, as in Jules Laforgue's 'Complainte des pianos qu'on entend dans les quartiers aisés',[22] or Tailhade's 'La plainte grise / Des pianos' ('Sonnet', *P.E.*, p. 86). Although Vigny's melancholy horn still sounds at night, commoner instruments are harps, brasses, cymbals, and even sistrums. The mention of individual musical instruments is reinforced by distant songs or by the use of musical terminology:

Et triste chant dans la bruine sur la grève,
Chant triste et si lent et qui jamais ne s'achève,
Lent et voluptueux, cerf qui de désir drame,
Et tremolo banal, aussi, de mélodrame.
                            [Moréas, 'Dans le jardin taillé', p. 63]

In a remarkable synesthesia Merrill blends not merely sensations but the media and forms of different arts:

Du Marivaux et du Watteau!
Du pastel et des mousselines!
Sur un air de pizzicato
Des crincrins et des mandolines!   ['Fête au parc, ɪɪ', p. 13]

The flowers in decadent verse entail the colour descriptions which were mocked in Les Déliquescences. An example is Rodrigue's 'Chrysanthème', in which he specifies the various tints of red:

J'adore ton velours écarlate où s'éteint
La mourante splendeur d'un soleil qui décline,
Où la pourpre a des tons rouillés où l'on devine
Les bises, les ciels bas, l'horizon incertain . . .

The purpose of decadent language was to permit nicer descriptions than had previously been possible, and we see this effort as poets define precise nuances of colour: 'Le marbre, veiné de fissures, / A des pâleurs de vert-de-gris',[23] or 'ces cheveux d'un blond roux, nimbe d'or flavescent'.[24] Jules Frédéric conveys nuances of both colour and shape in the couplet 'Comme un argent que mord l'échoppe ou le poinçon, / La lune s'échancrait blême sur l'horizon.'[25] The decadents were fascinated by close definitions of the off-white of moonglow, with its *laiteuse pâleur*[26] and its *pâleurs infinies*;[27] Moréas called the moon 'Pâle comme un grand lys, pleine de nonchaloirs' ('Conte d'amour, i', p. 25), and Merrill says, 'Sous la blême clarté de telle nuit sans voiles' ('Pendant qu'elle chantait', p. 37).

We shall now consider how these decadent traits set apart a typical poem on a Romantic theme so that the poem is specifically decadent. Our example is Jean Lorrain's 'L'Etang mort':

Comme un lointain étang baigné de clair de lune,
Le passé m'apparaît dans l'ombre de l'oubli;
Mon coeur, entre les joncs cadavre enseveli,
S'y corrompt lentement dans l'eau saumâtre et brune.

Les croyances d'antan s'effritent une à une
Tandis qu'à l'horizon suavement pâli
Un vague appel de cor, un murmure affaibli
Fait vibrer le silence endormi sur la dune.

O pâle vision, étang crépusculaire,
Songe en paix. Pleure en vain, olifant légendaire,
O nostalgique écho des étés révolus!

Un trou saignant au front, les Espérances fées
De longs glaïeuls et de lys morts coiffées,
Au son charmeur du cor ne s'éveilleront plus.[28]

The theme that the past is dead and that hope can rise no more is both Romantic and an expression of the philosophical pessimism of decadence There are the moonlight swamp and the Baudelairean cadavre, buried in the rushes and slowly rotting in the water: neither is inherently decadent, but both are common fixtures of decadent verse. Similarly, the horn recalls Vigny and the Middle Ages, and it is also characteristic of decadent verse. In addition, there are the flowers in line 13, the precise colour descriptions (*l'eau saumâtre et brune, l'horizon suavement pâli*), the archaisms *antan* and *olifant*, and, as we shall explain below, impressionist traits of style, all of which are specifically decadent. These features need not make 'L'Etang mort' a better poem in terms of literary worth, but they do distinguish it from general, Romantic treatments of a commonplace theme.

In chapter 1 we discussed the relationships among naturalism in the novel, decadence in poetry, and impressionism in painting. To describe decadent verse we need now to deal with the impressionist style, also known as *écriture artiste*, a term which first appears in the preface to Edmond de Goncourt's *Les Frères Zemganno*, and as *style Goncourt*, since it was they who developed it in their novels and notebooks. A passage in *Manette Salomon* makes it apparent that the two brothers intended to translate the techniques of one art by those of another: 'cette langue qu'ont les peintres, ces mots qui redoublent l'expression, des paroles qui ressemblent à une succession de touches, à de petits coups de pinceau avec lesquels ils semblent vouloir se montrer à eux-mêmes les choses dont ils parlent'.[29] The chief characteristics of this style are:

1. Placement of modifiers, especially those of colour, *before* the noun. Modifiers may be adjectives, nouns, or adjectives used as nouns: thus, *le vert arbre, la verdure de l'arbre, le vert de l'arbre*.
2. Linkage of nouns in asyndeton and use of series of noun phrases: a nominal style.
3. Replacement of verbs by nouns, as in 'Renée *eut un sifflement* de douleur'.[30] Again, a nominal style.
4. Disruption of normal sentence structure by separating grammatically paired words such as subject and verb, verb and object, preposition and object.
5. Omission of verbs, or reducing them to weak forms like *c'est*: a verbless sentence.

These impressionist devices, and enlarged, esoteric vocabulary (which is also a feature of the Goncourts' style), are the chief characteristics of decadent style, both in prose and in verse.[31]

In Lorrain's poem, above, metaphors are made by listing two nouns in asyndeton (*mon coeur–cadavre enseveli; appel de cor–murmure*); adjectives are placed before their nouns (*lointain étang, vague appel, pâle vision*); in the last tercet, *Espérances fées* is separated from its modifier, *coiffées*, by the long inversion *De longs glaïeuls flétris et de lys morts*. The fact that such procedures, as well as Verlaine's fondness for dashes to set off parenthetical expressions, were parodied in 'Cantique avant de se coucher' indicates that they were generally regarded as typical of decadent poetry. A poem by Tola Dorian is a good example of the omission of verbs:

Vers, II

Danger et délire et délice,
Irréalisable désir!
Lys immaculé sur qui glisse
L'écarlate sang du plaisir!

Ivresse et rayon et révolte,
O fougue et furie et langueur,
Semence, floraison, récolte,
Fatale et féconde liqueur!

Beauté,—créatrice cruelle,
Voile ardent sur la mort jeté!
Ame-chair! Chaste et sensuelle!
Rose-Eros! . . . Fauve Aphrodité![32]

The only verb in the poem, *glisse* in line 3, is not the main verb of a sentence but that of a relative clause; otherwise, the poems consists entirely of nouns, either listed in asyndeton or joined by the conjunction *et*—that is to say, normal grammatical structure has been jettisoned entirely in favour of a pattern based on successive impressions and connotations expressed by a series of nouns and noun phrases. Verlaine omitted verbs altogether from his poem 'Walcourt' (p. 197). and elsewhere he reduced them to the minimal form *c'est*, as in the opening lines of his first 'Ariette oubliée' (p. 191).

Impressionist painting aims to reproduce the *impression* that a subject, bathed in light, makes upon the painter's sensibility, and to do so it concentrates on rendering effects of light and colour at the expense of form, composition, and intellectual content. Besides its direct use of colour, impressionist painting is noteworthy for its *pointillism*, or dabs of colour placed next to each other on the canvas. When seen from a distance, these spots mingle in the viewer's eye and give a very lively impression of airiness, light, and colour; but, of course, when seen too close they again become mere dabs. For this reason, together with the difficulty of rendering sharp contours by such means, impressionist painting is said to destroy the solidity of forms: a house or an apple, like an expanse of sea, is never more than a field of coloured brush strokes. Similarly, in literature the impressionist style destroys the syntactic form of the sentence. The absence of verbs and the constant disruption of normal grammatical clusters reduce the 'sentence' to a series of sense notations, for each noun, noun phrase, or word cluster is like a dab of paint on canvas, and they are presented to the reader pell-mell, without the hierarchical organisation of the sentence.

In the stanza below we receive an impression of whiteness before we recognise it as a sail, an effect which we often feel in looking at impressionist paintings, and which the poet underlines with the question in the last line:

> Blanche ailes des barque frêles,
> Vois ces taches d'un ton plus clair
> Sur le vert sombre de la mer:
> Sont-ce des voiles ou des ailes?[33]

Le vert sombre de la mer, of course, also emphasises the impression of colour at the expense of its cause, the sea.

In his essay on Baudelaire, Paul Bourget identified as an inherently decadent quality the disintegration of syntax, which he likened to the dissolution of the decadent society in which too many individuals are unsuited to group effort:

> Une même loi gouverne le développement et la décadence de cet autre organisme qui est le langage. Un style de décadence est celui où l'unité du livre se décompose pour laisser la place à l'indépendance de la page, où la page se décompose pour laisser la place à l'indépendance de la phrase, et la phrase pour laisser la place à l'indépendance du mot. Les exemples foisonnent dans la littérature actuelle qui corroborent cette féconde hypothèse.[34]

This is one reason for the syntactical aspects of the *écriture artiste* to persist in the decadent style, even after they no longer serve the original purpose of reporting sense impressions. In 'L'Etang mort' Jean Lorrain places an *abstract* adjective before its noun: *nostalgique écho*. Another reason, as Stephen Ullmann emphasises, is that abstractness seems to be an inherent, if unexpected, quality of this style. The Goncourts use their style to express abstract notions from the very beginning; impressionist painting, after all, was the first step toward abstraction in modern art, and 'nominal syntax is abstract in its very essence'.[35]

In turning from style to versification, we find that the metrics of decadent poetry, for the most part, are surprisingly traditional. Nowhere is the movement's debt to the *Parnasse* more apparent than in the unending parade of sonnets, alexandrines, and rich rhymes that appear in the pages of decadent reviews. Decadence expresses its reaction against impassive formalism more readily in its themes, language, and moods of dark introspection than in experiments with poetic form. Still, metric innovations are to be seen. The frequent appearance of poems in octosyllabic and decasyllabic verse suggests that poets were

less than satisfied with the traditional alexandrine. Even in alexandrines
poets tend to place the caesura elsewhere than in its time-hallowed
postition following the sixth syllable. After 1883 one notes an increased
use of *vers impairs*. As early as the 2–9 February, 1883 issue, Georges
Herbert's 'Simple Aquarelle' in the *Nouvelle Rive Gauche* has seven-
syllable lines; so has Guy-Valvor's 'Raquettes et volants' in the 7–14
September 1883 issue; in that of 29 June–6 July 1884, Morèas' 'Rythme
boîteux' includes a stanza in five- and seven-syllable lines; and, two
months later (1–7 September), Charles Vignier published a group of
poems, obviously imitated from Verlaine, of which two are in *vers
impairs*.

The impeccable rhymes of many decadent poems have the effect of
camouflaging some very serious designs on the integrity of the poetic
line. These have less to do with inadequate rhyming, such as *rimes
faibles*, than with the role of rhyme as the end-marker of a line of
poetry. In French versification the last, or rhyming syllable of a line
is always stressed, and for this reason it is normally also the last syllable
of a *groupe phonétique*. In the following examples, however, the rhyme
word occurs in the midst of a phonetic group, where it could not
possibly be stressed:

> Je ne le dois! Et ce serait le plus impie
> Péché contre le Saint-Esprit, que rien n'expie;
>
> [Verlaine, 'A Edmond Thomas', p. 436]

> Une moire de vains soupirs pleure sous les
> Trop seuls saluts riants par nos voeux exhalés
> Aussi haut qu'un néant de plumes vers les gnoses![36]

In French diction the phrases *le plus impie péché* and *sous les trop seuls
saluts riants* are pronounced as a single word, with an accent on the last
syllable; there is no way that *impie* or *les* could be stressed without an
incongruous violation of the normal practices of French speech; thus,
in spite of the fact that *impie–expie* and *sous les–exhalés* are rich rhymes,
their position in the phrase tends to slur over the end of the poetic line
instead of emphasising it. Other poets do the same: 'La phalène en
silence vers / La flamme d'or se précipite' (Samain, 'Heures d'été, IV',
p. 21); 'Des ailes calmes / Caressent nos / Fronts lourds . . .' (Tailhade,
'Sonnet', *P.E.*, p. 86); 'Tâche donc, instrument des fuites, maligne /
Syrinx, de refleurir aux lacs où tu m'attends!' (Mallarmé, 'L'Après-
midi d'un faune').[37] There are precedents for this practice. Victor
Hugo's *enjambement* in the opening lines of *Hernani*, '. . . C'est à

l'escalier / Dérobé . . .' shocked classicists in 1830; in 1859 he wrote,
'. . . ce n'est / Ni l'outre où tout le vent de la Fable tenait,' and '. . .
tandis / que l'oiseau plane au fond d'un paradis',[38] Baudelaire wrote,
'. . . un amour / Eternel et muet . . .' and '. . . Le remords n'a-t-il pas /
Pénétré . . .';[39] as with their verbal music, the decadents merely use
much more frequently a device already thought of by their predecessors.

Another way of de-emphasising the end of a line, one which the
decadents do seem to have originated, is the use of identical rhymes. In
'Vitrail'[40] Vignier has only two rhymes for twelve lines, and these are
masculine and feminine spellings of the same sound: *cyclamen*, *caté-
chumènes*, *inhumaines*, *Yémen*, and so on, which he alternates according to
the traditional rules for the alternation of masculine and feminine
rhymes. However, since the final syllable of *cyclamen* is not nasalised
(and all the other 'masculine' rhymes are similarly irregular in pro-
nunciation), it *sounds* as if the poem were based exclusively on feminine,
and even identical, rhymes. This practice is not uncommon: Michelet
rhymes *fleur*, *fleure*, *t'effleure*, and *pleure*;[41] Gustave Kahn rhymes
future, *mâtures*, *aventures*, *déléaturs*, and *tortures*;[42] Stuart Merrill has
horizon, *chantonne*, *monotone*, *saison*, and *automne*,[43] which, while not
identical, are masculine–feminine versions of the same vowel sound.
The point is that any tampering with the traditional arrangements of
rhyme weakens its function as an end-marker, especially when prolifera-
tion of assonances, interior rhymes, and refrains makes it difficult for
the *listener* to tell *which* occurrence of a rhyme sound is the right one
for the end of a line. This uncertainty increases when run-on lines and
complete stops at the caesura in the middle of the line tend to eliminate
that other end-marker, the completion of a sentence or thought. The
process is particularly evident in a poem by Georges Khnopff:

La pluie est lasse et vous, ces cris
De toutes choses du soir, brises
De frolées ramures grises
Et dans les sillons, les cris-cris;

Et vous semeurs, l'air de songer
De geste lent et large, et lasse
L'ombre molle qui se déplace
D'agnelle lasse de manger.

Quelle source en mols gouttelis
Flue et soupire son sourire
Ou si triste revire et rire
La paix de feuillages pâlis?

La pluie est lasse, et si c'était
Lente et lasse, au fond de la drève
Celle en prières de mon rêve,
Pour qui la brise s'attristait!⁴⁴

Not all lines end at a pause in the thought, nor do all pauses in thought occur at the ends of lines; moreover, the repetitions of rhyme sounds are very confusing to the auditor, who listens for them, only to realise that some are end rhymes, others not. This is particularly true of the rhymes *lasse* and *déplace* in the second stanza, since *la pluie est lasse* also serves as a refrain at various points in the poem, and *lasse* itself is repeated, as in lines 8 and 14, independently of either rhyme or refrain. In this way, while decadent poetry is usually quite regular to the eye, and sometimes also to the ear, in other cases it would be distinctly difficult for a listener—and these poems were often read aloud in cafés—to recognise the rhythmic recurrence of standard poetic lines. In this manner decadent poetry anticipates the future, when free verse will compete with conventional versification.⁴⁵

Looking now at the subject-matter of decadent poetry, we find that a major theme is the modern city and its denizens—a theme obviously inherited from Gautier, Baudelaire, and Verlaine, not to mention the novel as early as Balzac. Urban landscape fascinated the decadents for several reasons: their preoccupation with 'modernity' and artificiality as the key notions of their philosophy; their efforts to imitate naturalism and impressionism, both of which proposed the urban working class as a subject for study; the lesson of the Parnasse, that objective description, while apparently an end in itself, could actually serve to express the poet's emotional reactions. Hence the wealth of urban landscapes, such as Jean Ajalbert's 'Gennevilliers', which describes an industrial suburb of Paris, with its erstwhile babbling brook now serving as an open sewer ('C'est ici que Paris déverse ses eaux sales . . .'), as the epigraph, 'O rus. . .' casts an ironic light on the whole scene.⁴⁶ In a reminiscence perhaps of Zola's *Thérèse Raquin*, Stuart Merrill describes in 'A la Morgue' unclaimed cadavers stretched out on their slabs, with a stream of flowing water in lieu of refrigeration: 'Les voilà, quatre ou cinq, étendus sur leurs dalles, / Sous l'eau des robinets aux glouglous attendris.'⁴⁷ Laurent Tailhade describes the evening leisure of a retired pharmacist in the backyard of his home at Grenelle ('Rus', *P.A.*, p. 14), and in 'Place des Victoires' he describes couples emerging from a concert, the women discussing the performance, their husbands bored, while the equestrian statue of Louis XIV, . . . le vainqueur de Namur, /

S'assomme à regarder les portes de la Banque.' (*P.A.*, p. 20). Finally this type of subject provided an opportunity to use a different and esoteric vocabulary. We see how a 'slice of life' involves the use of decadent language in Miguel Fernandez' 'Nocturnités':

> Le soir à la clarté des becs fuligineux
> La cité réfulgeant dans l'ébèneur de l'ombre
> Se vêt d'astres gazeux, couvre de sa pénombre
> Les pékins absinthés au teint rubigineux.
>
> A minuit, le sergot d'un oeil calamiteux
> Guette, molosse adroit, le tripot bas et sombre,
> Traîne sa nullité, zéro dans un vain nombre,
> Réflectant sur les murs son profil malingreux.
>
> La cocotte éreintée, aux farineurs de plâtre,
> Le visage appâli par un reflet blêmâtre,
> Balade effrontément ses airs cataractifs.
>
> Parfois dans les lointains, un bourgeois soligrade,
> Flaneur vespéral terminant sa promenade,
> Sternute au vent du soir des dégoûts olfactifs.[48]

The 'modernity' of the scene requires technical, 'non-poetic' terms like *bec* (de gaz), *gazeux*, *pekin* (here, army slang for 'civilian'). *Sergot*, *tripot*, and *cocotte* resemble slang in that they are colloquial terms designating objects associated with the underworld. The description involves precise terms of colour and light, such as *fuligineux* (also found in Verlaine's 'Effet de nuit', p. 67), *rubigineux*, *réflecter*, *appâli*, *blêmâtre*. Finally, Fernandez expresses his scorn for the solitary bourgeois stroller by describing his sneeze in ponderous Latinisms.

That the decadents intended such descriptions of urban scenes to express an implied judgement against modernity is clear from the preface to Jean Ajalbert's *Sur le Vif: vers impressionnistes* (Stock, 1886). Robert Caze, himself a decadent poet, describes how the ravages inflicted by modern industry on the countryside surrounding Paris affected his friend, Ajalbert:

> Un soir nous causions; vous levâtes tout à coup les yeux vers un cadre de bois laqué, qui contient un mélancolique et doux pastel signé J. F. Raffaëlli. Un terrain vague de banlieue, sali par une herbe galeuse et rare; des arbres poitrinaires au premier plan, et, dans le fond, des maisons à six étages avec des coins de puisards noirs entrevus: tout l'envahissement *de la maladive civilisation dans la malade campagne suburbaine* [our italics].
>
> '—Ce sont des choses qu'il faudrait mettre en poésie,' me dites-vous.[49]

Ajalbert, as Caze points out elsewhere in his introduction, admired the Goncourts and Huysmans, both of whom, the former in *Manette Salomon*, the latter in *Croquis parisiens*, had described the little La Bièvre river, south-west of Paris, in terms of its pollution by the surrounding industrial areas. (The river passes by the Gobelins tapestry factory and ends in a sewer!) Huysmans opens his sketch by writing, 'La nature n'est intéressante que débile et navrée,' and he continues, 'Au fond, la beauté d'un paysage est faite de mélancolie. Aussie la Bièvre, avec son attitude désespérée et son air réfléchi de ceux qui souffrent, me charme-t-elle plus que toute autre . . .'[50] Thus Ajalbert's view of a sickly and artificial suburban landscape was peculiarly decadent.[51] Indeed, a difference between impressionism in painting and that of the decadents is that, while impressionist paintings, with their sunshine and bright colours, seem celebrations of life, decadent writers usually emphasise the sullied aspect of landscapes touched by man.

It goes without saying that classical antiquity furnished the inpsiration for many poems. In chapter III we drew attention to Jean Lorrain's 'Bathylle', in which a homosexual Greek slave boy sums up the corruption and exoticism of ancient Rome. For several poets this theme became the concise and intense image of their rather particularised conception of decadence, because, as the Marquis de Sade observed, sexual perversion is man's parry against nature. In the poem below, the artificiality motif is heightened by the boy's hair-do (*calamistrer* means to curl the hair with a hot iron) and by the make-up (*fard*) on his toes:

Epigramme

Lourdement, ses cheveux calamistrés d'or roux
Tombent sur un bandeau de pourpre violette,
Devers ses yeux inquiétants où se reflète
La clarté des soleils enamourés et fous.

Ses pieds sur le pavé de chaude mosaïque
Se posent, les orteils avivés par le fard;
Son corps d'affranchi grec, blanc comme un nénufar,
S'épanouit, orné d'une grâce archaïque.

Très souples et marquant le rhythme des baisers,
Ses hanches que fleurit le printemps des Luxures
Erigent leurs autels aux offrandes peu sûres
Pour la cruelle ardeur des appétits blasés.

Dans l'étuve où l'odeur âcre des aromates
Et des vinaigres monte avec un goût d'encens,

L'imberbe—insoucieux des rires peu décents—
Offre aux bourgeois velus l'orgueil de ses chairs mates.

[Laurent Tailhade, *P.E.*, p. 57[52]]

As the eighteenth century was for Verlaine in *Fêtes galantes*, so for the poets of the '80's antiquity was a period of unabashed sexual indulgence. Pierre Quillard's 'L'Impassible' is a dialogue between an ephebe and a courtesan,[53] and Ernest Raynaud recounts how some Greek ephebes, 'tout haletant des jeux', admire their own nude forms in the reflection of a sylvan pool, while Pan 'Compare leur poitrine aux blancheurs des troènes / Et rit caché derrière un rideau de glaïeuls'.[54] Jean Lorrain has a series of nine poems grouped together under the rubric 'Les Ephèbes' in his *Sang des dieux* (Lemerre, 1882).

Again, the similarity between Paris and Rome, with debauchery as the factor common to both, is implied in Henri Beauclair's 'Les Feux du ciel de lit'. Paris, the prince of debauchery, is stretched out on a couch in an alcove with his faithful companion Luxuria at his side. Although the poem clearly takes place in Paris, the classical names Paris and Luxuria, the idea of an organised orgy, and an epigraph from Hugo's *Orientales* mentioning Sodom and Gomorrah, imply an ancient decor. To Paris's jaded request, '—Hé bien! Luxuria, tu n'as donc rien appris / De neuf! Toujours même rengaine?'[55] Luxuria replies that in spite of much research, nothing better has been found since Adam and Eve. Here we meet again the essentially decadent idea that, in vice as in literary style, only the new and unusual can satisfy the satiated tastes of an old civilisation. At Luxuria's command all kinds of women—laundry girls, seamstresses, prostitutes, adulterous wives in their coaches—pass in review. Then, at midnight,

> Les bras entrelacés, marquises et ribaudes,
> Cousettes et catins, sous le commandement
> Superbe et triomphal de Paris, doucement
> Se mirent à danser la valse Lesbienne . . .

When Paris tires, pale, swishing young men bring him wine to drink, and in an ironic echo of Hugo 'Toute la vieille garde entra dans la fournaise'.

It would be an error to ascribe all the racy poems appearing in periodicals to the cult of decadence—one has less a feeling of jaded voluptuaries than of high-spirited young men enjoying a bawdy anecdote—nevertheless, several styles of licentious verse do reflect the decadent aesthetic. On the analogy of Baudelaire's 'Les Bijoux' ('La très-chère était nue, et, connaisant mon coeur, / Elle n'avait gardé que ses bijoux sonores', p. 141), or 'Une nuit que j'étais près d'une affreuse Juive' ('Car j'eusse avec ferveur baisé ton noble corps, / Et depuis tes pieds jusqu'à tes noires tresses / Déroulé le trésor des profondes caresses', p. 32), there are numerous poems in which the poet instructs his mistress how to please him, or details how he will go about the love ritual. On the basis that in a decadent society sex is a form of illicit pleasure, preferably unnatural, rather than a normal expression of love, decadent poetry treats all manner of erotic activities. Prostitution is a common subject; Laurent Tailhade's 'Troisième Sexe'[56] has to do with homosexuality, and Emile Goudeau handles lesbianism in 'Sapho-Lorette à Lesbie-Trinité'.[57] A gentleman emerging from a public bath importunes little girls:

> Voici que, dans la rue, au sortir de sa douche,
> Le vieux monsieur qu'on sait un magistrat farouche
> Tient des propos grivois aux filles de douze ans.[58]

The sensuous descriptions of undraped female forms—artist's models or mistresses—frequently invoking Venus or nymphs as ideals of classic pulchritude, as in Eugène Berrichon's 'Le Modèle',[59] are another instance of the decadent view of sexual indulgence as a form of refinement or as an attribute of classical antiquity.

The religious theme in decadent literature, which was parodied in *Les Déliquescences*, go back to Chateaubriand, whose thesis in *Le Génie du christianisme* was that the aesthetic beauty of Christianity vouches for the truth of its dogmas. In the same way Delphin de Girard sees the Church as a storehouse of beautiful artifacts in his 'Alla Madonna':

> Dans les plis emperlés d'une étoffe de moire
> Blanche, le front neigeux embué d'ors éteints,
> Des lys altiers dans ses royales mains d'ivoire,
> Pareille aux Sainctes des vieux missels byzantins;
>
> Chaste Madone orant sur un thrône de gloire,
> Ointe d'âpres parfums, de menthes et de thyms,
> Elle déchiffre et lit un très ancien grimoire;
> Une flamme s'allume en ses regards hautains.
>
> A quelque vision sombre d'Apocalypse
> Qui sur le parchemin s'enlumine et s'éclipse
> Sa face resplendit d'une mate pâleur,
>
> Rayonnant sous la tiare aux pierres de couleur,
> Candide comme la Vierge des Paraboles,
> Image mystique à la façon des Symboles.[60]

We saw in chapter II that decadence had two different interpretations of religion. The one held that Catholicism (especially if seen as a sumptuously artistic rite of Byzantine or medieval times) was an elitist reaction against modern democracy and its anti-clericalism. A literary expression of this view is the prose sketch in the very first number of *Le Décadent* which describes Sunday services at the elegant, high-society parish of Saint-Germain-hors-les-murs. Just as des Esseintes preferred the early Church Fathers for their corrupt Latin style, so Church Latin has an added appeal for the modern visitor: 'Les paroles du roi prophète se répondent dans ce latin du cinquième siècle légèrement déliquescent, dont la simplicité permet une demi-compréhension qui ajoute un charme mystérieux aux verbes magnifiques des psaumes.'[61] When Laurent Tailhade attends vespers of a reformed Gallican sect, held in a café of the Mouffetard quarter, he complains about the quality of the sermon and of the hymns, translated into bad French poetry and played on a harmonium.[62] In such a context Verlaine's religious poetry is not at all out of place: his 'Un Crucifix' appeared only two issues after Augustin Boyer's 'Les Litanies du jeune homme' (from his *Psautier à l'usage de mon siècle*),[63] and a year before Laurent Tailhade's 'Cantique pour implorer la grâce de Notre-Dame'.[64]

Another decadent interpretation, also derived from Chateaubriand, was the blend of mysticism and sadism which is seen in Baudelaire's satanic Catholicism. In *Les Déliquescences* 'Remords' parodied this attitude, and Verlaine cultivated it carefully in the very title of *Parallèlement*.[65] We also see it in decadent treatments of the cult of the Virgin, which can assume a sensual tone: 'Coupe lustrale des ivresses libertines, / Tes yeux sont un ciel calme où le désir s'endort',[66] and, in an even more Baudelairean tone:

> Mon amour devant toi se prosterne et t'admire
> Et s'envole avec la vapeur des encensoirs
> Dans un parfum de nard, de cinnamme et de myrrhe!

The doctrines of the incarnation and of the immaculate conception are stated in a carnal vocabulary:

> Ta robe à longs plis droits drape ta taille sainte
> Et moule le trésor adoré de tes flancs—
> Que ne souilla jamais aucune humaine atteinte.[67]

Armand Sylvestre's 'Te Deum', from the hymn *Te Deum*, is a paean of adoration for his lady,[68] in 'Fête Dieu' Alaric Thome (Francis Vielé-Griffin) compares himself to an acolyte in the Corpus Christi procession, while his mistress carries the host which symbolises their love; the imagery becomes sacrilegious when in voluptuous terms he proposes to devour the host of their love.[69] The theme of the Virgin lends itself further to the decadent taste for artificiality. Madonnas are usually represented as Byzantine paintings ('Dans le nimbe ajouré des Vierges byzantines, / . . . / Je veux imprisonner Vos grâces enfantines', Tailhade, 'Sonnet liturgique', *P.E.*, p. 184), or as stained-glass windows: 'Sur le fond lumineux du vitrail et du ciel / Tu m'apparais drapée en tes atours magiques'.[70] Art and satanism are combined in Jean Lorrain's 'Angelica',[71] which relates how the figures in a stained-glass window come to life at night. Mallarmé handles the theme of religious art in 'Démon de l'analogie' and 'Sainte'.

Another way of gaining a perspective on decadent poetry is through the collections of verse appearing during the 1880's—and, again, it is more informative to consider the work of minor poets, who are often more exaggeratedly decadent, than that of major poets with whom we are already familiar. Less representative of decadence than of the strong and widespread influence of Baudelaire is Maurice Rollinat's volume *Les Névroses* (Charpentier, 1883), which is a concentrate of the macabre and frenziedly neurotic elements of Baudelaire's verse. Grotesque mistresses—a ventriloquist ('La Voix'),[72] a moribund skeleton ('L'Amante macabre', p. 255; 'Mademoiselle squelette', p. 259), or a sadist ('Le Succube', p. 66)—recall Baudelaire's handlings of women; poems to Chopin (p. 53), Edgar Allan Poe (p. 56), and Balzac (p. 57) suggests 'Les Phares'; 'L'Enterré vif' (p. 278), 'L'Ensevelissement' (p. 371), and 'La Bière' (p. 372) echo the macabre side of Baudelaire. 'Les Becs de gaz' (p. 238) presents one of the scenic descriptions of Paris which are typical of decadent verse, while the section entitled 'Les Refuges' recalls, by its formal virtuosity, the Parnassian origins of decadence.

Verlaine's influence on the new generation is evident in two volumes we have already discussed, *Les Syrtes* (1884) of Jean Moréas and *Le Centon* (1887) of Charles Vignier.

The collection which best exemplifies the spirit of decadence is Jean Lorrain's *Modernités*,[73] which affirms that modernity is synonymous with moral corruption and sexual perversion. His originality is to present in a series of verse scenes the *haut-* and *demi-mondes* of actresses, models, servants, and even poets who manage to profit from the pursuit of pleasure by the idle rich. Many poems have a theatrical format consisting of dialogue, often in slang, and terse statements resembling stage directions; with no exposition, the reader must infer the situation which leads to the scene. In this respect they are like 'Paris' of the later Corbière, although Lorrain's poems are quite inferior to Corbière's.

Quite another aspect of decadence is represented by Jean Ajalbert's *Sur le Vif: vers impressionnistes* (1886) and *Sur les Talus* (1887), which we have also discussed previously. With both Ajalbert and Lorrain the use of realist description in an indictment of a society in decline is an example of the naturalist side of decadence.

Stuart Merrill's *Les Gammes* (Vanier, 1887) continues the mode announced by Moréas and Vignier, as the poet expresses moods through songs and through scenes more suggested than described. This type of poetry looks forward to symbolism in its effort to find language combinations, verbal music, and evocations of scenes which, all together, are intended to involve the reader in the poet's emotional state. Such is the goal of a stanza like the following:

> Mon coeur, ô ma Chimère, est une cathédrale
> Où mes chastes pensers, idolâtres du Beau,
> S'en viennent à minuit sous la flamme lustrale
> Râler leur requiem au pied de ton tombeau.   ['Oubli, 1', p. 35]

Laurent Tailhade's *Poèmes aristophanesques* (1904) and *Poèmes élégiaques* (1907) bring together poems which had first appeared in decadent reviews and then in small volumes throughout the 1880's, since he was a prolific poet and an active figure in the movement. *Poèmes aristophanesques* is fairly sharply divided into two sorts of inspiration. 'Au pays du mufle' contains a series of sonnets on decadent themes, such as 'Rus' and 'Place des Victoires', which we have already seen. 'A travers les groins [also, *grouins*]', 'Dix-huit ballades pour exaspérer le mufle', and 'Quelques variations pour déplaire à force gens', on the other hand, reflect the parodying, *pince sans rire* side of decadence and anticipate Tailhade's statement to Jules Huret in 1891 that decadence was nothing but a *mystification*.[74] Continuing in the spirit of *Le Parnassiculet contemporain* in 1867, from *Les Déliquescences* to Jean-Charles Laurent's 'Les Fleurs blêmes'[75] and Alaric Thome's poem in Volapük,[76] to the Rimbaud forgeries and poems of Mitrophane Crapoussin in *Le Décadent*, parodies of decadence seem almost as typical of the movement as more serious poetic expression.

We have culled from some several hundred poems those which best illustrate how the idea of decadence was expressed in lyric poetry, and our selection has resulted in an assortment of admittedly minor verse. To place in correct perspective these forgotten poems, whose chief virtue is apparently to have carried valid procedures to sometimes tasteless extremes, it is necessary to review our uses of the term 'decadence'. We saw in chapter II that decadence began as a notion of social degeneration and of the artificial; that writers in particular quickly associated contemporary France with Rome of the decadence; and that this view of their times, far from causing dismay, appealed to their Romantic sense of the exotic; finally, that Gautier, Bourget, and Huysmans associated decadence with a particular syndrome of literary values until, in 1884, Barrès could call a rather limited group of authors *les décadents*. Thus in current usage the term underwent a narrowing and shifting of meaning until an interpretation of history became an epithet for a literary school. [77]

As we saw in the case of Jean Lorrain's 'L'Etang mort', features that distinguish a poem as decadent do not necessarily enhance its literary value. Rather, the reverse was generally true: it is the verse of minor poets, who exaggerated the decadent aspects of Baudelaire, Verlaine, and Mallarmé, which best illustrates decadence while having little other claim to permanent value. It would even be correct to state that the poets whose reputations have survived at all are those who outgrew decadence. Nevertheless, for a few years the decadent school represented what was best and most progressive in French poetry, in the sense that Verlaine and Mallarmé were nominally members of the group, and that the writers who admired them enlarged upon the tradition of Baudelaire and worked to create a new poetic idiom based on his discoveries. Since an avowed purpose of this group was to write for themselves and to read each other's verse, they also provided the first audience for Verlaine and Mallarmé, whose fortunes, so long as their reputations remained obscured, thus depended on those of the group. As we shall demonstrate in chapter VIII, this state of affairs did not last long: there was a reaction against the excesses parodied by *Les Déliquescences*, and Verlaine and Mallarmé had less and less to do with those who continued to call themselves *les décadents* Seen in this way, the decadents composed the milieu from which emerged Verlaine, Mallarmé, and French symbolism, and as a consequence, their activity acquires an historical interest which surpasses their artistic achievement.

Notes

In the case of quotations from collections of poetry, the source will be given in a footnote on the first occurrence, and thereafter quotations will be identified in the text by name of author, title of poem, and page reference to the edition cited in the footnote.

1 Gabriel Vicaire and Henri Beauclair, *Les Déliquescences: poèmes décadents d'Adoré Floupette* (Crès, 1911), p. 71.

2 See Joris-Karl Huysmans, *A Rebours* (Fasquelle, 1955), p. 228.

3 'Or, de même que les décadents de Verlaine et de Mallarmé ont outré les *défauts seuls* de ces deux *leaders*, arrivant ainsi à la cacophonie et au galimatias le plus complet, de même M. Jules Laforgue, trempé, imbu, sursaturé de Corbière, a poussé jusqu'à l'extravagance le procédé de l'auteur des *Amours jaunes*.' Mostrailles (Léo Trézenik), 'Les Quais de demain', *Lutèce*, 9–16 August 1885.

4 (Paul Duval), 'Parade', *Modernités* (Giraud, 1883), p. 3.

5 'Sonnet', *Poèmes élégiaques* (Mercure de France, 1907), hereafter referred to as *P.E.*, p. 11.

6 'Thème et variations, VIII', *Premiers Poèmes*, second edition (Mercure de France, 1897), p. 54.

7 'Nocturne', *Les Gammes* (Vanier, 1887), p. 21.

8 Charles Vignier, 'Tristesses, I', *Lutèce*, 1–7 September 1884.

9 'Sensualité', *Oeuvres*, I (Mercure de France, 1923), p. 23.

10 *Oeuvres poétiques complètes*, Y.-G. Le Dantec and Jacques Borel, eds. (Gallimard, 1962), p. 107.

11 That this was the decadents' intention is brought out by Charles Morice's observation, 'Pour Moréas, les vers ne sont plus que notations musicales dont il tire d'admirables effects.' *La Littérature de tout à l'heure* (Perrin, 1889), p. 309. See also note 13 below.

12 'Réponse à un acte d'accusation', *Les Contemplations* (Garnier, n.d.), p. 14.

13 *Cf.* Mallarmé's remark about this word, 'On m'assure qu'il n'existe dans aucune langue, ce que je préférerais de beaucoup à fin de me donner le charme de le créer par la magie de la rime.' Guy Michaud, *Mallarmé, l'homme et l'oeuvre* (Hâtier-Boivin, 1953), p. 75.

14 (Vanier, 1888).

15 *Ibid.*, pp. ii–iii.

16 Charles Darantière, 'Les Epoques littéraires', *Décadent*, 4 December 1886.

17 E.g. *cavale, los, lapider, lustre, plectre, mante, translucide* in poems by Moréas (I, pp. 68 and 71).

18 Laurent Tailhade, 'Rus', *Poèmes aristophanesques*, third edition. (Mercure de France, 1910), hereafter referred to as *P.A.*, p. 14.

19 *Basoche*, I, 4 (February 1885), 150.

20 'Chrysanthème', *Lutèce*, 11–18 October 1885. For autumn as a symbol of decline and death, see Emile Peyrefort's poems. 'L'Adieu suprême' and 'La

Toussaint' in *Lutèce*, 5–12 July 1885. For Moréas' use of the same symbolism, see P. Niklaus, *Jean Moréas, poète lyrique* (Presses universitaires, 1936), pp. 105 and 117.

21 *P.E.*, pp. 80–2. Was Tailhade aware of the fact that in the lines 'Et sur vos fraîches chrysoprases / Glisse l'intangible baccante', p. 81, *chrysoprase* is a form of agate and not a flower?

22 *Oeuvres complètes*, I (Mercure de France, 1962), p. 80.

23 Jean Lorrain, 'Coin de parc', *Basoche*, II, 2 (February 1886), 78.

24 Jean Lorrain, 'Amour posthume', *ibid.*, I, 9 (July 1885), 301.

25 'Perspective vespérale', *ibid.*, I, 12 (October 1885), 421.

26 Adolphe Ribaux, 'Lune d'avril', *ibid.*, I, 2 (December 1884), 83.

27 Albert Samain, 'Invitation', *Oeuvres*, I (Mercure de France, 1824), p. 87.

28 *Décadent*, December 1887.

29 Quoted by Stephen Ullmann, *Style in the French Novel* (New York: Barnes & Noble, 1964), p. 143, n. 1.

30 Quoted by Ullmann, p. 132.

31 For an excellent treatment of French impressionism in literature, music, and the arts, see Ruth Moser, *L'Impressionnisme français* (Geneva: Studer, 1951, and Droz, 1952). For literary impressionism in the nineteenth century, see Helmut Hatzfeld, *Literature through Art; a New Approach to French Literature* (New York: Oxford University Press, 1952), especially chapter VI, 'Impressionism and surrealism', pp. 165–90. For the Goncourts' style, see Ullmann, *Style in the French Novel*, especially chapter III, 'New patterns of sentence-structure in the Goncourts', pp. 121–45, and chapter IV, 'Word-order as a device of style, 4: E. and J. de Goncourt', pp. 167–73.

32 *Revue Indépendante*, n.s., VI, 17 (March 1888), 421.

33 Jacques Madeleine, 'Sur la plage', *Basoche*, I, 3 (January 1885), 120 (not to be confused with his other poem of the same title, I, 4 (February 1885, 156).

34 'Charles Baudelaire: III, Théorie de la décadence', *Essais de psychologie contemporaine* (Lemerre, 1883), p. 25.

35 Ullmann, p. 138.

36 René Ghil, 'A Villiers de l'Isle-Adam', *Décadent*, 21 August 1886.

37 *Oeuvres complètes*, Henri Mondor and G. Jean-Aubry, eds. (Gallimard, 1945), p. 51.

38 *Oeuvres complètes; Théâtre*, I (Ollendorff, 1912), p. 529; and 'Plein Ciel', *La Légende des siècles*, II (Garnier, n.d.), pp. 333 and 337.

39 'La Beauté' and 'Le Reniement de Saint Pierre', *Oeuvres complètes*, Claude Pichois, ed. (Gallimard, 1961), pp. 20 and 115.

40 *Lutèce*, 1–7 September 1884.

41 'Remords léger', *Basoche*, I, 1 (November 1884), 22.

42 'Thème et variations, II', p. 45.

43 'Crépuscule d'automne', p. 56.

44 'Vers oubliées, III', *Revue Indépendante*, n.s., III, 8 (June 1887), 388.

45 Actual instances of free verse by decadent poets are rare. One thinks of

Marie Krysinska's poem in *Le Chat Noir* ('Symphonie en gris', 4 November 1882), of Ajalbert's *Sur Les Talus*, and of Kahn's *Palais nomades*. In the latter collection, as well as in Albert Samain's *Au Jardin de l'infante*, occur also what the French call *vers libre*: stanzas of fixed form but with varying line lengths and rhyme schemes, as in La Fontaine's *Fables*.

46 *Lutèce*, 23–30 August 1885.

47 *Basoche*, I, 5 (March 1885), 192.

48 *Décadent*, 22 May 1886.

49 Quoted by Jean Ajalbert, *Mémoires en vrac* (Michel, 1938), p. 125.

50 'La Bièvre', in *Croquis parisiens* (Plon, 1908), p. 83. *Croquis parisiens*, with illustrations by Forain and Rafaëlli, first appeared in 1880 (Vaton), in ample time for Ajalbert to have read it. See A. E. Carter, *The Idea of Decadence in French Literature, 1830–1900* (Toronto University Press, 1958), p. 18, and also Mario Praz, *The Romantic Agony*, Angus Davidson, trans., second edition (London: Oxford University Press, 1951), p. 310. (Praz refers to an expanded version, *La Bièvre*, Amsterdam, 1886, which Ajalbert might not have seen.) For Baudelaire as the source of 'the tendency in French painting both of the last century and up to our own day, to portray aspects of landscape which are tortured and violated by man . . .' see Praz, p. 45.

51 For a landscape of human artifacts, see his poem, 'Croquis d'hiver', *Basoche*, I, 3 (January 1885), 102, dedicated to Verlaine.

52 Originally published as 'Aliptes' in *Lutèce*, 29 June–6 July 1884, and re-published in *Décadent*, 1–15 November 1888 as 'Garçon de bains'. For other poems on the same subject, see Daniel Denfert, 'Décadisme antique', *Décadent*, 16 October 1886; Albert Samain, 'L'Hermaphrodite' and 'Fin d'empire', *Oeuvres*, I pp. 103 and 215; Jean Lorrain, 'Bathylle', *Chat Noir*, 1 July 1882, and *Le Sang des dieux* (Lemerre, 1882), p. 117; Jean Ajalbert, 'Hamman', *Chat Noir*, 6 June 1885. For a nineteenth century version of this character type, see Jean Lorrain, 'Décadence', *Modernités*, p. 39.

53 *Basoche*, I, 4 (February 1885), 144–6.

54 'Sonnet', *Lutèce*, 2–9 November 1884.

55 *Lutèce*, 19–26 October 1884. The poem was taken from Beauclair's forth-coming volume *Les Horizontales* (Vanier, 1885), *horizontale* being the slang term for 'prostitute'.

56 *Décadent*, 1–15 August 1883.

57 *Chat Noir*, 22 December 1883.

58 'Hydrothérapie', *P.A.*, p. 28. *Cf.* Paul Hervieu's naturalist sketch 'Attentat à la pudeur', which describes the trial of an elderly business executive charged with seducing his foreman's twelve-year-old daughter (*Revue Indépendante*, n.s., VIII, 22, August 1888, pp. 196–200.

59 *Lutèce*, 2–9 November 1884.

60 *Décadent*, 11 September 1886. An apparent typographical error furnishes a facetious comment on the decadent's contradictory love of both the ancient and the modern, since the title reads 'Alla Moderna'!

61 Charles Evendal, 'Religiosité', *Décadent*, 10 April 1886.
62 'Les Eglises des garçons: la chapelle de la rue d'Arras', *Lutèce*, 1–7 September 1884.
63 *Lutèce*, 8–15 June 1883.
64 *Lutèce*, 18–25 May 1884.
65 Charles Morice wrote that Verlaine's modernity lay in the *duplicité* (in the sense of complexity, not hypocrisy) of his pagan–Christian, mystical-sensual inspiration. See his *Paul Verlaine* (Vanier, 1888), pp. 69–79; also Praz, *Romantic Agony*, pp. 306–8, on sadism and Catholicism.
66 Laurent Tailhade, 'Sonnet liturgique', *Décadent*, December 1887.
67 Raoul Russel, 'Vitrail,' *Basoche*, I, 10 (August 1885), 362.
68 *Lutèce*, 23 February–2 March 1883.
69 *Lutèce*, 23 July–2 August 1885.
70 Raoul Russel, 'Vitrail'.
71 *Lutèce*, 18–25 May 1883.
72 (Charpentier, 1926), p. 29.
73 '*Modernités* me semble el livre le plus représentatif du genre décadent: rapprochements constants entre Athéniennes, Romaines et Parisiennes; études de cabotins, de décavés et de drôlesses, de coquines et de névrosés. Au milieu du volume, *Corps de ballet* (six pages) est imprimé en rouge: raffinement jusque dans l'impression!' Noël Richard, *A L'Aube du symbolisme* (Nizet, 1961), p. 262, n. 20.
74 See Jules Huret, *Enquete sur l'évolution littéraire* (Charpentier, 1891), p. 329.
75 *Lutèce*, 28 September–5 October 1884.
76 (Francis Vielé-Griffin), 'Soladel', *Lutèce*, 3 March 1886. See also Richard, pp. 168–9.
77 Consider Jacques Lethève's succinct presentation: 'Lieu commun de la littérature à la fin du XIXe siècle, la constatation d'une "décadence" a été admise alors par la plupart des bons esprits. Mais les uns dénoncent cette décadence, tandis que beaucoup d'autres l'acceptent, s'en réjouissent ou s'y complaisent. Finalement et pendant quelques années, être "décadent", c'est par un curieux paradoxe, appartenir à une élite et relever d'une école littéraire.' 'Le Thème de la décadence dans les lettres françaises à la fin du XIXe siècle', *Revue d'Histoire Littéraire de la France*, LXIII, 1, January–March 1963, 46–61.

Chapter VII
Verlaine's decadent manner

A key moment in the chronology of Verlaine's relationship with the decadents may well have been May, July and August of 1883, when he published eight poems in *Le Chat Noir*, including 'Langueur', 'L'Aube à l'envers', and 'Madrigal', for these are the most decadent in manner of all the poems he had published to that time. A year later, in 1884, the publication of *Les Poètes maudits* and of Huysmans' *A Rebours* spread his fame and reinforced the notion that he, too, was a decadent poet.

In the same year *Jadis et naguère* made much more of Verlaine's poetry available to the public, and its very title invited readers to consider his earlier verse as well as his current work. Like Baudelaire and Mallarmé, Verlaine revealed decadent qualities from the very beginning of his career, in *Poèmes saturniens*. The opening tercet of 'Résignation' mentions the Roman emperor Heliogabalus, notorious for his excesses, as well as the Assyrian Sardanapalus. In 'Crépuscule du soir mystique', 'Promenade sentimentale', and 'Le Rossignol' the ponds, flowers, sunsets, and melancholy view of the past anticipate poems like Lorrain's 'L'Etang mort', with its water-lilies and swamp. Urban poems like 'Croquis parisien' or *La Bonne Chanson*, XVI, depict the sordidness of the modern city and its working class fauna; that is to say, men and an environment far removed from their natural state. The second 'Nevermore' reproduces Baudelaire's liturgical jargon and imagery and states the notion of irreversible corruption. The impressionist rendering of physical sensation in *Fêtes galantes* and *Romances sans paroles* and, more generally, the personalised quality of his language and the constant presence of music and painting in his verse (aestheticism; nature translated into human artifacts) are decadent. *Les Amies*, with their theme of lesbianism, were first published clandestinely in 1868 by Poulet-Malassis, Baudelaire's publisher. In 'Nevermore' and *Les Amies* the young Verlaine selected for imitation, as young poets would two decades later, the most decadent aspects of Baudelaire's work. Significant is the way in which he singled out for emphasis in an 1865 article on Baudelaire the same aspects of modernity that Gautier and Bourget would describe only in 1868 and 1881:

> La profonde originalité de Charles Baudelaire, c'est, à mon sens, de représenter puissamment et essentiellement l'homme moderne . . . l'homme physique moderne, tel que l'ont fait les raffinements d'une civilisation excessive, l'homme moderne, avec ses sens aiguisés et vibrants, son esprit douleureusement subtil, son cerveau saturé de tabac, son sang brûlé d'alcool, en un mot, le *bilio-nerveux* par excellence. . . .[1]

His dramatic conversion to Catholicism in 1874 merely anticipates that of Huysmans a few years later; it was a decadent trait, to paraphrase Barbey d'Aurevilly, to prefer the foot of the Cross to the mouth of a pistol. Seen in this light, it seems small wonder that Verlaine's work promptly appealed to young poets preoccupied with their own decadence. Where he differs from a Baudelaire or a Mallarmé, however, is in the extent to which his mature work seems to have been influenced by the decadent milieu. An appreciation of Verlaine's poetry composed during the 1880's, however, involves placing it in proper perspective with his earlier work.

For a quarter of a century now it is *Fêtes galantes* and *Romances sans paroles* that Verlaine critics have esteemed the most highly. Phenomenological critics have examined the psychological tensions of *Fêtes galantes*, where Verlaine seeks to compensate for the amorous frustrations of real life by projecting an imaginary world of *commedia dell' arte* figures enjoying an endless orgy of desire and gallantry unmarred by sexual achievement.[2] *Romances sans paroles* is seen as a universe shimmering with sensations which hover for ever just this side of extinction. In his rendering of their *fadeur*, in his translations of these sensations into musical–verbal equivalents, Verlaine has developed a brilliant mode of communication with his reader, for these *equivalences sensorielles* which he holds at arm's length with *c'est* and similar impersonal constructions are no more than arm's length from the reader, either, so that our perception and Verlaine's meet at a mid-point of common communication.[3] Dream and sensation—and music is the sensation *par excellence* for communicating the data of other senses—are the chief elements of this highly original formula.

In a happy fusion of biographical and textual criticism, this interpretation of Verlaine's creative endeavour posits the role played by his emotional imbalance. The dream *région où vivre* of his poetry depends on the poet's biographical need to sublimate the dissatisfactions of his real existence. When Verlaine did achieve a satisfactory, if temporary, resolution of his emotional problems, as during his engagement to Mathilde Mauté and after his conversion to Catholicism, the effect on his inspiration was unhappy, Hence the critics' denigration of *La Bonne Chanson* and of parts of *Sagesse*, which they call prosaic, banal, unimaginative, and given to conceptualism and allegory, for Verlaine's dream *poétique* does not permit his singing a real and present attainment. His own contemporaries placed a high value on the sincerity and emotional intensity of *Sagesse*, and intellectual currents such as the Catholic aspect of decadence and the idealism of symbolism further nourished their high estimate of this work. Modern criticism, on the other hand, has condemned Verlaine's verse beginning with *Sagesse*— after his mystic experience of 1874 would be a more accurate expression —so that for some readers the term *la conversion de Sagesse* has become almost a pun, denoting both a religious experience and a changed poetic theory.[4]

It is true that, while Verlaine always wrote some bad poetry, he wrote more and more of it after his prison term at Mons in 1873–75, and that as he used up his supply of unpublished early verse in *Jadis et naguère*, *Amour*, and *Parallèlement* his collections of verse become increasingly dreary. The same is true of his contributions to periodicals during the decade of the 1880's: except for an occasional early poem, titles like 'Un Crucifix', 'Saint Benoît Joseph Labre', or 'La Mort de S. M. le Roi Louis II de Bavière' reveal all too eloquently the limited scope of his poetic imagination. It was unusual for him to collect his poems of the previous two or three years and to publish them immediately, as was the case with *Fêtes galantes*, *La Bonne Chanson*, and *Romances sans paroles*. On the contrary, his normal practice was to collect poems composed over a number of years into variegated and uneven volumes like *Poèmes saturniens*, *Sagesse*, or *Jadis et naguère*. Hence the critic must select poems for discussion according to their date of composition, their similarity to other poems, or some other criterion which suits his purpose. To single out those poems composed between 1880 and 1890 which reveal decadent characteristics, therefore, is no more presumptuous than to discuss any other aspect of Verlaine's work. Jacques Borel's studies of *Jadis et naguère* and *Parallèlement* for the latest editions of Verlaine's complete works[5] draw attention to hitherto unnoticed aspects of his verse of this period. The subtlety with which Borel analyses the 'ambiguity' of Verlaine's simultaneous rejection, in 1884–87, both of his earlier work based on a *poétique* of dream and of sensation, and of the new-found religious orthodoxy which causes him to reject it,[6] suggests that Verlaine's poetry after *Sagesse* is ripe for reappraisal. When Borel calls *Parallèlement*, rather than some earlier collection, 'le dernier sans doute des recueils intéressants',[7] it has the effect of prolonging Verlaine's creative period for another fifteen years, thus proposing for our examination poems which perhaps deserve more attention than they have received.

On 26 May, 14 July and 18 August 1883, then, Verlaine published eight poems in *Le Chat Noir* under the collective title 'Vers à la manière de plusieurs' ('Le Poète et la muse' was added to this series in *Jadis et naguère* only in 1884). While most of these were composed in the 1860's or early 1870's, 'L'Aube à l'envers', and perhaps 'Madrigal' and 'Langueur' too, were composed after his return to Paris in 1882, and in any case the first two illustrate his decadent manner.[8] In spite of the importance traditionally attached to it, 'Langueur' is not particularly representative of Verlaine's decadent manner, and possibly, as Eléanor Zimmermann argues, it was composed in 1872–74, with the 'Ariettes oubliées', rather than after his contacts with the decadent milieu.[9] Still, the poem is useful as an indication of the direction his poetry would take.

While other poets of the period chose the homosexual as the epitome of classical decadence, for Verlaine decadence was aestheticism, represented by the poet who composes acrostic verses as victorious armies of barbarians march past, just as Nero is said to have fiddled while Rome burned. It is appropriate that Verlaine, who sought to fix in verse the nuances of *langueur*, should choose lethargy and superficiality as attributes of decadence: 'O n'y pouvoir, étant si faible aux voeux si lents, / O n'y vouloir fleurir un peu cette existence!'[10] The tone of languid, careless aestheticism recalls Nero's 'Qualis artifex pereo', The 'style d'or' (today we speak rather of 'Silver Age' Latin) is rendered by the excessive anaphora of the last eight lines and by the use of diminutives: *L'Ame seulette, fleurir un peu, mourir un peu*. Diminutive endings were a feature of vulgar Latin, as is evident from the number of modern Romance words derived from them rather than from standard classical forms (e.g. *oreille<auricula<auris*). Could Verlaine have had in mind the emperor Hadirna's poem to his departing soul, the charm of which is due largely to its use of affectionate diminutive endings?

'L'Aube à l'envers', a landscape of the modern industrial city, and 'Madrigal' are examples of Verlaine's new manner, a *poétique* based on

style and diction.[11] 'Madrigal' also illustrates the elaborate imagery and
a somewhat obscure allusiveness which comprise this manner:

> Tu m'as, ces pâles jours d'automne blanc, fait mal
> A cause de tes yeux où fleurit l'animal,
> Et tu me rongerais, en princesse Souris,
> Du bout fin de la quenotte de ton souris,
> Fille auguste qui fis flamboyer ma douleur
> Avec l'huile rancie encor de ton vieux pleur!
> Oui, folle, je mourrai de ton regard damné.
> Mais va (veux-tu?) l'étang là dort insoupçonné,
> Dont du lys, nef qu'il eût fallu qu'on acclamât,
> L'eau morte a bu le vent qui coule du grand mât.
> T'y jeter, palme! et d'avance mon repentir
> Parle si bas qu'il faut être sourd pour l'ouïr.   [p. 376]

The pond is a typically decadent setting. In lines 1–3 and 9–10 closely
connected grammatical elements are separated by interrupting phrases.
The vocabulary is elaborately chosen: in line 1 *pâle* (before its noun!)
and *blanc* repeat each other; *quenotte* and *souris* in line 4 are colloquial
terms, *nef* in line 9 and *ouïr* in line 13 are archaic. The poem concludes
with an antithetical *pointe*, that one must be deaf to hear his softly
uttered repentance. Esoteric vocabulary terms are drawn not from a
single class but from several lexical categories, so that comparatively
few such items suffice to give an impression of pronounced strangeness.
Souris (smile) puns with *souris* (mouse), and their use as rhyme words
draws attention to the pun. Of the numerous alliterations and assonances
we notice line 5, with its '*F*ille auguste qu*i f*is *f*lamboyer . . .' and
'l'hu*i*le rancie' in the following line; in line 9 the combination of [k]
and [y] render the line cacophonous and even hard to pronounce. In
the phrase 'Mais va (veux-tu!)' *veux-tu* is a colloquial expression for
reinforcing an imperative; the three vowels [a], [oe], and [y] form a
progressive closing and tightening of the mouth; this tensioning of
the vocal organs is set off and contrasted by the open, relaxed, and
harmonious vocables immediately following: *l'étang là dort.* (Such
cacophony, caused by the repetition of plosives and of tense, shrill
vowels like [oe] [y], [i], and often followed by more relaxed and
musical vocables, is a distinctive feature of Verlaine's decadent manner.)
Lines 9 and 10 are very confused grammatically: the proper sequence is
'l'étang, dont l'eau a bu le vent qui coule du grand mât du lys, (lequel
est une] nef qu'il eût fallu qu'on acclamât'. This involved and inverted
grammatical construction, and the accumulation of *de*'s (lines 4 and

9–10), are but two of several factors which in combination create an impression of obscurity. Here, as in other poems addressed to his ex-wife, Mathilde Mauté, or to Arthur Rimbaud, Verlaine does not explain the biographical frame of reference, whence an air of mystery and of private association which are troubling to the uninitiated reader. In the poem at hand, the girl to whom the poem is addressed is compared to a mouse, and this figure is completed by the animality of her look and by the gnawing teeth of her smile; it is not necessary to know that the girl is Mathilde Mauté, nor the circumstances of their separation. The next figure, however, is hermetic: a lily floating on a pond is compared to a ship, and the water in the pond has drunk the wind flowing from the mainmast. While appreciating the tone of dark foreboding which this figure adds to the poem, still we should like to see it clarified. While Verlaine is never hermetically obscure, nevertheless confused grammar, allusiveness, and complex imagery do produce a murkiness of expression which is unusual in his verse and hence distinctive of his decadent manner.[12]

About two years later, in May and June of 1885, *Lutece* published a group of six poems, collected subsequently in *Parallèlement* under the heading 'Lunes (pp. 503–7), which also illustrate Verlaine's decadent manner:

> Je veux, pour te tuer, ô temps qui me dévastes,
> Remonter jusqu'aux jours bleuis des amours chastes
> Et bercer ma luxure et ma honte au bruit doux
> De baisers sur Sa main et non plus dans Leurs cous.
> Le Tibère effrayant que je suis à cette heure,
> Quoi que j'en aie, et que je rie ou que je pleure,
> Qu'il dorme! pour rêver, loin d'un cruel bonheur,
> Aux tendrons pâlots dont on ménageait l'honneur
> Es-fêtes, dans, après le bal sur la pelouse,
> Le clair de lune quand le clocher sonnait douze.   ['Lunes, **1**', p. 503]

Again, in lines 1 and 6 we have a harsh alliteration of plosives, the mysterious allusions to *Sa main* (Mathilde's) and *Leurs cous* (those of the street-walkers with whom he was living), a classical allusion to Caesar Tiberius in line 5, and, in the last four lines, a combination of inter-rupted word-order and of choice vocabulary (*tendrons, ès, pâlots*). We recognise in these poems traits which we have come to regard as typically decadent: exaggerated alliterations and assonances, all manner of word plays, impressionist style, conversational mannerisms of language, classical allusions, the presence of a pond and of flowers, and, in 'L'Aube à l'envers', a modern, urban landscape. 'Lunes I, III, IV, and V' hint at the depravity of some decadent poetry.

The figures of the lily compared to a ship in 'Madrigal' and of Tiberius, to whom the poet compares himself in 'Lunes, I', are examples of the elaborate, sometimes hermetic imagery which distinguishes Verlaine's manner in *Parallèlement*, but which is not otherwise typical of decadent verse. In 'Fernand Langlois' the poet's heart is compared to a lock which Langlois patiently opens, in 'Autre Explication' there are the tropes of constancy (compared to a prostitute), the cuttlefish, and the hour. Curiously, it is in two of the *Poèmes saturniens*, 'Crépuscule du soir mystique' and 'Le Rossignol', with their decadent ponds, flowers, and birds, that we find a previous instance of such extended imagery. In 'Le Rossignol' the poet's memories are likened to a flock of birds swooping down on the tree of his heart, mirrored in the water of Regret; and the nightingale is the poet's first love. On the other hand, his practice in these poems of capitalising words taken in a symbolic sense is a common one in decadent verse; in *Les Déliquescences* 'Pour avoir péché' and 'Platonisme' parody this Baudelairean device.

As with decadent verse in general, an intensification of his usual traits distinguishes 'Madrigal' and 'Lunes' from Verlaine's earlier verse and makes them appear as self-parodies. Recent critics who have drawn attention to this parodying quality in Verlaine's poetry of the 1880's suggest that the very intention of the 'Lunes' cycle, and of 'A la manière de Paul Verlaine' in particular, is to reject his earlier manner by making fun of it.[13] As we shall see in chapter VIII, Verlaine's relationship with the decadents was an ambivalent one, since he did not take the decadence very seriously, and it is therefore always possible that the target of his caricatural poems was decadence itself as well as his own earlier manner. If so, in the perverse logic of decadence, which was fascinated by what it loathed, such poems are all the more decadent!

It is in any case certain that Verlaine consciously adopted decadent mannerisms during the 1880's. His use of Latinisms and classical allusions corroborates this point. Although his unpublished verse included three schoolboy translations from Latin, which he apparently valued enough to save, in the 110 poems of *Poèmes saturniens*, *Fêtes galantes*, *La Bonne Chanson*, and *Romances sans paroles* there are only five[14] containing Latin phrases or allusions to classical antiquity—and two of these reflect merely his Parnassian affectation of Greek mythology. In contrast, of the 128 poems of *Jadis et naguère*, *Amour*, and *Parallèlement*, we count twelve[15]—almost one in ten—containing Latin expressions or classical allusions; this proportion would undoubtedly be still greater if we excluded poems composed before 1880.

Collating two versions of the same poem provides further corroboration. 'L'Aube à l'envers' is clearly contemporary with Verlaine's residence at Boulogne-sur-Seine in the summer of 1882, while the second version, 'Nouvelles Variations sur le Point-du-Jour', published in *Lutèce* at the very end of 1885, must be an elaboration of the first poem.

L'Aube à l'envers

Le Point-du-Jour avec Paris au large,
Des chants, des tirs, les femmes qu'on 'rêvait',
La Seine claire et la foule qui fait
Sur ce poème un vague essai de charge.

On danse aussi, car tout est dans la marge
Que fait le fleuve à ce livre parfait,
Et si parfois l'on tuait ou buvait,
Le fleuve est sourd et le vin est litharge.

Le Point-du-Jour, mais c'est l'Ouest de Paris!
Un calembour a béni son histoire
D'affreux baisers et d'immondes paris.

En attendant que sonne l'heure noire
Où les bateaux-omnibus et les trains
Ne partent plus, tirez, tirs, fringuez, reins!   [p. 375]

Already the poem is distinctly decadent on account of its naturalist subject, with commuter steamers and trains the play on *Point-du-Jour*, which means 'daybreak' as well as designating a landmark to the west of Paris, and the artificiality implicit in the book trope of line 6. It is precisely these elements that Verlaine expands in the later version:

Nouvelles Variations sur le Point-du-Jour

Le Point du Jour, le point blanc de Paris,
Le seul point blanc, grâce à tant de bâtisse
Et neuve et laide et que je t'en ratisse,
Le Point du Jour, aurore des paris!

Le bonneteau fleurit 'dessur' la berge,
La bonne tôt s'y déprave, tant pis
Pour elle et tant mieux pour le birbe gris
Qui lui du moins la croit encore vierge.

> Il a raison, le vieux, car voyez donc
> Comme est joli toujours le paysage:
> Paris au loin, triste et gai, fol et sage,
> Et le Trocadéro, ce cas, au fond,
>
> Puis la verdure et le ciel et les types
> Et la rivière obscène et molle, avec
> Des gens trop beaux, leur cigare à leur bec:
> Epatants ces metteurs-au-vent de tripes!   [pp. 519–20]

The basic play on words now fills the first stanza with variants: *Le Point du Jour, le point blanc, Le seul point blanc; Point du Jour, aurore des paris; Paris–paris*. These are followed up with homonyms: **tant** *de bâtisse*, **t'en** *ratisse; Le* **bonneteau**, *La* **bonne tôt**. Popular locutions abound, such as *je t'en ratisse, à leur bec, dessur, birbe, Il a raison, le vieux, les types*, and in general the diction is rhetorically self-conscious. In lieu of the book and margin figure, Verlaine has introduced the old man who seduces the young maid (in the sense of *bonne*, since he spells out that she is no longer *vierge*!), a decadent motif. *La Seine claire* has been replaced by *La riviere obscene et molle*, in which the adjectives somehow make us think of putrefaction and of flabby degeneracy. While even the 1882 version could be contrasted with Verlaine's landscapes in *Poèmes saturniens* or *Romances sans paroles*, the revisions of the 1885 version have emphasised those qualities which *Les Déliquescences* and minor poems like them have led us to call decadent.

Turning now from the analysis of individual poems, we shall make a general survey of decadent qualities in verse which he composed during the 1880's. What stands out in his verbal music of this period is a tendency toward cacophonous effects of plosives and very tense vowels; these are sometimes contrasted with more harmonious combinations, as we saw in both 'Madrigal' and 'Lunes'. There are numerous lines on the order of 'Des bas de dos très beaux et d'une gaîté folle' ('Lombes', p. 507); 'Pour que ce goût les acclamât / Minces, grands, d'aspect plutôt mat' ('L'Impénitent', p. 511); 'Qui qu'en grogne ou quel que soit son niveau' ('Ballade Sappho', p. 528). Again, this sort of procedure is not new: a line from *Romances sans paroles*, 'Qu' as-tu voulu, fin refrain incertain' ('Ariettes oubliées, v', p. 193), would not be out of character in 'Lunes'. Especially in *Fêtes galantes* we find similar passages, such as this stanza from 'En patinant', with its alliterations, its shrill [y], its precious diction and archaic *férir*:

> Nous fûmes dupes, vous et moi,
> De manigances mutuelles,

> Madame, à cause de l'émoi
> Dont l'été férut nos cervelles.   [p. 111]

or the final stanza, where a pair of conventional lines are followed by alliterations in [f], and where the final alliteration in [k] provides a phonetic stop at the end of the poem:

> Les deux mains dans votre manchon,
> Tenez-vous bien sur la banquette
> Et filons!—et bientôt Fanchon
> Nous fleurira—quoi qu'on caquette!   [p. 113]

Homonyms, plays on words, and affectations of spoken French are typical of Verlaine's decadent manner. He is fond of coupling different forms of the same word—'Plus fière fierté, plus pudique pudeur' ('Délicatesse', p. 431), or different words which sound the same: 'Passe et rit sur ta *chère chair* en fête' ('Ballade Sappho', p. 528); 'Et de Saturne penchant son urne / Et de ces *lunes l'une* après *l'une*' ('A la manière de P.V', p. 503). In a typical stanza we observe several different practices: plays on words whose sounds are similar but not identical; replacement of verbs by nouns or participles; foreign words; and an emphatically asyndetic structure. The effect of bringing all of these together into a single stanza is to create a highly personalised idiom, remote from standard literary French:

> Cet oiseau, ce roseau sous cet oiseau, ce blême
> Oiseau sur ce pâle roseau fleuri jadis,
> Et pâle et sombre spectre, et sceptre noir: Moi-même!
> *Surrexit hodie*, non plus: *de profundis*.   ['A Fernand Langlois', p. 400]

Oiseau–roseau differ only in the first syllable, *spectre* and *sceptre* are differentiated only by the metathesis of *c* and *p*. The most general principle underlying Verlaine's word games is these subtle, unexpected analogies, which he was always very quick to spot.

The impressionist style is pushed to the point where sentence structure disintegrates completely, and a stanza of verse may consist merely of disconnected word groups:

> Homme de primesaut et d'excès, je le suis,
> D'aventure et d'erreur, allons, je le concède,
> Soit, bien, mais illogique ou mol ou lâche ou tiède
> En quoi que ce soit, le dire je ne le puis,
> Je ne le dois! . . .   ['A Edmond Thomas', p. 436]

Word order becomes capricious if not almost unintelligible:

> Je pardonne à ce mensonge-là
> En faveur en somme du plaisir
> Très banal drôlement qu'un loisir
> Douleureux un peu m'innocula.
>
> ['A la manière de Paul Verlaine', p. 504]

He uses a telegraphic style: 'Puis, la soif nous creusant à fond comme une mine, | *De nous précipiter, dès libres des convois,* | Vers des bars attractifs . . .' ('A Germain Nouveau', p. 562; note the anglicism of *bars attractifs*). Elsewhere Verlaine is particularly fond of English terms, which he can use effectively:

> Les courses furent intrépides
> (Comme aujourd'hui le repos pèse!)
> Par les steamers et les rapides.
> (Que me veut cet at home obèse?)   ['Laeti et errabundi', p. 522]

Another aspect of this style is the prevalence of constructions drawn from colloquial French. He may compose an entire stanza in slang:

> Vous souvient-il, cocodette un peu mûre
> Qui gobergez vos flemmes de bourgeoise,
> Du temps joli quand, gamine un peu sure,
> Tu m'écoutais, blanc-bec fou qui dégoise?   ['Dédicace', p. 484]

(See also 'Poème saturnien', fifth stanza, p. 509.) He reproduces the patterns of spoken French with conversational expletives: 'Il est l'entrain, il est tout, quoi!' ('Gais et contents', p. 429); 'Nous allions,— Vous en souvient-il, | Voyageur où ça disparu?—' ('Laeti et erranbundi', p. 522); or by spelling out popular mispronunciations: 'Le bonneteau fleurit 'dessur' la berge' ('Nouvelles Variations', p. 519);[16] or with tautological repetition, for emphasis, of nouns already represented by personal pronouns: 'Il a raison, le vieux, car . . .' (*ibid.*, p. 52); 'La plénitude! Ils l'ont superlativement'; and 'Je le crois bien qu'ils l'ont la pleine plénitude' ('Ces passions qu'eux seuls . . .', pp. 521 and 522). A curious construction which is indigenous to Verlaine's native north-eastern France, and which occurs in the Paris region, too, is the use of a disjunctive pronoun as subject of an infinitive to replace a clause: '. . . un peu d'innocence | En moins, pour toi sauver, du moins, | Quelque ombre encore de décence?' ('L'Impénitent', p. 511).[17] Again, this tendency to mimic colloquial discourse has always been present in

Verlaine's poetry; as early as 1868 he affects the jargon and the silent mute *e*'s of spoken French:

> J' crach' pas sur Paris, c'est rien chouett'!
> Mais comm' j'ai une âm' de poèt',
> Tous les dimanch's j' sors de ma boît'
> Et je m'en vais avec ma compagne
>   A la campagne.   ['L'Ami de la nature', p. 216]

Since he now regards verse as a means of informal communication, Verlaine no longer makes a clear distinction between prose and poetic styles, casual and formal modes of discourse, whence the close similarity between his poetic diction and his epistolary style in intimate letters to friends. When in a poem he coins the neologism *défoudroyé*, 'un-thunderstruck', for 'cured' or 'recovered' ('A Fernand Langlois', p. 430), he is indulging in the same playful transformation of words as in his conversation or intimate correspondence, where 'Hôtel des Mines' becomes 'Hôtel des Mauvaises Mines',[18] or Madame Verlaine (a woman whom he met at Broussais Hospital and who claimed to be a distant relative) becomes 'Mme mon homonyme'.[19] The telegraphic style of his verse duplicates that of his letters:

> Rien encore reçu de B. . . ., ni lettre ni télégramme. Nulle autre lettre un peu importante. 1 volume de vers d'un ami de Jullien. Lettre de celui-ci, où me parle de tout excepté de Jeanne.[20]

'. . . —Et *quid* de notre chair? . . .—' ('Laeti et errabundi', p. 523) in a poem repeats a Latinism which is prevalent in his letters: 'Je travaille boco. Quid de Lily, *Figaro* et *Chat*?'[21] The adjectives *edmonschéresque* and *francisquesarceyse* in 'A la louange de Laure et Pétrarque' (p. 200) are formed on the same fanciful basis as *astierréhuesque* (from Astier Réhu, a character in Daudet's *L'Immortel*) and *doncesardebasanesque* (from Don César de Bazan in Hugo's *Ruy Blas*) in his correspondence.[22] A slang passage from a letter echoes the use of slang in his poetry:

> Eté hier, comme dit, chez le sculpsit, mais il y avait à la porte un LANDAU tellement rupin que j'ai, moi violette, hésité, puis m'armant de courage, trouvé *copurchic* de chalter. J'y retournerai aujourd'hui et entrerai, bouffre! y eût-il là tout un train d'attelages à la Daumont avec des Schahs et des Norodams dedans!
>
> Profité de cette course que je qualifierai tout simplement d'inféconde pour flanocher un peu plus loin que mon usuel périmètre. (O Adam, ô Guiches, ô Rosny!)[23]

Again, we notice how Verlaine mingles terms from various sources: slang: *rupin, copurchic, chalter*; Latinisms: *sculpsit*; a neologism, *flanocher*, from *flâner;* an erudite term mixed with English word order: *mon usuel périmètre.* As always, the principle is to create a personal idiom by mingling words of different origins.

The most general conclusion to be made concerning Verlaine's decadent style is simply that it incorporates pell-mell all manner of previous tendencies: exotic and esoteric vocabulary, colloquialisms, impressionist style, original syntax, As critics from Gautier to A. E. Carter have pointed out, concern with language and with new forms of diction is an essential element of decadence.[24] The progressive exaggeration of his own personalised diction over a twenty-year period, perhaps even for the sake of self-parody, parallels the development of decadent poetry. In its final form Verlaine's asyndetic style reduces the sentence to a series of word groups, the alliterations of plosives have a staccato effect which literally detaches some syllables from their context, interjections are set off by dashes or parentheses, and strong caesuras destroy the entity of the poetic line. Thus the whole of a poem, stanza, or line disintegrates into isolated, autonomous fragments, and this fragmentations of the whole into its parts is typical of decadent style. The conversational tendency in Verlaine's style, and the development of the friendship theme, with its apostrophes to Mathilde and Rimbaud, its frequent poems addressed to personal acquaintances (nine in *Amour* alone; consider also the very title of *Dédicaces*), with a poem such as 'A Fernand Langlois' (especially stanzas 6–8), which is structured on a conversational situation, recall the language of the naturalist novel, similar poems we saw in early issues of *La Nouvelle Rive Gauche* and *Le Chat Noir*, some poems of Jean Lorrain, and, of course, Corbière and Laforgue. Verlaine, to be sure, lacks the latter's pungent, humorous irony, and in no case do we see their influence on his verse.[25] On the other hand, Claude Cuénot seems to have missed the point when he condemns the vulgar, slangy quality of Verlaine's late verse;[26] such language, like his divergent use of both popular and literary diction,[27] is simply a feature of the decadent preoccupation with language for its own sake.

To look now at themes, Verlaine's changing attitudes toward homosexuality and toward licentious verse in general can perhaps be ascribed to his decadent manner as well as to personal considerations. In July of 1883 he omitted from 'Vers à la manière de plusieurs' the compromising 'Le Poète et la muse'. Now, although the nature of his relationship with Rimbaud had always been known—so much so that in 1874 it was Lepelletier who had to dissuade him from dedicating *Romances sans paroles* to Rimbaud—from the time of his imprisonment until after his return to Paris Verlaine maintained a firm and tactful silence on the whole subject of perversion (indeed, until his death he always denied that their relationship had been sexual). But in March of 1884 he published the compromising 'Vers pour être calomnié', followed in December by 'La Dernière Fête galante', with its revealing conclusion, 'O que nos coeurs . . . / Dès ce jourd'hui réclament . . . / L'embarquement pour Sodome et Gomorrhe!' (p. 508). Then the publication of 'Explication' and 'Autre Explication' in *Lutèce* for 19–23 July 1885 initiated a series of poems in which during the next several years he was to write ever more openly of his relationship with Rimbaud and even to justify homosexuality. Jacques Borel[28] argues convincingly for the psychological reasons which, when he was preparing *Parallèlement*, induced Verlaine to take up again the Rimbaud theme, with its candour and its exaltation of '. . . ceux-là que sacre le haut Rite' (Ces passions qu'eux seuls . . .', p. 521): nostalgia for the mystic exhilaration of their adventure, or the false rumours of Rimbaud's death in 1887, which inspired at least one poem. Similar considerations apply to a reprise of the theme of female eroticism; Verlaine's early penchant for erotic verse appears in *Les Amies* (1868) and in the indecent poems appended to *La Bonne Chanson* (1870). But these were clandestine works, and less than two decades later he was openly publishing poems of this sort.

Perhaps there was no longer the same need for prudence. While until 1882 Verlaine had good reason to maintain his pose as a respectable gentleman misunderstood by his contemporaries, by 1884 he had little to gain from further claims to respectability. For one thing, the truth was by now widely known; for another, after his dismissal from the Collège de Rethel, after the rejection of his application for re-employment in the city administration, and in view of the impossibility of rejoining Mathilde (who remarried in 1885), it was apparent that he was to be permanently excluded from conventional, self-respecting bourgeois life. On the other hand, with the growth of his 'legend' and with his decision to stake everything on a full-time literary career, he had rather more to gain than to lose by frankly accepting the role of an incorrigible if penitent sinner, as richly endowed with the grace of poetry as he was deprived of that of common morality. But to admit past indiscretions is not the same as singing current offences. Would not Verlaine's new-found candour also have been brought about by the decadent milieu, with its treatment of vice, its preference for perversion because it is unnatural, and its implication that Paris rivalled Rome as a centre of debauchery? Since Baudelaire, since *A Rebours*, since the more lurid decadent novels like Péladan's *Le Vice suprême*, homosexuality was becoming less taboo and more, if not acceptable, at least tolerated in avant-garde circles. The first issue of *Le Décadent*, for example, contains an instalment of Luc Vajarnet's *La Grande Roulotte*, in which the lesbian attachment of Countess Jeanne and her chambermaid Mariette is presented in such detail as to be erotically stimulating to male readers.[29] Against this background we can understand Verlaine's including in *Parallèlement* poems such as 'Sur une statue de Ganymède', 'Ces passions qu'eux seuls nomment encore amours', and 'Laeti et errabundi'. Heterosexual love, which, if less original, still figures prominently in the decadent aesthetic, was handled quite freely, to the point where *La Plume* saw some of its issues seized by the police. In comparison to his relative shyness in 1883, Verlaine's plans for *Parallèlement* are revealing. Although the first edition already included *Filles* and *Les Amies*, for a projected new edition he wanted to include 'Nous ne sommes pas le troupeau', 'Billet à Lily' (from the pornographic volume *Femmes*), 'Le Bon Disciple' (from *Hombres*), as well as 'un dialogue entre éphèbes et vierges à la Virgile; le cadre me permettra les dernières hardiesses. Inititulé Chant alterné.'[30] The use of a classical setting as an excuse for licentious verse is particularly indicative, as we saw in our previous chapter, for this common practice of decadent poets reflects their fundamental interpretation of Greco-Roman antiquity.

Notes

1 'Charles Baudelaire', *Oeuvres complètes*, 1 (Club du meilleur livre, 1959), p. 54.
2 See Jacques-Henry Bornecque, 'Le Problème des *Fêtes galantes*', *Mélanges d'histoire littéraire offerts à Daniel Mornet* (Nizet, 1951), pp. 209–20, and his critical edition, *Lumières sur les Fêtes galantes de Paul Verlaine* (Nizet, 1959).
3 See Jean-Pierre Richard, 'Fadeur de Verlaine', *Poésie et profondeur* (Seuil, 1955), pp. 163–85, and Octave Nadal, *Paul Verlaine* (Mercure de France, 1961). For *équivalences sensorielles*, see Nadal, chapter 11, 'Impressionnisme pictural', pp. 96–118, especially p. 111, and Richard, pp. 175–7.
4 'Ce qu'on nomme la conversion de *Sagesse*, qu'avait annoncée la première conversion de *La Bonne Chanson*, n'est guère en effet qu'un essai pour se ressaisir et pour ressaisir les choses selon les habitudes du sens commun.'

Richard, p. 181. See also Claude Cuénot, *Etat présent des études verlainiennes* (Belles Lettres, 1938), pp. 63-4, and Nadal, p. 68.

5 *Oeuvres complètes*, two vols., Jacques Borel and Henry de Bouillane de Lacoste, eds. (Club du meilleur livre, 1959, 1960), introduction by Octave Nadal (the same text as his *Paul Verlaine*, above); *Oeuvre poétiques complètes*, Y.-G. Le Dantec and Jacques Borel, eds. (Gallimard, 1962), not to be confused with the first Pléiade edition ot 1954 by Le Dantec alone. Since Borel's studies for both editions, as well as his article 'L'Envers de l'érotisme verlainien', *Critique*, 157 (June 1960), 496–507, are almost the same, for subsequent references to Borel we shall use the 1962 Gallimard edition.

6 See Borel, 'Notice' for *Parallèlement*, pp. 467–82.

7 *Ibid.*, p. 480.

8 For a discussion of the chronology of these poems, see *Oeuvres poétiques complètes* (1962), pp. 1157–60. The most tantalising poem is 'Madrigal': was this composed after 1882, as the style might indicate, or in 1875, for instance, when an unsuccessful effort at reconciliation could have provoked such an outburst against his ex-wife?

9 *Magies de Verlaine* (Corti, 1967), p. 87.

10 'Langueur', *Oeuvres poétiques complètes* (1962), p. 371. Hereafter all quotations from the poetry of Verlaine will be identified in the text by title and page reference to this edition.

11 Claude Cuénot calls the following poems decadent: 'Prologue' to *Jadis* (p. 319), 'Conseil falot' (p. 372), 'Madrigal', 'A Fernand Langlois' (p. 429), 'Lunes, I' and 'Limbes' (p. 505). See *Etat présent*, p. 66. To these we would add 'A Edmond Thomas' (p. 435), 'Dédicace' to *Parallèlement* (p. 484), 'Poème saturnien' (p. 508), and 'L'Impénitent' (p. 510), as well as the poems mentioned in the text.

12 *Cf.* Cuénot: 'Ce qui prouve l'influence des Décadents sur Verlaine, c'est qu'il est passé par un système poétique qu'on peut appeler le système "obscur-exprès" et qui se définit en quelques mots: pessimisme, cynisme, sensation et obscurité. C'est bien là l'expression des tendances décadentes.' *Etat présent*, p. 66.

13 See Borel, p. 475, and Zimmermann: '. . . une section de *Parallèlement* intitulée *Lunes* et toute consacrée à la parodie du passé, comme l'illustre "A la manière de Paul Verlaine" . . .' (p. 24).

14 'Prologue', 'Résignation', 'Croquis parisien', 'Voeu', and 'Epilogue'.

15 'Prologue' to *Jadis*, 'Princesse Bérénice', 'Langueur', 'A Fernand Langlois', 'Autre', 'Lunes, I', 'Sur une statue de Ganymède', 'Laeti et errabundi', 'Ballade de la mauvaise réputation', 'Ballade Sappho', 'Projet en l'air', and 'Le Bon Disciple'.

16 See Pierre Guiraud, *Le Français populaire* (Presses universitaires, 1965), p. 86. Verlaine's altertness to the intonations of popular speech was proverbial. *Cf.* in a letter to Morice, ' "Celle-ci" est pour vous dire seulement que je suis-t-arrivé-z-à bon port (style de chez Courtois),' *Lettres inédites à Charles*

Morice, Georges Zayed, editor. (Minard, 1964), p. 13. Courtois was a wine merchant and Verlaine's landlord at 17 Rue de la Roquette.

17 See Guiraud, pp. 36–7.

18 'Verlaine, toujours gavroche, prenait un plaisir enfant à déformer certains noms; il disait: "L'Hôtel des Mauvaises Mines, la rue Descartes transparentes, la rue des Feuilles intimes," etc.' F.-A. Cazals and Gustave Le Rouge, *Les Derniers Jours de Paul Verlaine* (Mercure de France, 1911), p. 103, n. 1.)

19 See Georges Zayed, *Lettres inédites de Verlaine à Cazals* (Geneva: Droz, 1957), p. 171.

20 *Ibid.*, p. 124.

21 *Ibid.*, p. 205; *cf.* 'Et quid de Miss Maria?' p. 195.

22 *Ibid.*, p. 81.

23 *Ibid.*, p. 177.

24 See Théophile Gautier, 'Charles Baudelaire', in *Les Fleurs du mal* (Lemerre, n.d.), pp. 1–90, and A. E. Carter, *The Idea of Decadence in French Literature, 1830–1900* (Toronto University Press, 1958), especially chapter 5, 'The glamours of syntax', pp. 123–43.

25 Granted that Verlaine is obviously working in somewhat the same manner as Corbière and Laforgue, it still seems an exaggeration to declare, 'Verlaine's best ironic verse greatly resembles that of the Jules Laforgue of *Les Complaintes*.' Albert Sonnenfeld, 'The forgotten Verlaine', *Bucknell Review*, XI (December, 1962), p. 78. So far as the influence of Corbière is concerned, except for 'L'Impudent', of which the last stanza recalls somewhat the situation of Corbière's 'Bonne Fortune et fortune' and hence that of Baudelaire's 'A une passante', we can see no influence of Corbière in Verlaine's verse.

26 *Cf.* 'A force de simplicité, Verlaine est tombé dans la prose, dans une prose pleine de vulgarité et même d'argot. Dès les premiers recueils, on sentait l'influence de la langue familière, mais maintenant c'est une invasion que rien n'arrêtera plus.' *Etat présent*, pp. 63–4. Cuénot correctly indicates one of the weaknesses of Verlaine's late verse, of course, but allowance should be made for those poems in which Verlaine does cultivate a conversational idiom for artistic effect.

27 'C'est un problème vraiment étrange que cette double tendance, d'un côté vers une langue artificielle, de l'autre vers la prose, et il ne semble pas que cette dualité ait jamais été expliquée.' *Etat présent*, p. 88.

28 See Borel, pp. 472–82.

29 *Décadent*, 10 April 1886.

30 *Lettres à Cazals*, p. 194.

Chapter VIII
Decadence as a school of poetry

The year 1886 saw *la jeune littérature*, as Ferdinand Brunetière called it,[1] solidly established: its existence was recognised, even though grudgingly, by the general press; its leaders, Verlaine and Mallarmé, were generally known; and the younger generation was beginning to make its influence felt through articulate spokesmen like Jean Moréas, René Ghil, and Gustave Kahn. The growth of the new current in poetry since Morice's first article on 'Boileau–Verlaine' had been phenomenal; it was only in April and May of 1884 that *Les Poètes maudits* and *A Rebours* first indicated the presence of new currents in poetry; just a year later, in May and June of 1885, *Les Déliquescences* attracted the attention of the general public; and now 1886 witnessed the appearance of several new magazines and proliferating statements of poetic doctrine.

Against this background of success for the decadent movement, there was a real decline in Verlaine's personal fortunes. On 21 January 1886 his mother died; confined to his bed by the bad knee that was to plague him for the rest of his days, he was unable to see her or to attend the funeral, although overhead he could hear the preparations for burial. A few days later court officials seized his last securities to satisfy Mathilde Mauté's alimony judgement. In the spring he began a liaison with Marie Gambier, a common prostitute he had met at the *hôtel borgne*, where he had been living with his mother. On 30 October Mathilde Mauté remarried. Henceforth Verlaine was alone in the world, altogether destitute, and in deteriorating health. The year 1886, then, introduces the final decade of Verlaine's life, the decade consecrated by the *Pauvre Lélian* legend, with its public acclaim, its poverty and sordidness, its succession of whores who disputed the poet's favour, its odyssey between charity hospitals and furnished Latin Quarter rooms.

For decadence, the price of success was competition from rival branches of *la jeune littérature*, so that the appearance of new magazines in 1886 represents the transformation of the new poetry into different currents, decadence and symbolism, with symbolism itself divided into several groups. One might say, roughly speaking, that the distinction between decadence and symbolism was their chronological sequence, while the distinctions among the various symbolist groups were political, since they resulted from the rivalries among the individuals claiming leadership of the new movement. From 1882 up to the publication of *Les Déliquescences* it is accurate to call the new trend in poetry decadence, in the sense that it exemplifies the decadent outlook we have described; or it can be called symbolism, in the sense that these same poets later became known as symbolists. 'La littérature décadente s'appellera désormais le Symbolisme, et l'école des décadents, école symbolique'[2] is an oversimplification with which, nevertheless, the symbolists did not bother to disagree.

For a while the two terms were concurrent. In December of 1884 Maurice Barrès called the poets descended from Baudelaire 'décadent', but he also called Mallarmé's verse 'cette poésie symbolique'.[3] In his manifesto of 11 August 1885 Jean Moréas called his group 'Les Décadents', although in the body of his article he said, 'Les prétendus décadents cherchent avant tout dans leur art le pur Concept et l'éternel Symbole,' and 'la critique . . . pourrait les appeler plus justement des *symbolistes* . . .'[4] In 1886, however, when *Le Temps* invited him to submit a statement on the new poetic school, Moréas called it 'Le Symbolisme'.

Actually, in spite of the fact that the notion of decadence in litterature had been in the air since the 1868 edition of *Les Fleurs du mal*, with Gautier's 'Notice', use of the term *les decadents* to designate poets grouped around Verlaine and Mallarmé was relatively recent; while Huysmans described Verlaine, Corbière, Thomas Hannon, and Mallarmé as typical of the 'écrivan subalterne de la décadence' preferred by des Esseintes,[5] it was only Maurice Barrès who took the obvious step of calling certain writers 'Les Décadents' in December of 1884,[6] and, of course, *Les Déliquescences* confirmed the epithet six months later. Nevertheless, as an example of how widely tradition can differ from fact, two legends credit Verlaine with having coined the term, either in 'Langueur' or in reply to some young men who invited him to preside over a new magazine to be called *La Décade*: 'On va se foutre de vous, on va vous appeler les Décadents.'[7] Ernest Raynaud claims that the word was first used as an insult by Paul Bourde, and that the young school proudly took it up as a challenge.[8] Other names were tried but failed to gain wide currency: *les maudits*, from Verlaine's articles, *les déliquescents*, from Vicaire's and Beauclair's title, and Anatole

Baju's *le décadisme*.[9] The chief objection to 'décadence' seems to have been its contradictory connotations when applied to writers who were seeking to improve poetry, and, perhaps, the fact that 'décadence' does not imply an aesthetic program as succinctly as 'symboliste' does.

And aesthetic programmes were uppermost in people's minds, judging from the number of declarations which appeared in the autumn of 1886; Moréas' 'Le Symbolisme' appeared in *Le Temps* on 18 September, drawing a scornful reply from Anatole France in the same newspaper a week later. Significant of the changed situation within the movement is the fact that Moréas also drew a rebuttal from Alfred Vallette in *Le Scapin* for 16 October.[10] On 1 October the first issue of *La Décadence*, devoted specially to the *école symbolique et harmoniste*, published Renés Ghil's manifesto 'Notre Ecole'. A week later Paul Adam had a statement in the first issue of *Le Symboliste*, 'La Presse et le symbolisme'. His remarks are typical of the confusion surrounding the term, for he blames the press for confusing symbolists and decadents, while he himself uses 'decadent' as a synonym of 'classical', since for him the seventeenth and eighteenth centuries were the decadent period of French letters. He adds, 'Par suite, nous répudions absolument ce titre, *Decadence*, puisque nous cultivons précisément une littérature contraire à celle de ces écrivains.'[11] Four statements of differing literary positions in the space of a month illustrate the extent to which the movement was dividing into parallel currents.

Of the magazines with which we are familiar. *La Revue Indépendante* is the only one to continue past 1886 (the new series appeared until 1893). *Lutèce* ceased publication with the issue of 3 October 1886; *Le Chat Noir*, although it continued to appear through 1895, was no longer important as a vehicle for serious poetry, largely because of the flowering of new magazines; *La Basoche*, founded in 1884, would cease publication at the end of 1886, and the last four numbers—those appearing during 1886—contain little poetry and are of slight relevance to the history of decadence. Turning to the new magazines, we come to *La Revue Wagnérienne*, founded in 1885, which would continue through 1888. Edited by Edouard Dujardin (celebrated as the first writer to have used stream-of-consciousness dialogue, in *Les Lauriers sont coupés*), *La Revue Wagnérienne* was particularly interested in the relations between music and poetry—a subject close to the intent of symbolist poetry. It was at this period, and largely through the enthusiasm of symbolist musical criticism, that Wagner came to be appreciated in France. For the issue of 8 January 1886 Dujardin invited eight poets to contribute sonnets dedicated to the memory of Wagner; among them were Verlaine's '*Parsifal*' and Mallarmé's 'Le silence déjà funèbre d'une moire'. *La Vogue* (1886), edited by Léo d'Orfer and Gustave Kahn, we have seen, is of immediate interest for its publication of poems by the major decadent poets, Téodor de Wyzewa's essay 'Notes sur M. Mallarmé', the second series of Verlaine's 'Poètes maudits', and also Rimbaud's 'Les Premières Communions', *Illuminations*, and *Saison en enfer*.

On 1 December 1885 appeared the first issue of *Le Scapin*, published by E. G. Raymond, the two series of which would appear regularly until 19 December 1886. The same editorial staff produced the three issues of *La Décadence* in October of 1886. The long list of contributors included many familiar names: Paul Alexis, Paul Bourget, Joris-Karl Huysmans, Charles Morice, Verlaine, and Mallarmé, as well as minor figures like Rodolphe Darzens, Edouard Dubus, Fernand Icres, Victor Margueritte, Léo d'Orfer, Pierre Quillard, Jean Lorrain (was there a magazine to which he did *not* contribute?), and Rachilde; then there were new names, such as René Ghil, Charles Cros, Stuart Merrill, Ephraïm Mikhaël, Henri de Régnier, and Albert Samain. The chief articles in the two magazines are Alfred Vallette's 'Les Symbolistes', in which he contests Moréas' claim that symbolism is the literature of the future, and René Ghil's 'Notre Ecole'. Politically, these two magazines championed René Ghil against Jean Moréas, and they also sought to discredit Anatole Baju and *Le Décadent*. Nevertheless, many of their contributors also published poems in *Le Décadent*, and a number of poems in *Le Scapin* are distinctly decadent in tone; among these are Mallarmé's 'Hérodiade';[12] Jean de Guillou's 'Perversité', with its evocation of the debauchery of ancient Rome;[13] two poems by André Mesnil experimenting with colloquial language;[14] Edouard Dubus' 'La Diva', which presents a café concert in naturalist terms,[15] and 'Complainte': 'Je suis un piano brisé / Parce qu'il a trop amusé',[16] which echoes Laforgue; and Charles Cros' 'Novembre', with its images of death-bearing autumn.[17] Thus, in spite of a growing tendency to renounce decadism and its overdrawn effects, the decadent mood was still strong. Only the year before, Victorien Sardou's *Theodora*, a lurid tale of Roman Byzantium, with Sarah Bernhardt in the title role, had been the smash hit of the 1884–85 theatrical season.

Le Symboliste (four issues in October and November of 1886), to the contrary, was definitely opposed to decadence. The editors were

Gustave Kahn, Jean Moréas, and Paul Adam, and although the list of contributors includes names as illustrious as those of Laforgue, Huysmans, Mallarmé, and Verlaine, absent are the numerous minor poets associated with *Lutèce*, *Le Décadent*, and *Le Scapin*. The common ground that still existed between decadence and symbolism is indicated by the names we have cited, by an advertisement for Vanier, 'le Lemerre des décadents', as 'le bibliopole des symbolistes', and by Moréas' and Paul Adam's use of decadent language.[18] On the other hand, in the first issue Paul Adam's 'La Presse et le symbolisme'[19] spells out that symbolism is dissociated from the parody of Vicaire and Beauclair, and from the 'très jeunes gens' who rallied around it; indeed, the error of the press is to confuse them with the 'réelles personnalités du mouvement symboliste'; similarly, 'les diaboliques naïvetés' of Baju and Ghil, of *Le Décadent* and *Le Scapin*, have nothing to do with symbolist doctrine. Finally, poems published in *Le Symboliste*, which seem to us conventional and nondescript, lack the specifically decadent paraphernalia of lush language, classical references, debauchery, naturalist description, and sense of decline.

One passage in particular reveals the magazine's orientation. In reviewing Félix Fénéon's *Les Impressionnistes en 1866*, Moréas recognises that, by their originality, the impressionists are opposed to banality and the *lieu commun*, which are also enemies of the new poetry, and he concedes the worth of their paintings. But when Moréas continues, 'Mais hâtons-nous de proclamer la souveraineté du maître Puvis de Chavannes, dont l'oeuvre, hors les parvités de l'impression, s'essore parmi les halos corruscants du Pur Symbole.'[20] his preference for the symbolist painter reveals his belief that, in painting as in poetry, art should do more than record sense-impressions, it should express lasting ideas through symbols. Another instance of how writers in 1886 regarded decadence as only a stage in the development of art is René Ghil's statement, in his highly original French:

> Certes heureusement, quand régnait, aux vers de seigneuriale emphase monotone, l'Art seul de dire et de narrer, se révéla le dissident Paul Verlaine. Telles phrases éloquentes devinrent ris et murmures et soupirs spécieux de langueurs . . . Mais, d'un goût exquis et prudent en l'aventure périlleuse, il sut l'heure où devait s'éteindre son sourire délicieux et moqueur devant la gloire et la raison du Passé.[21]

Only two years before, by way of contrast, Maurice Barrès had equated Verlaine's verse with 'le zutisme, le dernier mot de l'indépendance'.[22]

The evolution of decadence into symbolism, the presence of competing schools, and the assertion that Verlaine was outmoded render all the more important *Le Décadent*,[23] which appeared (with a one-year interval) from 10 April 1886 to 1–15 April 1889, for it was the magazine which championed Verlaine and which was devoted solely to expressing the decadent viewpoint: 'On ne saurait exiger de nous des jugements portés à un point de vue classique. Nous sommes Décadents. Toutes les nuances de la décadence sont représentées dans notre journal: décadence de la forme, décadence de l'idée, jusqu'à la déliquescence pure.'[24] The magazine was founded by Anatole Baju and, perhaps, Maurice du Plessys;[25] for three months Paul Pradet (Luc Vajarnet) was editor-in-chief, but very promptly Baju alone became editorial staff, typographer, and printer, as well as director! The fact that *Le Décadent* was the work of one man is a tribute to Baju's indomitable energy, but it is also ground for our having reservations about some of the statements made in the magazine, for Baju's idiosyncratic editorials were the expression of his own confused views and do not always accurately reflect the decadent view.

Like so many of the decadents, Anatole Baju was not a Parisian; he was born at Confolens (Charente) and grew up at his father's mill at Saint-Germain-de-Confolens. Verlaine's statements in his biographical *Hommes d'aujourd'hui* that the father had been a poet and a friend of Lamartine and George Sand, like the one attributing a collection of verse to the son, need to be taken with a grain of salt. What does seem true is that in 1884, after the death of the father, Madame Bajut [*sic*] moved to Paris with her two boys. The future director of *Le Décadent* dropped the final *t* from the family name and traded first names with his younger brother, so that our Anatole Baju was actually named Adrien Bajut.[26] Baju (to continue to use the name he adopted for himself) obtained a post as substitute teacher in the suburb of Saint-Denis, a position whose meagre salary still permitted him to devote his leisure time to literature. The unusual part of the story is how Baju, who had not finished his *baccalauréat* and whose knowledge of literature was obviously deficient, threw himself into his editorial activities with such untiring enthusiasm, devotion, and poor judgement. A photograph taken when he was twenty-six or twenty-seven (since he was born in 1861, this photograph would have been made in the middle of his editorial career),[27] from which the cartoon portrait for *Les Hommes d'aujourd'hui* was taken, shows a lean, intense face, neatly combed hair, and a look of sharp intelligence in the eyes; yet something in his expression reinforces the feeling one gets from reading his editorials that the man was less than well-balanced. In an account of which the dramatic nature is perhaps more accurate in spirit than in fact, Ernest Raynaud describes his first meeting with Baju. A group of admirers were paying a call on Verlaine at the Tenon Hospital, when a copy of *Le Décadent* was produced. Those present snickered at the title, and Verlaine asked,

'Quel est l'imbécile qui a osé ramasser ce titre ridicule?'

'L'imbécile, c'est moi!' répondit une voix nette, tranchante comme un défi. Je me tournai et tout Baju m'apparut alors, ramassé, âpre, têtu, avec, dans une petite figure vieillotte, la flamme d'un regard vibrant.[28]

The reaction described by Raynaud is typical of the Baju that we come to know through the pages of his magazine. As he had done with Charles Morice four years before, Verlaine diplomatically smoothed Baju's ruffled feathers, and the fledgling editor became his most ardent admirer; indeed, *Le Décadent* was the only magazine to entertain such an enthusiastic and exclusive cult for Verlaine.

The first series of thirty-five issues appeared on Saturdays from 10 April to 4 December 1886. Each issue had four pages. After a lapse of a year, the second series, which was to run for thirty-two bi-weekly issues, smaller in format, but each one containing sixteen pages or more, began to appear in December of 1887. Baju himself regularly composed an editorial, and Louis Villatte furnished the 'Chronique littéraire'; however, since Louis Villatte and Pierre Vareilles were both pseudonyms of Baju, obviously it was he alone who kept the magazine afloat. (Similarly, prose pieces signed 'Pierre Vareilles' reveal his ambitions in the field of creative writing.) In the second series Ernest Raynaud, who was the *Décadent's* most competent critic, often shared the 'Chronique', as well as composing critical articles. Except for Verlaine, a very few poems by Mallarmé, and a single poem by Laforgue, no important poets published in *Le Décadent*; otherwise we do meet the familiar names of Albert Aurier, Paul Vorsin, Miguel Fernandez, Rodolphe Darzens, Jean Lorrain, Léo d'Orfer, Jean Ajalbert, and Laurent Tailhade. Thus *Le Décadent* was essentially a periodical of minor figures, now forgotten.

We shall look at the first issue because it is so representative of what the magazine was like throughout its existence, and because even this one issue is a comprehensive example of the decadent syndrome. On the first page a statement of purpose by Baju, 'Aux lecteurs', illustrates the rather hysterical tone of his literary and social criticism:

Se dissimuler l'état de décadence où nous sommes serait le comble de l'insenséisme.

Religion, moeurs, justice, tout décade, ou plutôt tout subit une transformation inéluctable.

La Société se désagrège sous l'action corrosive d'une civilisation déliquescente.

L'homme moderne est un blasé!

Affinement d'appétits, de sensations, de goût, de luxe, de jouissances; névrose, hystérie, hypnotisme, morphinomanie, charlatanisme scientifique, schopenhauérisme à outrance, tels sont les prodomes le l'évolution sociale.

C'est dans la langue surtout que s'en manifestent les premiers symptômes.
. . .

C'est lui [l'art] que nous allons suivre dans ses fluctuations. Nous vouons cette feuille aux innovations tuantes, aux audaces stupéfiantes, aux incohérences à 36 atmosphères dans la limite la plus reculée de leur compatabilité avec ces conventions archaïques étiquetées du nom de morale publique.

Nous serons les vedettes d'une littérature idéale, les précurseurs du transformisme latent qui affouille les strates superposées du classicisme, du romantisme et du naturalisme; en un mot, nous serons les mahdis [*sic*] clamant éternellement le dogma élixirisé, le verbe quintessencié du décadisme triomphant.   [1, 1]

While satisfying our amused curiosity, this passage illustrates how Baju drove home the decadent viewpoint by dint of repetition and over-statement, although at the cost of being patently silly. The notions of social decay, the decline of civilisation, the hyper-refinement of modern man, with his vices and maladies, a specially adapted literary style, literary evolution, and the cult of aestheticism, are all intimated here. Other magazines touch on these ideas, too, but much less vigorously than Baju!

The first instalment of Louis Villatte's (Anatole Baju) 'Chronique littéraire' is in the same vein:

Le présent est au naturalisme.

Celui-ci triomphe sur toute la ligne grâce à l'affaissement du niveau intellectuel.

Fils naturel du Romantisme, il taloche son vieux père caduc avec la plus hyrcanienne des cruautés.

Chose épatante, le public se plaint qu'il sent l'ordure.

Je ne vois qu'il puisse fleurer la violette.

Le romantisme était un ulcère, une tumeur. Le naturalisme, c'est le romantisme en putréfaction, les purulences d'un abscès crevé. On le voit commencer à tituber tout gluant des crachats de la foule.

Les écrivains de cette ècole me rappellent des vidangeurs et des charretiers journalisant leurs faits et gestes dans leurs moments de loisirs.

. . . [1, 1]

Baju was virulently opposed to naturalism throughout the existence of his magazine. In the first issue of the second series he declared. 'Pour nous, Mesdames et Messieurs, innocents de toute sorte de symbole et d'instrumentation, nous poursuivrons au bénéfice de l'Art pur la lutte contre le Naturalisme' ('Chronique', II, 1). Conferral of the *Legion d'honneur* on Zola on 14 July 1888 drew two vituperative editorials;[29] thus Baju shares the decadents' occasional hostility to Zola, while going counter to their generally favourable view of the naturalist novel. Baju was also opposed to the Russian novel, which was beginning to achieve success in France, to Paul Bourget's pessimism, to symbolism, and to the political establishment. He was chauvinist, but against General Boulanger. Editorial views in *Le Décadent* are Baju's personal opinions, which interest us perhaps because of the extent to which this irrational young man shared some of the decadent convictions of intellectuals of his time.

Charles Evendal's 'Religiosité', which we noted in chapter VI, is typical of the decadents' concern with Catholicism as an aesthetic pose. In 'Lions' Evendal describes the wild-animal act of a travelling carnaval, compares it to a circus in ancient Rome, and concludes with an apostrophe to the lions of Rome, applauded by fifty thousand spectators drunk with the blood of martyrs. The animal act is described in naturalistic terms, showing how both naturalism and decadence sought to adapt language to the needs of exact description; and the apostrophe to the lions dwells sadistically on their devouring Christians ('Avec quelle grâce pleine de force vous enfonciez vos griffes dans le sein lilial des vierges impolluées!'). *Le Décadent* stands out for its harping on the comparison between ancient Rome and modern Paris, as in Baju's 'Le Progrès' (1 1, signed 'Pierre Vareilles'), 'Zim Boum' (I, 9), and 'Sadités' (I, 14); no other review we have seen paid as much attention to this notion, so fundamental to decadence. 'Théo's' poem, 'Pierrot d'aujourd'hui', describes Laforgue's clown figure, burnt out and thoroughly bored; like much of the poetry in *Le Décadent*, what it lacks in poetic merit is more than compensated for by the intensity of its decadence. Pierre Vareilles' (again, Baju's) prose poem, 'Clair de lune: fantaisie déliquescente', and excepts from two novels, Luc Vajarnet's *La Grande Roulotte* and Paul Pradet's (whose pen name was 'Luc Vajarnet') *Espada negra*, demonstrate that *Le Décadent* was the best periodical source for decadent prose. *La Grande Roulotte* is the story of two lesbians, and *Espada negra* is interesting for the gory sadism in its description of a bullfight and for its treatment of the matador as a typical decadent hero. 'Clair de lune' is decadent by virtue of its style:

> Après une journée torrescente, atmosphère languide, papillotante d'électricité. Ciel d'azur tacheté de laiteurs chloroti ques. Sidération stellaire moins ardescente que de coutume et pleine de langourosité universelle.
>
> A l'occident, hémicycle lumineux aux rutilences pâlissantes, sous les loines et ultimes réfulgences du soleil disparu. A l'Orient, ronde comme la plus impeccable des circonférences, la lune au milieu d'un grand cercle presque incandescent, dans l'azuration pâlotte des surfaces éthériennes.
>
> (1, 1)

Thanks to Baju's ubiquity under different names,[30] *Le Décadent* starts off with great verve, unlike some of the other magazines, which seemingly had trouble obtaining sufficient copy for their early issues.

Subsequent issues of *Le Décadent* continue to be a treasury of information on the personalities and intellectual attitudes of the movement. F.-A. Cazals, the young painter with whom Verlaine was emotionally involved during the latter part of the 1880's, composed 'Croquis littéraires', a series of word portraits of literary figures which, in an amusing pun, he signed 'Des Cadenzals'. Pierre Vareilles did a similar series called 'Silhouettes décadentes'. Critical articles abound; during the second series Ernest Raynaud's are particularly useful for their informed, intelligent tenor. He observes, for instance, that the stereotyped classical style taught in the *lycée* forces him to lie by saying what he does not feel,[31] and Louis Villatte points out that Buffon's maxim 'le style, c'est l'homme' means that each writer must adapt his personal style to his own individual apprehension of life.[32] Even superficial and querulous criticism at least indicates which issues the decadents regarded as important: Anatole Baju condemns pessimism as un-French,[33] suggests that 'quintessents' is a better term than 'décadents' for these writers who refine and condense their thought, eliminating all verbiage,[34] and he calls the symbolists mere followers of the decadents.[35] For Louis Villatte the symbolists are anti-modern and obscure in contrast with the 'simplicité humaine' of Verlaine and the decadents.[36] Both as Pierre Vareilles[37] and as Louis Villatte[38] Baju is self-conscious about the sparse production of the decadents; their opponents scornfully pointed out that the plethora of literary theory published by the decadents and symbolists was not as yet vindicated by a work of substantial proportions; for the decadent, however, quality counts more than quantity. Thus as Raynaud and especially Baju reply to criticism and in turn criticise their rivals their writings present a comprehensive view of decadent beliefs.

Furthermore, in the pages of *Le Décadent* we find literary compositions most aptly described as 'decadent', to the exclusion of overlapping terms like 'naturalist' or 'symbolist'. For the novel, there are selections from *La Marquise de Sade* and *Candaulette* by Rachilde (Marguérite Eymery), the authoress of *Monsieur Vénus*, one of the most celebrated titles in this series, and excerpts from Pierre Vareilles' *Laïda ou l'île des amours* and Albert Aurier's *Le Magnétiseur*. Decadent novels are generally characterised by lurid, far-fetched plots, often involving sexual deviations, and it is the extravagant nature of their plots, which reflect the decadent concern with social and moral decay, or with the decadence of Rome, rather than extended use of decadent style which distinguishes these novels. (Passages of truly Latinate decadent style seem limited to sketches, short stories, and similar bravura pieces.) *Monsieur Vénus* was charged with endangering public morals, it fared badly at the hands of decadent reviewers even, and it has failed the test of time.

In the area of poetry, the contribution of *Le Décadent* is to have published precisely that sort of poetry which, too narrowly period-style to survive, has the merit of representing the extreme expression of decadence. Four poems that we quoted *in toto* in chapter VI, 'L'Etang mort' by Jean Lorrain, 'Nocturnité' by Miguel Fernandez, Laurent Tailhade's 'Aliptes' (or 'Garçon de bains'), and Delphin de Girard's 'Alla Madonna' appeared in *Le Décadent*. The Greek slave motif is repeated in Daniel Denfert's sonnet 'Décadisme antique' (I, 28), the religious motif in Tailhade's 'Sonnet liturgique' (II, 1). Laurent Tailhade's 'Troisième sexe' (III, 16) deals with modern homosexuality. Théo's 'Pierrot d'aujourd'hui' (I, 1), Martial Besson's 'Poétique nouvelle',[39] and Miguel Fernandez' 'Dégénérescence' express an attitude of morbidness and degeneration:

> 'Décadence—dit-on—mensonge et fiction'
> —Erreur— Oui, tout décade et l'igneur prolifique
> S'éteint dans l'énerveur d'un corps épileptique;
> C'est un fruit orescent qui n'a plus d'embryon.
>
> Contemnable dégoût de parturition!
> Boréales frigueurs d'un amour antarctique!
> Bâtardes siccités d'un flanc anhélitique
> Où périt le foetus en germination!

Les modernes Phrynés ont des coeurs de banquise
Un regard terne et froid comme un pavé d'église
Qui glace et réfrigère en sa blêmeur de mort.

Les hommes allouvis d'une crainte érophobe
Semblent s'être entendus pour dépeupler le globe
Et le faire occomber au Néant dont il sort.

[Fernandez, 'Dégénérescence', 1, 10]

The twenty-fifth issue, 25 September 1886, brings to light an incident in the rivalry among different schools. In a note Baju states that henceforth the *Décadent* will cease to be exclusively the organ of *les jeunes* and instead will become that 'of the new literary school'. He yields his 'Chronique littéraire' column to Gustave Kahn and announces that in future issues it will be handled by, among others, Edouard Dujardin, Félix Fénéon, Jules Laforgue, Jean Moréas, and Théodore de Wyzewa. Other contributors to this issue include Charles Vignier, Moréas, Laforgue (whose 'Aquarelle en cinq minutes' was his sole contribution to *Le Décadent*), and Paul Adam. This arrangement lasted for only the one issue. Baju wanted his own contributors back, with whom Kahn and his group refused to collaborate, and by issue No. 26 things were as they had been before. As Rachilde pointed out in a letter of protest to Trézenik in *Lutèce* (3–10 October 1886), this episode apparently represented an unsuccessful attempt by symbolists, Kahn, Moréas, and Wyzewa, to appropriate Baju's publication for their own purposes.[40]

In spite of a year of silence in 1887 between the two series, the *Décadent's* growth is impressive. Like Trézenik before him, Baju had to print the magazine himself, and he required the principal collaborateurs to set their own articles in type and to help with the printing. This arrangement undoubtedly explains the consistently inaccurate typography, which led to quarrels between Baju and some of his poet–contributors. An amusing anecdote has to do with his efforts to smuggle a small press, piece by piece, past the *concierge* and up to his room; alas! the noise of the press in operation annoyed the neighbours anyway, and they had to be placated. *Le Décadent* held receptions on Tuesday evenings, and it seems incongruous to read the invitation, printed in the magazine, to ring at 5 bis rue Lamartine and ask for Monsieur Baju or Monsieur Pradet. In the second issue Pierre Vareilles, stating that the new magazine will be addressed to youth, who have no preconceived ideas and are free of any entanglement, proudly adds, 'Nous aussi nous sommes des jeunes. La Rédaction du *Décadent* ne compte pas un seul écrivain en renom. Nous sommes des nouveaux venus dans le monde littéraire' ('Aux jeunes', 1, 2). Six months later, however, Baju justifiably congratulates himself on the magazine's growth: circulation has grown to the point where he has been obliged to have it printed commercially (the second series ran to 6,000 copies), and he has obtained the participation of two major writers, Paul Verlaine and Stéphane Mallarmé. Henceforth the magazine will be the militant journal of the new literary school! *Le Décadent's* success, in spite of its journalistic inexperience, is due to the worthiness of the idea it defends.[41]

Verlaine first met Baju, according to Raynaud, in July of 1886; the issue of 31 July, which announces the future collaboration 'du si délicatement grand poète Stéphane Mallarmé', reprints Verlaine's 'A Louis II de Bavière' from *La Revue Wagnérienne*. In the next issue, 7 August, Paterne Berrichon, the future brother-in-law of Arthur Rimbaud, is listed on the masthead, and he makes his *début* with a sympathetic interview with Verlaine, in which he draws attention to the master's unjust exclusion from literary success and expresses the hope that the *Décadent* will be able to bring him to the attention of the 'grands confrères cotidiens tout-puissants' (is not this pious wish just a little bit belated, considering Verlaine's notoriety since the *Déliquescences* the previous year?) ('Paul Verlaine', 1, 18). Following his article is an announcement, 'Nous publierons dans notre prochain numéro des vers inédits que notre collaborateur Paul Verlaine rythme spécialement pour le *Décadent*, de son lit d'hôpital,' and in fact in the following issue appears his 'A un mort', followed by 'Pierrot gamin' (1, 22), 'Je vois un groupe sur la mer' (1, 32), 'Ballade à Louise Michel' (1, 35), as well as prose selections from *Louise Leclercq* and *Mémoires d'un veuf*. Mallarmé's collaboration, in the meantime, was distinctly slighter than Verlaine's: after the prose poem 'Fusain' (1, 18) *Le Décadent* published 'Le Tombeau d'Edgar Poe' (1, 21), 'Eventail' (1, 27), and 'Le Guignon' (1, 33)—all of them reprints, since Mallarmé did not publish a single *inédit* in *Le Décadent*.

During the first three and a half months of 1888 the pages of *Le Decadent* reveal with particular vividness how the magazine and Verlaine together served as the focal point of the decadent movement, thus realising Baju's avowed purpose of grouping the 'forces éparses en un faisceau unique'.[42] Everything seemed to happen at once, as if by prearrangement: Verlaine made statements on *décadisme* and rhyme; articles in the magazine discussed rhyme, decadence, and symbolism; Jules Lemaitre published a study of Verlaine's poetry, and *Le Décadent* rebutted it; and the magazine published a series of counterfeit Rimbaud poems. In the penultimate issue of the first series (27 November 1886) there was a sonnet over the name of Arthur Rimbaud, 'Il splendit sous le bleu d'athlétiques Natures', which was actually a *pastiche*. Three more such poems appeared in January, February, and March of 1888, and another three in the course of the next half-year. One of these, 'Les Corbeaux' (15–31 March 1888) was actually from Rimbaud's hand, but it was in no way distinguished from the others. *Le Décadent* did not acknowledge these forgeries until February of 1889, and then only in a dubious fashion. In March Baju again claimed that the poems were authentic.[43] All this naturally antagonised Verlaine. Meanwhile, the magazine obtained publicity by printing these poems at a time when interest in Rimbaud was keen, and when even authentic texts of his work were scattered and unknown.

To begin with the first issue of the new series in December of 1887, Baju announces the return of *Le Décadent*, indicating that what it stands for is not the same thing as the decadence being brought upon the country by its ruling class, and, in a more literary vein, rejoicing that some of the more *fumistes* among the decadents have been exiled by public clamour to Belgium, where they 'ululent, là-bas, le Verbe symbolo-instrumentaliste' in *La Wallonie*. For true decadents the struggle is against naturalism *à la Zola* ('Chronique', II, 1). This editorial is followed by Verlaine's poem, 'Ballade pour les décadents'. In the following issue (III, 2) appears Verlaine's 'Lettre au *Décadent*', in which he begins by merely asking that the title of his ballad be changed to something else, because he is working on a still better one for his friends; he then goes on to felicitate Baju on inventing the word *décadisme*:

> *Décadisme* est un mot de génie, une trouvaille amusante et qui restera dans l'histoire littéraire; ce barbarisme est une miraculeuse enseigne. Il est court, commode, 'à la main', *handy, éloigne précisément l'idée abaissante de décadence*, sonne littéraire sans pédanterie, enfin fait balle et fera trou, je vous le dis encore une fois . . .[44]

The literary school, then, has nothing to do with decline or deterioration; on the contrary, *décadisme*,

> . . . qui est proprement une littérature éclatant par un temps de décadence, non pour marcher dans les pas de son époque, mais bien tout 'à rebours', pour s'insurger contre, réagir par le délicat, l'élevé, le raffiné si l'on veut, de ses tendances, contre les platitudes et les turpitudes, littéraires et autres, ambiantes,—cela sans nul exclusivisme et en toute confraternité avouable.

The same issue (III, 2) carries a plagiarism of Rimbaud, 'Instrumentation', and a discussion of rhyme by Ernest Raynaud in the 'Chronique littéraire' column. Raynaud's article is as interesting for the insight it gives into Verlaine's relationship with the decadent school as for its views on rhyme. Simply stated, Raynaud believes that the regular appearance of rhymed words is harsh and unpleasant to the ear, rather than necessary, and that the decadent's efforts to render the line musical, to orchestrate their poems, will soon make rhyme superfluous. He is surprised that Verlaine dwells on the Parnassians' theories of rhyme; he, of all people, should be the first to raise the flag of revolt instead of drawing back before the daring efforts of the young poets who, after all, are his disciples and are motivated by his 'Art poétique'. Raynaud concludes by observing that if Verlaine himself does not encourage their innovations, his work does, and that they need no further encouragement.

In the issue of 15–31 January 1888 (III, 3) Raynaud undertakes to define decadence, since some critics are still uncertain of its meaning. Viewing the question in historical terms, he states that at the moment when Verlaine published his *Poètes maudits*, 'ce formidable coup de tonnerre qui eut le retentissement que l'on sait', there was already at work a small group of writers whose only common ground was a sincere love of literature and a hatred of popular, commercially success-ful writing, and whose idols were a half-dozen unknown masters like Verlaine, Mallarmé, Barbey d'Aurevilly, and Huysmans. Being few in number, they wrote chiefly for each other, and out of disdain for popular literature they deliberately made themselves incomprehensible to the public by the arduousness of their form and the abstruseness of their ideas. Consequently the sole valid criteria of decadence are con-scious artistry and scorn for public acclaim ('Chronique littéraire', III, 3). This statement further demonstrates the paternal role into which Verlaine was cast, and it enunciates the position consistently held by decadent critics, that decadence is nothing but up-to-dateness and excellence in literature: estimable qualities which the public is not yet ready to accept.

The same issue carries Verlaine's second ballad on the decadents, 'Ballade touchant un point d'histoire', and Baju's editorial. Verlaine's statement, according to Baju, is the condemnation of symbolism, the triumph of *Décadisme*, and their assurance of victory ('La Déclaration de Paul Verlaine', III, 3). Baju's admiration for Verlaine, as fervent and unreasonable as his other beliefs, is expressed in dogmatic terms like

'Le Maître a parlé' (*ibid.*), 'notre grand poète national Paul Verlaine' ('La Vraie Littérature', III, 12), and 'Ce serait naïvement prétentieux que de vouloir faire la critique littéraire d'*Amour*. De telles oeuvres ne se discuttent point' ('*Amour*', III, 8). 'Les Décadents et la vie' indicates that Baju could be accurate and to the point; while ending with a rather pointless discussion of woman in literature, he does begin by stating, 'Ce qui distingue le Décadisme des autres écoles littéraires, ce n'est pas seulement le nom; c'est aussi le style et surtout la façon de voir . . . qui est la génératrice du style'. The force and originality of the decadents, he writes, are due to the fact that they see differently from other people and are courageous enough to translate their impressions faithfully (III, 5).

Meanwhile, on 7 January 1888, Jules Lemaitre published his 'M. Paul Verlaine et les poètes symbolistes et décadents' in *La Revue Bleue*. This was, so to speak, Verlaine's consecration as a leading poet and *chef d'école*, since it was 'le premier grand article qu'un critique officiel, décoré, consacre à Paul Verlaine'.[45] As a measure of Verlaine's increased fame, it should be remembered that only three years before, in the course of two different articles on the new literature, Lemaitre had barely mentioned Verlaine's name in connection with des Esseintes! *Le Décadent* seldom let a derogatory remark about decadence in the public press go unanswered. Baju makes a vigorous retort to this article in the issue of 15–31 January ('Revue génerale-échos', III, 3), and in the issues of 15–29 February and 1–15 March (III, 5 and 6)Ernest Raynaud published a rebuttal. We shall consider it and Lemaitre's article later.

The two March issues (III, 6 and 7) carry Verlaine's 'Un mot sur la rime', written specifically to repudiate Raynaud's interpretation of his poetry. Verlaine argues that rhyme is indispensable in a language like French which has no tonic accent; that it is not rhyme which is at fault, but the misuse of it. Quoting a poem of his own where, for want of a rhyme, he was obliged to settle for the assonance *Cécile–faucille*, he admonishes, 'Mais que ceci ne serve pas d'exemple!'[46]

Still in the issue of 15–31 March, Raynaud reproduces a statement on symbolism and an illustrative poem by Edouard Dubus ('Du symbolisme'). His purpose in quoting this material is to clarify the decadent position by contrasting the symbolist one with it, since the public is still confused about decadence and tends to put all the different poetic factions together. Raynaud sees the war among the various schools as an advantage, in that it causes each one to define its position. To us, however, Raynaud seems over-optimistic, for the statements by the

various leaders consist largely of generalities, platitudes, and vitupera-
tion of their rivals, and sometimes their views even coincide; nor is it
always helpful to analyse poems, for the same individuals published
poems in magazines with opposing views, and anyway most of the
verse is too banal and conventional to indicate a literary orientation.
Even *Le Décadent* still published verse which can only be described as
Parnassian!

The remaining twenty-five issues of *Le Décadent*, while interesting,
do not record events of major importance. Verlaine's participation
ceases in the spring of 1888—his last poem to appear was 'Sainte
Thérèse veut que la pauvreté soit . . .' in the issue of 1–15 July. Baju's
and Raynaud's columns continue to appear (Raynaud's only until
March 1889). Some parodies in the final issues are amusing and continue
to remind us of the decadent penchant for *mystification*. In the issue of
1–15 February 1889 there is a notice that the poems which had been
erroneously attributed to Arthur Rimbaud, Ernest Raynaud, Maurice
du Plessys, and Laurent Tailhade were actually the work of 'Mitrophane Crapoussin' ('Avis'). In the same issue *Le Missel* by Raoul Pascalis
is criticised for having parodied Tailhade's liturgical style (Jules Maus,
'Critique anti-littéraire'); apparently no such book existed. Yet in the
next issue (IV, 29) appears Crapoussin's 'Antienne', dedicated to
'monsieur Raoul Pascalis pour le congratuler de sa dévotion', and
'Oiseaux'. The next two issues contain five more poems by the genial,
if non-existent, Crapoussin: they resemble the parodies of *Les Déliquescences*. In the last issue (IV, 32) poetry is completely given over to
fun: 'Voeu', as an example, is ascribed to Louis II of Bavaria and
dedicated 'Au frère en Baudelaire, Arthur Rimbaud', and it has comic
epigraphs from St Joseph de Cupertino, Victor Hugo, and Philothée
O'Neddy. Such paradoxes and hoaxes are almost the *sui generis* of
decadence, and it is appropriate for *Le Décadent*, which was a mirror
of the tastes, achievements, and shortcomings of the movement, to
end on such a note.

With the demise of *Le Décadent* in April of 1889 the decadent school
went out of existence, for it no longer had a spokesman, a magazine, or
even writers who advocated its principles. Occasional poems still
expressed the decadent outlook, but they were scarce and seemed
outmoded.

Verlaine's participation on the *Décadent* sheds light on his role as
mentor of the younger generation of poets, with its satisfactions,
advantages, and tribulations. Since it was these young men who had

recalled him from oblivion in 1883, naturally he was prompt to cultivate their enthusiasm and to show a friendly interest in their work. The publicity surrounding them was to Verlaine's advantage, too: as late as 1887 he saw in Anatole Baju's *L'Ecole décadente* 'un petit regain de réclame autour des 'Décadents' à propos d'une brochure de Baju',[47] and he proposed to Vanier that they profit from it by doing a biographical article about him: 'Battre le fer tandis qu'il est chaud'.[48] Probably it was desirable in the years 1888 and 1889 to have one's own coterie and review, as Kahn, Moréas, and Ghil did, yet he found Baju's uncritical and unrestrained enthusiasm bothersome. 'On a ri jusq'aux larmes,' he wrote, 'parce que Baju dans sa brochure me proclame le plus grand poète de tous les temps, On a eu tort de rire. D'abord parce que peut-être Baju pense ainsi *pour de bon* . . .'[49] Might not a person as sensitive as Verlaine also have been pained by the contrast between such fulsome praise and his own awareness that many a poem of *Amour* and *Parallèlement* was substantially less than his best? Moreover, Verlaine was completely indifferent to the quibbling over poetic theory which characterised much of the criticism in *Le Décadent*, and he must have been amused or annoyed by some of the more exaggeratedly decadent verse. '. . . Les théories et le style décadents me puent furieusement, comme dirait Molière. . . . L'autre [Baju] est un monsieur ennuyeux et faussement savant au dire des vrais savants. N'importe il aura mes livres—pour réclame,'[50] he wrote in 1889.

Verlaine had genuine cause for dissatisfaction with Baju, who failed to get copies of *Le Décadent* to him in hospital, printed poems he had asked be withheld, and made unauthorised statements in his name. After Verlaine's 'Lettre au *Décadent*' (III, 2), Baju published a 'Déclaration de principes' (III, 3), expanding Verlaine's remarks according to his own interpretation. Now this was an issue Verlaine did not receive, learning about it only while in hospital, so that he had double reason to be annoyed: hence a letter to Baju, threatening to terminate his participation and to state publicly his reasons for doing so.[51] In the issue of 1–15 May 1888 Baju berated Paul de Foss for writing *décadentisme* instead of *décadisme* and cited Verlaine as his authority ('Revue de la presse', III, 10). The same day Verlaine apologised to Foss in a letter interesting for its nice delineation of the situation:

> Mon cher poète,
> Ai-je besoin de vous dire que la Note du *Décadent* No. 10 n'est pas de mon fait et même pas de mon *su*? Je ne suis pas le maître dans ce journal, sans quoi les choses y prendraient une tournure plus sérieuse, sans peine.

Baju et ses amis sont d'excellents garçons trop jeunes à mon gré. Excusez-
les et comptez sur moi pour, dès que je le pourrai, là ou ailleurs, redresser,
entre autres, ce tort.
 . . .[52]

When Baju took it upon himself to criticise Verlaine's own schoolmates and friends for failing to support him financially ('Paul Verlaine',
III, 14) he caused Verlaine considerable embarrassment, as can be seen
in the latter's complaint to Baju and apology to Théodore de Banville.[53]
Furthermore, Verlaine was angry over Baju's liberties with the memory
of Rimbaud, such as the forged poems of 1888 and a subscription for a
monument in March 1889. Laurent Tailhade apologised to Verlaine
for his role in both matters, and he and Ernest Raynaud both publicly
dissociated themselves from Baju's scheme for a monument. When, in
the issue of 15–31 March 1889, Baju again asserted the authenticity of the
Rimbaud forgeries, Raynaud left the magazine (in the middle of a
serialised article!), advising both *La Cravache*, which had been covering
the dispute, and Verlaine of his decision. Verlaine had already left in
1888. Tailhade finally broke with the magazine over its typographical
errors in printing his poems.[54] It seems prophetic that Baju had lost his
first editor, Paul Pradet, after only three months in 1886.

Similarly, the exchange with Raynaud over rhyme is illustrative of
the misunderstandings that arose between Verlaine and a younger
generation. Despite his condemnation of rhyme in 'Art poétique' and
his use of unrhymed lines in a very few poems, with no significant
exceptions Verlaine's poetry is rhymed, for the excellent reason that he
felt it was essential to the prosody of French. 'Art poétique', as he had
explained to Morice, referred to undue emphais on *rime riche*. Nevertheless, younger poets persisted in citing him as the patron of their
efforts to eliminate rhyme altogether, thus placing him in an ambiguous
position. How much more satisfactory and accurate was Raynaud's
article on decadence (III, 3), where he presents Verlaine, among others,
as a model of artistic integrity and vision, rather than as an arbiter of
poetic technique!

Although the thoroughly Parnassian 'Prologue' and 'Epilogue' of
Poèmes saturniens, his 'Art poétique', his 'système' of 1873–74, his self-
identification with the Catholic tradition, and finally his momentary
acclamation of *décadisme* make Verlaine appear to be a poet of schools
and programmes, in truth just the opposite was true. More so, perhaps,
than with other poets, the uniquely personal nature of his experience
and of his poetic skills led Verlaine to devise new modes of expression

as each experience suggested different means of recapturing it in verse. Hence the unplanned, non-intellectual nature of his best poetry, as well as his consistent emphasis that art must be sincere. 'Art poétique' must have been composed after the other poems of *Romances sans paroles* and as a commentary on one phase only of his inspiration. In contrast, young symbolists drew up poetic systems first, thereby leaving us with the impression that they produced more theories of poetry than poems. Verlaine wisely avoided these doctrinal discussions; when he did utter sallies like 'L'art, mes enfants, c'est d'être absolument soi-même', or his chauvinistic outburst against symbolism in the Huret interview of 1891,[55] he expressed his impatience with poets who placed theory before achievement, although he probably had an ulterior purpose, too, for Verlaine had to remember that acting in character kept up the publicity which sold the verse on which his livelihood depended. He expressed his attitude much more reasonably and sincerely in a letter to Henri de Régnier:

> J'ai véritablement longtemps réfléchi à demande de Griffin d'un 'exposé de principes' concernant l'art des vers, etc. Je n'ai pu tirer de ma conscience que cette conclusion: Tout est bel et bon qui est bel et bon, d'où qu'il vienne et par quelque procédé qu'il soit obtenu. Classiques, romantiques, décadents, symbolos, assonants ou comment dirai-je? obscurs exprès, pourvu qu'ils me foutent le frisson ou simplement me charment, même et peut-être surtout sans que, comme le Dindon de Florian, je sache pour quelle cause, font tous mon compte. Allez, poètes que nous sommes, aimons-nous les uns et les autres, cette maxime n'est pas plus bête en art qu'en morale et je crois qu'il faut s'y tenir. Telle ma théorie mûrement délibérée.[56]

The complaint that Verlaine's statements on poetry are inadequate as literary criticism misses an essential fact which, although too often overlooked, nevertheless sheds light on his career: this is Verlaine's role as an *homme de lettres*.[57] The professional man of letters takes up where the creative writer leaves off; he is a businessman, politician, and diplomat, the sort of congenial, outgoing individual who can look after the fortunes of his manuscript after he has completed his work as creator. A literary work leads a life of its own as a marketable, readable text, and it implies no aspersion on an author's integrity or sincerity to point out that he must defend his interests, push his own cause, and cultivate the critics and fellow writers who can help him in that large area where literature ceases to be an act of individual creation and becomes instead a joint human venture. Such is especially the case of the French writer, who lives in a capital with critics, publishers, other writers, and indeed some twenty per cent of the public who will buy and read his books. The gregarious Verlaine seems to have been unusually adept at this sort of activity; certainly at all stages of his career he possessed a host of friends and acquaintances in the world of letters, and in spite of the quarantine imposed on him as a result of the Rimbaud scandal, it is surprising how much a few strategic contacts, like Lepelletier, Vanier, Huysmans, and Morice, were able to do for him when he resumed his literary career in 1882. Verlaine's relationship with the decadence and symbolism, therefore, had as much to do with his personal contacts as with purely literary questions, for it was the former which he could manipulate and which were at first responsible for rescuing his poetry from oblivion. This consideration would also explain his unwillingness to give offence by taking sides with any of the mutually hostile factions during the second half of the decade.

We now leave Verlaine and his role in the movement in order to consider how decadent criticism dealt with the question of poetic theory. Our principle sources of information are the articles of Ernest Raynaud in *Le Décadent* and those of Téodor de Wyzewa and Gustave Kahn in *La Revue Indépendante*.[58] While Wyzewa and Kahn can appropriately be called symbolists rather than decadents, still their conception of poetry to a large extent coincides with that of the decadents, and Kahn's earlier poetry, particularly in its debt to Verlaine, displays decadent characteristics. Raynaud, Wyzewa, and Kahn agreed all three that the proper subject of literature is physical sensation, a notion that had been fundamental to decadence since Gautier's preface to *Les Fleurs du mal*. In one of the first articles on the new poetry, it will be remembered, Maurice Barrès saw that the bond uniting Baudelaire and his followers was their common concern with sensation,[59] and even the hostile Jules Lemaitre, in his 1885 article on pessimism in literature, correctly identified the treatment of sensation, in lieu of moral values, as the element common to Parnassians, naturalists, and impressionists.[60] It was for accurately recording sensations that the decadents revered the Goncourts. In an article on Edmond de Goncourt in 1884 Emile Hennequin emphasised the impressionism of his style, with its attention to fixing motion or evanescent emotions at a given instant in time, and this at a date when the decadent sensibility was just becoming aware of itself.[61] Looking back in 1889, Ernest Raynaud acknowledged the Goncourts' formative role in an article in *Le*

Décadent, 'Les Origines du mouvement décadent: Les Frères de
Goncourt' (IV, 26 and 27).

Just as decadent prose style specialised in rendering uncommon
sensations, so decadent critics see poetry devoted to expressing emotions
for which prose is unsuited. Téodor de Wyzewa credits the Parnassians
with having determined that so-called poetic ideas and vivid images
are better expressed by prose than by verse, and that the function of
poetry is to express musical emotions: those which appeal to our
senses, which are lyrical in nature, yet different from the ones expressed
by music.[62] Indeed, for him the function of poetry, with its special
kind of music, is to enable us to relive those pure emotions which
prose cannot recreate: 'La poésie est une musique verbale, destinée à
traduire des émotions. La plupart de nos poètes cependant, ignorants
ou insoucieux de cette haute destination esthétique, s'acharnent à un
stérile effort de versification. . . .'[63] This notion is so basic to Wyzewa's
criticism that the phrase 'la poésie est une musique', which reappears
throughout his articles, itself like a musical *Leitmotiv*, is his sole criterion
for evaluating new books of verse: Ajalbert, Vignier, Coppée, and
René Ghil fail by this yardstick; Jean Lorrain, Stuart Merrill, Viélé-
Griffin, Henri de Régnier, and Gustave Kahn succeed to the extent that
they come closer to his ideal. He received Kahn's *Palais nomades*
particularly cordially because of the musical quality of his free verse.
Kahn himself, when he replaced Wyzewa on *La Revue Indépendante*,
wrote that emotion is music: 'Le premier jour qu'un pâtre ayra modula
une onomatopée admirative ou joyeuse ou éclata en sanglots, le
poème était fondé, et le poème ne servit depuis qu'a développer le cri
de joie et le cri de douleur de l'humanité,' and farther on, 'car en
l'essence même de la poésie elle s'adresse à l'oreille tout en cherchant à
fixer des attitudes'.[64] Baudelaire's 'Correspondances' and Rimbaud's
'Sonnet des voyelles' (with which decadent poets were familiar since
Verlaine's 'Poètes maudits' article in *Lutèce* at the end of 1883, and
which René Ghil further popularised with his instrumentalist theories),
as well as Verlaine's 'Art poétique', firmly established that one sensation
can express phenomena proper to another and that emotion can be
suggested by sense-impressions. The recent cult of Wagner's music,
with which Mallarmé was involved, was another instance of music
being preferred over other sensations as a means of expression.

The basis of Verlaine's appeal to poets who thought this way is
apparent. Recent critics like Jean-Pierre Richard and Octave Nadal
emphasise the *équivalences sensorielles* by which Verlaine translates

emotions into sensory terms—usually impressionist descriptions—which appeal to the reader's emotional perception.[65] Verlaine's first admirers were less systematic in their analysis of his method, yet there was a general agreement that he had created a new art form for expressing nature's moods and man's subtle emotional states. 'Jean Mario' said that he understood and translated nature better than Baudelaire had, Huysmans found that he expressed vague, whispered avowals with consummate delicacy, Maurice Barrès saw in his treatment of sensations 'le dernier degré d'énervement dans une race épuisée. C'est de l'art, parfois le plus exquis que nous sachions.'[66] Thus the delicacy of Verlaine's art corresponds to the delicacy of the decadent mood. In 1888 we find a direct connection between Verlaine's poetry and the poetic expression of decadence, since for Ernest Raynaud both aim at a simpler, more direct, and at the same time more efficacious rendition of life:

> . . . le retour à une poésie initiale, impliquant plus de sincérité dans l'émotion, plus de naïveté et plus de mélodie à la fois dans l'expression, le rejet de toute rhétorique vaine et apprêtée, la phrase n'étant qu'une tunique légère moulée sur le nu de l'aine. Toute cette oeuvre et celle des décadents peut se résumer à ceci: perception plus immédiate de la vie, expression plus nerveuse et plus concise de ces phénomènes. De là vient que la forme la plus ordinaire de leurs poèmes est le sonnet, s'appropriant merveilleusement au rendu de toute émotion—l'intensité étant en raison inverse de la durée.[67]

For Kahn, who depreciates the use of misleading terms like 'decadent' and 'symbol' anyway, Verlaine is neither decadent nor symbolist, he is simply himself; still, his individuality consists of a decadent mode of experience: '. . . il interprète, il cliche ses sensations au passage en toute sincérité; et son critérium est sa sincérité même.'[68] Like Louis Desprez in 1884, Raynaud emphasises the painterly quality of Verlaine's verse, calling him:

> . . . par exemple, le paysagiste éminent, l'impressionniste subtil avec ses rappels d'aubes exaltées, de crépuscules allanguis, d'après-midis recueillis, véritablement adorables et dont le rendu défie la palette des plus habiles coloristes, furent-ils [*sic*!] Daubigny, Courbet ou Corot. Il aurait dû noter ces murmures d'eau sur la mousse, les chants d'alouette au réveil, ces clairs de lune sous bois, saisis dans leur toute intensité et merveilleusement imités par la musique et la coloration du vers.[69]

Jules Lemaitre correctly interprets Verlaine's poetry as having to do largely with sensation: 'On pourrait presque dire qu'il est le seul poète qui n'ait exprimé que des sentiments et des sensations et qui les ait traduits uniquement pour lui; ce qui le dispensait d'en montrer le lien, car lui le connaît.'[70] For the decadents, then, and even for an academic critic like Lemaitre, Verlaine was the poet who best carried out an ideal of expressing in a sensuous kind of writing the sensory experience of civilised, modern man.

Raynaud and Lemaitre express the decadent viewpoint, while Wyzewa and Kahn, who expect poetry to do more than just translate visual or tactile sensations into music, represent a symbolist one. We see this when Wyzewa wants emotions to be *re-created* by the music of the arts, and the arts to come together and re-create all of life:

> L'émotion est recréée artistiquement par divers moyens, dont chacun correspond à des émotions particulières: la peinture émotionnelle, traitant les couleurs et les lignes comme des notes musicales, les combinant au seul point de vue des émotions qu'elles suggèrent; la littérature émotionnelle ou poésie, traitant les syllabes et les rhythmes comme des notes musicales, les combinant au seul point de vue des émotions qu'ils suggèrent; enfin la musique, recréant le fond dernier des émotions, par des alliances de sons et de rhythmes. Et comme la vie n'est point des sensations, ni des notions, ni des émotions, mais une série enchevêtrée de ces modes divers, les divers arts doivent tendre à un Art total, unisant tous les signes artistiques pour recréeer toute la Vie.[71]

Kahn calls *Fêtes galantes* 'Cette façon de prendre, d'objectifier son âme en formes tangibles et extérieures . . .'[72] Here the work of art is not merely a report of what the artist saw, felt, or heard; it is its equivalent, its substitute (not inferior, but better than the original), a symbol of experience. This distinction between decadence and symbolism is a fine one, yet it comes inevitably: the first step in developing a personalised style is to find a technical substitute for experience—dabs of paint on canvas, words on paper, or the sounds of music; the second step, which comes almost instinctively, is to interpret sensations, to find a hidden meaning in them, to infer a conception of life from the incomplete data furnished by our senses. As Ruth Moser observes in connection with impressionism,

> . . . Dès que l'artiste ne se contente plus de jouir de la sensation, qu'il lui découvre un sens, une signification cachée, il s'achemine vers le symbolisme. D'ailleurs, les frontières entre les deux esthétiques sont flottantes, car elles sont parentes.[73]

Whenever the sensations so delicately recorded by style and by music acquire an intrinsic value as signs, or as substitutes for life, whenever the goal of the poet becomes Beauty, or some other aesthetic concept, rather than the depiction of reality, then the poem is symbolist rather than decadent. Wyzewa expects poetry to re-create life rather than depict it. Edouard Dubus states that the sole object of a poem is beauty (*le beau*), which consists of variety in unity, so that the more subjects of aesthetic emotion a poem offers in pursuing a single goal, the more it will correspond to this idea. An aesthetic emotion consists essentially of sense-impressions, but since nature is imperfect, the poet substitutes for them aesthetic forms, or symbols, consisting of *correspondances* and of musical evocations, and these symbols are figures or images expressing a purely moral quality.[74] Nature, in Dubus' view, is not to be imitated, and the aesthetic forms he has created have a symbolic, not a representative, value.

Symbolism, therefore, emphasises the aesthetic unity of a work of art, which decadence is willing to sacrifice for the sake of obtaining more striking effects in individual parts. Bourget, it will be recalled, drew attention to the fragmenting nature of decadence: society falls apart because individuals are unsuited to group effort, the literary composition distintegrates into individual pages, sentences, and words.[75] One thinks also of how in impressionism forms are broken down into effects of local colour and light, or of the disconnected structure of Corbière's conversational verse. In contrast, symbolists emphasise the unity which the poem imposes on its different elements. For Dubus the divers aesthetic forms in a poem must be 'logiquement reliées entre elles dans l'unité d'un sujet de composition'.[76] For Kahn a symbolic poem is '. . . un poème évoluant sur lui-même, présentant toutes les facettes d'un sujet, chacune isolément traitée, mais étroitement et strictement enchaînées par le lien d'une idée unique'.[77] Adolphe Retté complains when Dubus fails to extend such a principle of unity to an entire collection of poems: 'D'abord, contrairement à l'esthétique adoptée par les plus marquants d'entre les poètes récents, il n'a pas fait de son livre un tout, un poème dont les différentes parties se répondent entre elles et chantent des variations autour d'un thème représentatif d'une idée centrale.'[78] Thus at the aesthetic level decadence appears as a kind of raw material for symbolism, just as, at the chronological level, the decadent movement came first and symbolism second.

Up to this point we have regarded decadism from within, so to speak. Since the movement had become public knowledge with the publication of *A Rebours* and *Les Déliquescences*, it is appropriate and illuminating to consider what was going on during the latter half of the decade in that portion of the press which served the general public. There was, of course, continuing, mocking criticism of the new poetry. Anatole France, literary critic of *Le Temps*, could always be counted on for an acid reply to any notice about decadence. Ferdinand Brunetière expressed surprise that the decadents and symbolists had not thought of rehabilitating Maurice Scève's *Délie*, since it, too is hopelessly obscure.[79] One of the cleverer jibes was a short story in *La Revue Bleue*, in which a well bred young lady, Hélione d'Orval, follows the decadent fad in all its aspects, to the despair of her family, her fiancé, and her old family doctor; to cure her of her fantasy the family persuade her that she is dying of a slow, fatal disease, until, after months of languishing away in truly deliquescent fashion, she is moved to tears at the thought of her own approaching death; a cure is effected when the family doctor explains that she is realy quite well, and that the joys of conventional bourgeois life lie before her![80]

Such gems of sarcasm, however, are scarce; indeed, rather surprising is the absence from the staid columns of *La Revue des Deux Mondes*, *La Revue Bleue*, or *La Grande Revue*, of any indication that a literary war was going on. The regular articles of prestigious critics like Lemaitre or Ferdinand Brunetière involved substantial research and preparation, so that only rarely could one be devoted to a peripheral subject or an unknown author.[81] Many magazines of large circulation simply did not review small editions of poetry or cover the activities of the avant-garde. Nor could decadents constantly fight philistines, since some of them who wanted to become professional writers devoted part of their energies to serious critical studies for magazines of large circulation. So we find conventional, expository articles signed by names that we more readily associate with *la jeune littérature*: Georges Rodenbach's 'Le Catholicisme dans la poésie moderne', which dealt with Baudelaire, Marceline Desbordes-Valmore, and Verlaine in the conservative *Grande Revue*;[82] Emile Hennequin's studies of Poe and of Flaubert in *La Revue Contemporaine*;[83] or Morice's articles on Bourget and on 'Lamartine, Baudelaire, Shelley' in the same magazine.[84] Moreover, it should be said to the credit of the conservative press that, while their selections reflected the time lag between the taste of the avant-garde and that of the literate public (e.g. *La Revue Contemporaine* could stomach studies of Poe and Baudelaire by 1885!), and while their critics could on occasion be sarcastic, they often demonstrated an impartial fairness. Thus, in spite of 'Alceste's' aversion to decadence, *La Grande Revue* published the poetry of Jean Ajalbert, Pierre Quillard, Armand

Silvestre, and other decadents, as well as articles and stories by Joséphin Péladan (author of *Le Vice suprême*, and extreme example of decadence in the novel) and Jean Lorrain (author of *Modernités*). Poetry appearing in such magazines, of course, was usually more conventional than decadent, but, as we saw in our first chapter, men with advanced critical tastes were capable of writing the most banal of traditional verse. *La Revue Bleue* spoke sympathetically of Gabriel Vicaire,[85] whose *Emaux bressans*, to be sure, bear no similarity to *Les Déliquescences* (it was Paul Bourde who twitted him for the discrepancy between his two poetic styles). The same critic for *La Revue Bleue*, in an article on 'La Poésie parisienne', discusses Emile Goudeau's transposition of modern Paris into ancient Rome in *Les Fleurs du bitume*, apparently without realising that Goudeau's idea was the very essence of decadence.[86] Even Jules Lemaitre is neutral and expresses mixed reactions in his review of Tola Dorian's *Poèmes lyriques*,[87] although he is displeased with Mallarmé's translation of Poe, whose poetry he calls 'de la vapeur opiacée'.[88] Moreover, individual reviewers apparently enjoyed a certain freedom of taste: although *La Revue Contemporaine* found Laforgue's *Complaintes* 'le tohu-bohu d'une foire de mots, d'images et de coq-à-l'âne tout à fait réjouissante', even a parody of *Les Déliquescences*,[89] *La Revue Bleue*, while deploring its hermeticism, still found the *Complaintes* truly modern and a contrast to sentimentality in verse.[90] Seen from this perspective, those writers and their works which we have been calling decadent merge quietly with the regular weekly flow of new books.

Notes

1 In 'Charles Baudelaire', *Revue des Deux Mondes*, LXXXI (1 June 1887), 696.

2 Quoted from *L'Univers Illustré*, 2 October 1886, by Jacques Plowert (Paul Adam) in 'Parenthèses et incidences: contumellies illustrées', *Symboliste*, I, 1 (7–14 October 1886), 1.

3 In 'La Sensation en littérature: la folie de Charles Baudelaire', *Taches d'Encre*, I, 2 (5 December 1884), 26. Nevertheless Moréas stated in 1891: 'C'est moi le premier qui ai protesté, dès 1885, contre l'épithète de *décadents*, dont on nous affublait, et c'est moi qui ai réclamé en même temps celle de symboliste,' Jules Huret, *Enquête sur l'évolution littéraire* (Charpentier, 1891), p. 76.

4 Moréas' capitals and emphasis; 'Les Décadents', *Le XIXe Siècle*, 11 August 1885; see also *Les Premières Armes du symbolisme* (Vanier, 1889), pp. 27 and 30.

5 *A Rebours* (Fasquelle, 1955), p. 228.

6 In 'La Sensation en littérature', No. 2, p. 36. Of the first writers to discuss
   Verlaine, Charles Morice dealt only with 'Art poétique', 'Jean Mario' did
   not mention Verlaine's decadence, while Huysmans, who owed many of
   his ideas to Gautier, did so at length. Léon Bloy, in his *Chat Noir* article on
   Les Poètes maudits, called Verlaine 'maudit' and 'romantique', but not
   'décadent'. Subsequently Louis Desprez, Barrès, and others all call Verlaine
   and his followers 'décadent', Thus Jacques Plowert (Paul Adam) is wrong
   when he states in his *Petit Glossaire pour servir à l'intelligence des auteurs
   décadents et symbolistes* (Vanier, 1888), under 'décadence', that it was Maurice
   Barrès who first applied the term to Verlaine, Mallarmé, and their followers
   (p. 28); Barrès is merely the first to do so *after* Huysmans. Plowert does
   have some interesting observations on the background of the term. After
   stating that the word is 'employé volontiers par Gautier, Flaubert et Goncourt dans le sens de raffinement littéraire' (p. 27), he continues, 'L'origine
   du mouvement littéraire remonte à l'apparition des *Poètes maudits* de Paul
   Verlaine . . .' (p. 28), referring to a passage where Verlaine compares the
   portraits of Rimbaud, Corbière, and Mallarmé to bronze busts of the
   Roman decadence. See *Oeuvres complètes*, Henry de Bouillane de Lacoste et
   Jacques Borel, eds., I, Club du meilleur livre, 1959, pp. 466–7.
7 Paul Verlaine, *Oeuvres poétiques complètes*, Y.-G. Le Dantec, ed. (Gallimard,
   1954), p. 980.
8 The reference is to Paul Bourde, 'Les Poètes décadents', *Le Temps*, 6
   August 1885. See Ernest Raynaud, *La Mêlée symboliste*, I (Renaissance du
   livre, 1920), p. 63. In his *L'Ecole décadente* (Vanier, 1887), p. 12, Anatole
   Baju says the name was chosen for the same reason, but in retort to an
   article by Félicien Champsaur in *L'Evénement*.
9 See Raynaud, I, p. 65. The word is used in *Le Décadent* from the very first
   issue.
10 'Les Symbolistes' (16 October 1886), 73–81.
11 I, I (7–14 October 1886), 2.
12 2 January 1886, pp. 1–2.
13 16 August 1886, p. 3.
14 'En dépouillant l' scrutin', 1 December 1885, p. 4, and 'Au cours de M'sieu
   Caro', 15 December 1885, p. 7.
15 1 December 1885, p. 2.
16 2 January 1886, p. 5.
17 1 February 1886, p. 2.
18 See Jean Moréas, 'Peintures', *Symboliste*, I, 3 (22–9 October 1886), 9, and
   Paul Adam, 'Chronique', *ibid.*, 10.
19 I, I (7–14 October 1886), 1–2.
20 'Peintures'. The same distinction is made by André Barre, *Le Symbolisme*
   (Jouve, 1912), pp. 8–9, and Guy Michaud, *Le Message poétique du symbolisme*,
   I (Nizet, 1947), pp. 220–21.
21 René Ghil, 'Notre Ecole', *La Décadence*, I, I (1886), 1.

22 'La Sensation en littérature', No. 2, p. 29.

23 The only complete study of *Le Décadent* is Noël Richard, *Le Mouvement décadent; dandys, esthètes et quintessents* (Nizet, 1968), which, its title notwithstanding, has to do solely with the history of this periodical. Since much material concerning *Le Décadent* is either generally known or available in this work, to avoid an inordinate number of footnotes we shall limit our documentation to sources of direct quotations. In most cases, statements about persons, including pseudonyms, can be verified in the excellent 'Index des noms de personnes' in *Le Mouvement décadent*, pp. 273–9.

24 Anatole Baju, 'A nos lecteurs', *Le Décadent*, 17 April 1886. Hereafter references to *Le Décadent* will be identified in the text by year and issue number.

25 See Richard, p. 21.

26 *Ibid.*, p. 10.

27 This photograph is reproduced on the front cover of *Le Mouvement décadent*.

28 Raynaud, I, p. 63.

29 Baju, 'M. Emile Zola décoré', 1–15 August 1888, and 'M. Emile Zola', 1–15 November 1888. See Richard, p. 134.

30 Richard, p. 44, adds two more 'avatars' of Baju, Hector Fayolles and Raoul Vague.

31 'Un Point de doctrine', 15–28 February 1889.

32 'Le Style, c'est l'homme', 17 April 1886.

33 Baju, 'Pessimisme', 1 May 1886.

34 'Quintessence', 11 September 1886.

35 'Décadents et symbolistes', 15–30 November 1888.

36 (Baju), 'Les Livres', 1–15 June 1888.

37 'Le Poète décadent', 1 May 1886.

38 'Chronique littéraire', 15–30 April 1888.

39 15–30 June 1888. See also A. E. Carter, *The Idea of Decadence in French Literature, 1830–1900* (Toronto University Press, 1958), p. 137.

40 See Richard, chapter VII, 'Un Cheval de Troie dans la cité décadente', pp. 85–92, and Plowert, 'Parenthèses et incidences: les voltes de M. Baju', *Symboliste*, I, 1 (7–14 October 1886), 1.

41 See Baju, '*Le Décadent*', 2 October 1886. For circulation figures two years later, a notice on the last page of the 1–15 January 1888 issue states that, to give wider circulation to Verlaine's 'Lettre au *Décadent*', this issue will have 10,000 copies instead of the normal 4,500. Four issues later (1–15 March) the *tirage justifié* is given as 6,000 copies. Now, since many of the 4,000 subscribers are public places such as cafés and *salons de lecture*, Baju reasons, and since each issue in such a place could be read by more than a hundred persons per day, *Le Décadent* might well have as many as 200,000 to 300,000 readers! ('Publicité du *Décadent*', 1–15 March 1888.)

42 Verlaine, 'Anatole Baju', *Les Hommes d'aujourd'hui, Oeuvres complètes,*

Henry de Bouillane de Lacoste et Jacques Borel, eds., II (Club du meilleur livre, 1960), p. 650.

43 The retraction was buried in a page and a half of decadent obfuscation announcing that the poems previously attributed to Arthur Rimbaud, Ernest Raynaud, Maurice du Plessys, and Laurent Tailhade were actually the work of Mitrophane Crapoussin, who will henceforth contribute over his own name ('Avis', R. V. [Raoul Vague], 1–15 February 1889). Then in the issue of 15–31 March the editors, citing doubts as to the authenticity of the Rimbaud poems, claim to be the sole owners of his unpublished works. Thus truth and Verlaine's feelings both remained unsatisfied.

It was du Plessys, Raynaud, and Tailhade who composed both the Rimbaud and the Crapoussin poems, some of which appear in Tailhade's *Poèmes aristophanesques*.

For a thorough discussion, see Bruce Morrissette, *The Great Rimbaud Forgery* (St Louis: Washington University Press, 1956), pp. 1–10 and appendix 4, pp. 285–9, where he gives the texts of the forgeries. As a further complication, Mr Morrissette omits mention of 'Les Corbeaux', and he also lists 'Nirvâna' as a sonnet attributed to Crapoussin. Now this poem was called 'Renoncement' in the 1–15 March 1889, issue; an entirely different one, titled 'Nirvâna', was published by Emile Cottinet in the 15–30 July 1888 issue!

44 1–15 January 1888. See also Verlaine, *Oeuvres complètes*, I, pp. 893–4.

45 Gustave Kahn, ' "Paul Verlaine", par Jules Lemaitre', *Revue Indépendante*, n.s., VI, 16 (February 1888), 287.

46 Verlaine, *Oeuvres complètes*, I, p. 900.

47 Paul Verlaine, *Lettres inédites à Charles Morice*, Georges Zayed, editor. (Minard, 1964), p. 94.

48 See Paul Verlaine, *Correspondance*, II, Adolphe van Bever, editor. (Messein, 1923), p. 95; quoted by Richard, p. 182. The result, of course, was his article on Baju in *Les Hommes d'aujourd'hui*.

49 Quoted by Richard, p. 183, n. 30.

50 Georges Zayed, *Lettres inédites de Verlaine à Cazals* (Geneva: Droz, 1957), p. 149.

51 See *Oeuvres complètes*, I, p. 1296.

52 Unpublished letter quoted by Richard, p. 178.

53 See *Oeuvres complètes*, I, pp. 1321 and 1322, respectively.

54 See Richard, pp. 210–13.

55 E.g. 'Le symbolisme? . . . comprends pas . . . Ça doit être un mot allemand . . . hein? Qu'est-ce que ça peut bien vouloir dire? Moi, d'ailleurs, je m'en fiche. Quand je souffre, quand je jouis ou quand je pleure, je sais bien que ça n'est pas du symbole. Voyez-vous, toutes ces distinctions-là, c'est de l'allemand-isme; qu'est-ce que ça peut faire à un poète ce que Kant, Schopenhauer, Hegel, et autres Boches pensent des sentiments humains!' *Oeuvres complètes*, II, p. 1760.

56 *Oeuvres complètes*, I, p. 1256.

57 It is André Fontaine, in his *Verlaine, homme de lettres* (Delagrave, 1937), who argues convincingly that Verlaine, as a professional writer, was far more adroit at cultivating his literacy fortunes than most biographers have realised.

58 Téodor de Wyzewa handled 'Les Livres' from n.s., I, 1 (November 1886) to V, 14 (December 1887); enthusiastic over Mallarmé and Laforgue, he never reviewed a book of Verlaine's. Gustava Kahn replaced Wyzewa, doing the 'Chronique de la littérature et de l'art' from n.s., VI, 15 (January 1888) onward; thus he had occasion to review *Amour* and Lemaitre's article on Verlaine.

59 See 'La Sensation en littérature', I, 1 (5 November 1884), 3–26, and 2 (5 December 1884), 21–43.

60 'La Jeunesse sous le Second Empire et sous la Troisième République', *Revue Politique et Littérature (Revue Bleue)*, XXXV, 24 (13 June 1885), 742–3.

61 'Les Romans de M. Edmond de Goncourt', *Revue Indépendante*, I, 1 (May 1884), 28–43.

62 'Notes sur M. Mallarmé', *Vogue*, I, 11 (5–12 July 1886), 362.

63 'Poésie', *Revue Indépendante*, n.s., III, 8 (June 1887), 333.

64 ' "Paul Verlaine", par Jules Lemaitre,' 288 and 289.

65 See Jean-Pierre Richard, 'Fadeur de Verlaine', in *Poésie et profondeur* (Seuil, 1955), especially pp. 175–7, and Octave Nadal, *Paul Verlaine* (Mercure de France, 1961), especially chapter 11, 'Impressionnisme pictural', pp. 96–118.

66 Respectively, 'La Sensation en littérature', No. 2, p. 27; 'Les Vivants et les morts: Paul Verlaine', *Nouvelle Rive Gauche*, 9–15 February 1883; and *A Rebours*, p. 230.

67 'M. Jules Lemaitre et les poètes décadents', *Décadent*, 15–29 February 1888.

68 ' "Paul Verlaine", par Jules Lemaitre', p. 291.

69 'M. Jules Lemaitre et les poètes décadents'.

70 'M. Paul Verlaine et les poètes symbolistes et décadents', *Revue Politique et Littéraire (Revue Bleue)*, XLI, 1 (7 January 1888), 12.

71 'Une Critique', *Revue Indépendante*, n.s., I, 1 (November 1886), 66.

72 ' "Paul Verlaine," par Jules Lemaitre', p. 292.

73 *L'Impressionnisme français: peinture, littérature, musique* (Geneva: Studer, 1951), pp. 118–19.

74 Quoted by Ernest Raynaud in 'Du symbolisme', *Décadent*, 15–31 March 1888.

75 In 'Charles Baudelaire', *Essais de psychologie contemporaine* (Lemerre, 1883), p. 25.

76 'Du symbolisme'.

77 ' "Paul Verlaine", par Jules Lemaitre', p. 290.

78 'Chroniques', *Ermitage*, III, 5 (15 May 1892), 309.

79 In 'Revue littéraire: les éditions originales', *Revue des Deux Mondes*, LXXXVI (1 March 1888), 217.

80 Georges Peyrebrune, 'Une Décadente, modernité', XXXVII, 12 and 13 (20 and 27 March 1886), 353–61 and 392–401.

81 After waiting for the decadents to produce something important before writing about them, Brunetère finally discussed them anyway because of their wide influence on youth. His conclusion is that as a literary renewal decadence and symbolism will not be as permanent or as fertile as Romanticism. See his 'Symbolistes et décadents', *Revue des Deux Mondes*, XC (1 November 1888), 213–26.

82 *Deuxième année*, I, 2 (November 1888), 203–15.

83 'Edgar Poe, étude critique', I, 1 (25 January 1885), 24–56; 'Gustave Flaubert, étude critique', III, 2 (25 October 1885), 137–74.

84 'Paul Bourget, étude critique', II, 1 (25 May 1885), 72–90; 'Lamartine, Baudelaire, Shelley', IV, 2 (25 January 1886), 15–37.

85 Antony Valabrègue, 'Les Poètes du terroir', XLIV, 8 (24 August 1889), 253.

86 Valabrègue, XLV, 12 (22 March 1890), 369. Perhaps tempers had cooled in the course of five years!

87 'Causerie littéraire,' *Revue Bleue*, XLII, 13 (29 September 1888), 411–12.

88 *Ibid.*, XLII, 15 (13 October 1888), 475–6.

89 'Poésie', III, 1 (25 September 1885), 108–9.

90 Maxime Gaucher, 'Causerie littéraire', XXXVII, 1 (2 January 1886), 28.

Chapter IX
Verlaine's influence on younger poets

When Verlaine's influence on younger poets first became apparent in the season 1883–84 his style, language, and themes were imitated so closely as to resemble parody; we saw this in poems of a Jean Moréas or a Charles Vignier. By 1885, however, such exaggeratedly close imitations give way to more mature practices which, submerging Verlaine's diction in a sort of generalised decadent idiom, express the same moods as his poetry and seek to state emotions in terms of perceived phsyical sensations. Thus, as was the case with Baudelaire a few years before, we look for the effects of Verlaine's influence in the work of those poets who understood the significance of his *poétique*, rather than in superficial imitations of his mannerisms.

It is also important to distinguish between devices which are uniquely Verlaine's and those which he, too, inherited from his predecessors. Romanticism, the Parnassianism of Leconte de Lisle, and the work of Baudelaire, the three poetic currents which affected the young Verlaine in 1866, still prevailed in 1882, so that his followers actually underwent the same influences as he had. It is possible for the verse of a young poet of the '80's to resemble Verlaine's, not because he had read him, but because both had read Baudelaire, Leconte de Lisle, or Hugo. A passage from *Poèmes saturniens* could almost as well have been written by an obscure imitator of Baudelaire in 1882: 'Allons, mon pauvre coeur, allons, *mon vieux complice*, / Redresse et peins à neuf tous tes arcs triomphaux.'[1] A poet steeped in Victor Hugo (to judge from obituary articles in 1885, he was generally respected by the young generation) could unwittingly have written verse recalling Baudelaire, for Hugo and Baudelaire both portray autumn as the season of sadness and death, both draw on the suggestiveness of musical words like *linceul*, and Baudelaire probably derived his use of *clair-obscur* in descriptions from Hugo. The melancholy of autumn was a widespread Romantic theme, common to poets from Lamartine to Laforgue. It should be born in mind, therefore, that there was a common nineteenth-century poetic tradition which most poets shared and which causes them to resemble

each other. How often in the second half of the century does *automne*
rhyme with *monotone* or *chantonne*, how often *la bise détonne*, and, a little
later in the decadent period, does *la blanche lune luit*! This community
of themes, diction, and figures explains the inclusiveness of critics who
list multiple sources for the verse of a new poet, as when Adolphe
Retté finds 'Par ci et par là, pourtant, de fâcheuses rémiscences de MM.
Verlaine, Maeterlinck et Kahn . . .' in Fernand Roussell's *Le Jardin de
l'âme*,[2] or Marjorie Louise Henry finds that 'Par sa sensibilité frémissante,
Merrill est le frère de Poe, de Baudelaire et de Verlaine.'[3]

That the existence of this tradition makes it difficult to isolate
Verlaine's influence from that of the other masters of the century
becomes apparent if we trace two particular tropes. Verlaine's 'Clair de
lune' seems at first to be one of the most widely imitated poems in
French literature, to judge from the number of poems which compare
the heart or soul to a physical décor (e.g. 'Mon coeur est une crypte où
parmi les pilastres / S'enroulent les remous de l'encens des oublis'[4]), or
the verb *se mêler* is applied to the mingling of different sensations (e.g.
of moonlight and music). Yet Baudelaire had written, 'Notre âme est
un trois-mâts cherchant son Icarie,' and 'Pendant que le parfum des
verts tamariniers / . . . / Se mêle dans mon âme au chant des mariniers,'[5]
and Hugo, 'Ils sentaient par degrés se mêler à leur âme, / . . . / Le clair
de lune bleu qui baignait l'horizon.'[6]

Similarly, although it was generally agreed that Verlaine was
instrumental in relaxing the rules of French versification,[7] this tendency
was so strong anyway that Marie Krysinska's first free verse poems
appeared in *Le Chat Noir* in 1882, at the same time that 'Art poétique'
was published elsewhere. Hugo rhymed different meanings or forms
of the same word.[8] So not all infractions of traditional prosody can be
ascribed to Verlaine's influence.

Two devices, on the contrary, do seem to be Verlaine's own contribution to decadent prosody: *vers impairs* and the short, simple, song-
like stanzas of 'Chanson d'automne' or 'Il pleure dans mon coeur'.
Although Baudelaire had used *vers impairs* in *Les Fleurs du mal*, we
have not seen them used by minor poets until 1884, and then almost
always in company with other Verlainean mannerisms. While brief
stanzas of short lines were common in the verse of Banville and Gautier
(and sometimes in Hugo's), and Baudelaire used them as the refrain of
'L'Invitation au voyage', Verlaine seems to have originated using
them with repetitious assonances in a song-like manner.

It seems, consequently, that the best way to examine Verlaine's

influence on his contemporaries is to look for poets who understood
and put to use his aesthetic attitudes, rather than merely to enumerate,
as we did in chapter v, those who appear at least to have read his verse.
Here Téodor de Wyzewa is a useful point of departure, for his repeated
assertion that poetry is a verbal music suitable for transmitting emotions[9]
seems like an unconscious echo of 'Art poétique'. Although Wyzewa
does not happen to discuss Verlaine's work, the poets whom he singles
out for most nearly realising his ideal of verbal music are among those
whose verse resembles Verlaine's: Stuart Merrill, Francis Vielé-
Griffin, and Gustave Kahn.[10] The latter merits our attention for his
appreciation of Verlaine in his own criticism and because of the strongly
Verlainean tenor of his *Palais nomades*. The section entitled 'Voix au
parc' has for its epigraph 'L'inflexion des voix chères qui se sont tues',[11]
and Verlaine's influence is equally evident in the poem 'Mélopées, IV':

Chantonne lentement et très bas . . . mon coeur pleure . . .
Tristement, doucement, plaque l'accord mineur;
Il fait froid, il pâlit quelque chose dans l'heure . . .
Un vague très blafard étreint l'âpre sonneur.
Arrête-toi . . . c'est bien . . . mais ta voix est si basse? . . .
Trouves-tu pas qu'il sourd comme un épais sanglot?
Chantonne lentement, dans les notes il passe
Vrillante, l'âcreté d'un malheur inéclos.

Encore! la chanson s'alanguit . . . mon coeur pleure;
Des noirs accumulés estompent les flambeaux.
Ce parfum trop puissant et douloureux qu'il meure
Chant si lourd à l'alcôve ainsi qu'en un tombeau.
D'où donc ce frissellis d'émoi qui me pénètre,
D'où très mesurément, ce rythme mou d'andante?
Il circule là-bas, aux blancheurs des fenêtres,
De bougeuses moiteurs, des ailes succédantes.

Assez! laisse expirer la chanson . . . mon coeur pleure;
Un bistre rampe autour des clartés. Solennel
Le silence est monté lentement, il apeure
Les bruits familiers du vague perennel.
Abandonne . . . que sons et que parfums se taisent!
Rythme mélancolique et poignant! . . . Oh! douleur,
Tout est sourd, et grisâtre et s'en va!—Parenthèse,
Ouvres-tu l'infini d'un éternel malheur?   [pp. 65–6]

It is Verlaine's decadent manner that we find here; the unidentified
references, the unanswered questions, and the rich, yet disconnected,

imagery evoke the obscurity of some of the 'Lunes' poems; the succession of noun phrases, free of grammatical links, are typical of Verlaine; the bits of conversation, as in lines 5 and 6 (note the colloquial omission of *ne* in 'Trouves-tu pas . . .?) recall the theme of friendship, as in 'A Fernand Langlois' (p. 429). The use of words which are of low frequency-count, like *frisselis, apeurer, perennel*, is typical of Verlaine; *il pâlit, il sourd, il passe, il circule* recall several Verlainean mannerisms: the use of personal verbs in impersonal constructions, his sometimes careless grammar, and his tendency to express emotions obliquely with *c'est*, an impersonal verb, or a qualifier such as *comme si*. In lines 1 and 2 the assonances and alliterations, the soft, harmonious vowel sounds, and the uneven rhythm of pronounced mute *e*'s are very common effects in Verlaine's versification. The refrains *chantonne lentement* and *mon coeur pleure* certainly remind us of Verlaine, even if such diction is not uniquely his. Furthermore, Kahn has reproduced certain aspects of Verlaine's sensibility, as in the deliberate suggestions of vagueness: *il pâlit quelque chose, un vague très blafard, il sourd comme un épais sanglot, aux blancheurs des fenêtres.* (In other poems Kahn is very adroit at using *quelque chose, un peu, sans doute* to suggest inexactitude of perception; or he combines terms like *d'un incertain passé*, p. 49, or *Dans d'improbables firmaments*, p. 75.) A typically Verlainean attitude is to contrast sharpness and vagueness: '. . . la chanson grise / Où l'Indécis au Précis se joint' ('Art poétique', p. 326) or 'Un instant à la fois très vague et très aigu. . .' ('Kaléidoscope', p. 321).[12] Kahn does so in line 2, where the plosives of *plaque l'accord* contrast with the harmonies of the other vocables; in line 8, where *vrillante* (drilling, or gimlet-shaped) and *âcreté* are opposed to the vagueness of *malheur inéclos*; in line 22 *Rythme mélancolique et poignant* also juxtaposes contrasting adjectives. Furthermore, the entire tone of the poem, all its apparatus of slowness, low sounds, blurred chiaroscuro, and dying sounds and perfumes—'Tout est sourd et grisâtre et s'en va! . . .'—is the same atmosphere that Verlaine loved to create. A typical situation in Verlaine's poetry is that of a music, mysteriously detached from its source, a piano, which hovers for a while before dying out:

. . .
Un air bien vieux, bien faible et bien charmant
Rôde discret, épeuré quasiment,
. . .
Que voudrais-tu de moi, doux Chant badin?
Qu'as-tu voulu, fin refrain incertain

Qui vas tantôt mourir vers la fenêtre
Ouverte un peu sur le petit jardin? ['Ariettes oubliées, v', p. 193]

This is the condition evoked in Kahn's poem with his songs and perfumes, autonomous because their source is not indicated, and which are dying out: 'Encore! la chanson s'alanguit . . . ,' 'Assez! laisse expirer la chanson . . . ,' 'Abandonne . . . que sons et parfums se taisent!'

Kahn reproduces the same passive state as Verlaine, in which the poet is acted upon by an emotion; Verlaine asks, 'Quelle est cette langueur / Qui pénètre mon coeur?' and he quietly awaits the phenomena of nature:

Immobiles, baissons nos yeux vers nos genoux.
Ne pensons plus, rêvons. Laissons faire à leurs guise
Le bonheur qui s'enfuit et l'amour qui s'épuise,
Et nos cheveux frolés par l'aile des hiboux. ['Circonspection', p. 329]

Kahn writes,

Rien dans l'avenir, rien dans le remords!
Le coeur est blessé d'une flèche étrange;
Un désir pénétrant et vague qui le mord,
Concert inexpliqué qu'un accroc bref dérange! ['Melopées, II', p. 63

In a similar mood of calm and inertia, Kahn awaits the arrival from ‧ distant places of an imaginary mistress, and, as in Verlaine, a rustling above accompanies his patient waiting:

J'attends dans l'heure obscure et calme
L'héroïne, fanal de mes rêves fiévreux,
Qui vient sous les frissons approbateurs des palmes
Du fond des lents Edens des pays ténébreux.
['Thème et variations, x', p. 57]

Dream is the realm of much of *Les Palais nomades*, just as it is for Verlaine's poetry. There is the *imaginaire dame* of the poem quoted above, there is the sister–mistress who reminds us of the dream mistresses of *Poèmes saturniens*:

Je rêvais comme d'une soeur
aux lèvres uniques de douceur
et belle et chaste et femme et soeur. ['Soir par la ville, v', p. 208]

Like Verlaine, Kahn translates his dreams in terms of sensory experience: the gait of a horse is that of his dream, 'Ton allure si lente est le pas de mon rêve, / Desir devenu doux d'avoir tant attendu'

('Thème et variations, VIII', p. 54). Forgotten sounds (and for Kahn, as for Verlaine, memory is another unattainable realm in which much of his poetry is located) are described in terms of physical sensations:

> Timbres oubliés, Timbres morts perdus,
> Pas d'une autre glissant à la rue,
> Chansons d'amour et vols de grues
> Dans d'improbables firmaments.   ['Intermède, IV', p. 75]

Again, the rather indefinite term *chanson* is defined by equating it with specific, if imaginative music: 'C'est le son des flûtes aux accords des brises / Et la marche nuptiale des pâles lys' ('Chanson de la brève démence, IV', p. 104). As with Verlaine's sensory equivalents, the trope is emotionally satisfying because it does communicate, even if logically we have difficulty visualising a wedding march of lilies. Verlaine perceived a future dawn in a musical glow:

> Je devine, à travers un murmure,
> Le contour subtil des voix musiciennes
> Et dans les lueurs musiciennes,
> Amour pâle, une aurore future!   ['Ariettes oubliées, II', p. 191]

across similar sensory experiences Kahn perceives an infinity of grief:

> Oh! le douloureux infini
> Qu'on ressent aux larges musiques,
> Au delà des clartés plastiques
> Dans les puissances mécaniques,
> Oh! le douloureux infini!   ['Mélopées, II', p. 62]

Further examples of Verlaine's influence can be found in almost any poem of *Palais nomades*. The significance of Kahn's debt to Verlaine is in the way Kahn has adopted the older poet's very sensibility, seeing life as a dream or memory and rendering the ineffable portion of his experience in concrete, musical terms of sensation. So in Kahn's verse we do not find the superficial resemblances, verging on *pastiche*, which often cause such derivative verse to seem like third-rate Verlaine. Kahn, in fact, is vaguer than Verlaine, for the moods he evokes in poems like 'Mélopées, IV' or 'Thèmes et variations, x' are not based on anything as limited as a landscape, a *commedia dell'arte* situation, or an identifiable biographical incident. If both poets have a similar attitude, Verlaine reacts to a specific stimulus, while Kahn endeavours to establish a more general mood; furthermore, of course, Verlaine stopped his musical experiments well short of Kahn's free verse.

Although Henri de Régnier does not adopt Verlaine's aesthetics as completely as Kahn, still he defines a mood or an experience in terms of music and of equivalent physical sensations: 'Ton pas est un frisson de robe sur les mousses',[13] and, as in Verlaine's second 'Ariette', he perceives subjective values through a veil of sense-perceptions:

C'était, là-bas, aux lointains bleus des avenues
Parmi l'herbe fleurie et la forêt d'avril
Mon âme même qui disait son puéril
Poème par ce jeu de lèvres inconnues. ['Prologue', p. 199]

The area of contact between Régnier's and Verlaine's poetry consists of some dozen poems from *Les Lendemains*, *Apaisements*, and *Sites* which reproduce the same décor, mood, and themes as various poems of *Poèmes saturniens* and *Fêtes galantes*. In this rather limited zone Régnier resembles Verlaine more than Kahn does, yet the very similarities emphasise the difference between Régnier and Verlaine, for the latter's poems are more concise, his diction tenser and more specific. Both Régnier and Verlaine create an autumn evening at moonrise saddened by memories of the past or by the poet's dissatisfaction with the response of his mistress; in either case, the sadness is that nostalgic melancholy caused by an ideal of love which is beyond the poet's achievement—the kind of gentle, spontaneous melancholy Verlaine has made as distinctively his own as a trade mark. Very typical of Régnier's poems in this vein, and hence of his debt to Verlaine, is the first poem of *Les Lendemains*:

Vers le passe

Sur l'étang endormi palpitent les roseaux;
Et l'on entend passer en subites bouffées,
Comme le vol craintif d'invisibles oiseaux,
Le léger tremblement de brises étouffées;

La lune fait tomber sa divine pâleur
Sur le déroulement infini des prairies
D'où le vent, par instants, apporte la senteur
Des buissons verdoyants et des herbes fleuries;

Mais voici que, tout bas, chuchote la chanson
Que chantent, dans la nuit, les plaintives fontaines.
Dans le coeur secoué d'un intime frisson
S'éveille le regret des tendresses lointaines,

Et, du fond du passé, monte le souvenir

> Triste et délicieux de pareilles soirées,
> Et de bien loin on sent aux lèvres revenir
> Les paroles d'amour en l'ombre murmurées.   [pp. 13–14]

The sleeping pond, with its reeds, intermittent wind, and flight of birds reminds us of 'Promenade sentimentale' or 'Le Rossignol' in *Poèmes saturniens*; the plaintive fountains of the third stanza recall those of *Fêtes galantes*; the moonlight and its *divine pâleur* are typical of Verlaine's predilection for moonlight in *Fêtes galantes* and, more generally, for light which can be described by synonyms of off-white. Régnier echoes this taste in many passages, such as '. . . le ciel que blanchissait / La lente ascension d'une lune cachée / Avait des tons nacrés et transparents de lait' ('Vers le passé, III', p. 16) The impression of remoteness in space or time so common in Verlaine's verse is evoked by the expressions, *le déroulement infini des prairies, du fond du passé*, and *Et de bien loin on sent aux lèvres revenir*. *Le Regret des tendresses lointaines* and *le souvenir / Triste et délicieux de pareilles soirées* adumbrate the same undefined melancholy so distinctive of Verlaine. For Verlaine, emotions and memories occur on their own initiative and happen to the poet ('Souvenir, souvenir, que me veux-tu?', 'Nevermore', p. 61; 'Comme un vol criard d'oiseaux en émoi, / Tous mes souvenirs s'abattent sur moi', 'Le Rossignol', p. 73), so for Régnier a regret *s'éveille* in line 12, and memory *monte* in line 13. Finally, Régnier seeks to concretise, to incarnate his nostalgia by rendering as specifically and physically as possible the circumstances in which *paroles d'amour* were uttered; in so doing he recalls Verlaine's 'Et qu'il bruit avec un murmure charmant / Le premier *oui* qui sort de lèvres bien-aimées!' (p. 45).

How many readers have noticed, as Régnier has, Verlaine's predilection for birds in his early landscapes: the thrush (*la grive*, p. 61); the teal, with its beating wings (*la sarcelle*, p. 70); the nightingale ('l'oiseau que fut mon Premier Amour', p. 74; 'Voix de notre désespoir', p. 120; '. . . un langoureux rossignol / Clame la détresse à tue-tête', p. 114); and the owl ('Et nos cheveux frôlés par l'aile des hiboux', p. 329)? Five of Régnier's poems contain birds, and a sixth mentions the colour of the gull's wings ('Sur un ciel automnal dont les tons apaisés / Avaient le gris perlé de l'aile des mouettes,' 'Expérience', p. 19); in two poems, it is the dove which, like Verlaine's nightingale, images the poet's melancholy: 'Et la colombe y roucoule / Son éternel désespoir', ('Terrasse', p. 77).

Particularly in *Fêtes galantes* Verlaine heightens the note of psychological ambiguity, of poignant yet indeterminate emotion, by ending the poem on a note of interrogation, of uncertainty, of unresolved personal tensions, so that the emotions of the poem tend to hover in the reader's sensibility long after he has put it down. Thus, in 'Pantomime',

Colombine rêve, surprise
De sentir un coeur dans la brise
Et d'entendre en son coeur des voix.   [p. 107]

Similarly, two of Régnier's poems conclude with his beloved continuing to regard her poet, her emotional reaction still growing, rather than terminated: 'Je pris alors ses mains dans les miennes pour voir / Ses yeux s'alanguir d'une indicible tendresse' ('Vers le passé, III', p. 17), and 'Et tes yeux grands ouverts me suivent dans la nuit' ('Nocturne', p. 45). Like Verlaine's 'Fantoches', with its nightingale, 'Terrasse' ends with the dove's melancholy cooing. Verlaine's 'Circonspection' ends on a menacing note: 'Il n'est pas bon d'aller troubler dans son sommeil / La nature, ce dieux féroce et taciturne' (p. 329), as does 'Expérience' (and the poet's following a pair of lovers reminds us of Verlaine and his companion following their mistresses in 'Les Ingénus'), where the poet's prescience seems to bode no good: 'Ils étaient le présent et j'étais le passé / Et je savais le mot final de la chimère' (p. 19). Comparing 'Expérience' with 'Les Ingénus' contrasts the way the two poets handle the same theme: in 'Les Ingénus' a series of sharply noted observations lead convincingly to a moment of emotional ambiguity; although Régnier does present two precise visual notations in his first stanza, they do not seem to reinforce the mood of the poem or to help induce its conclusion.

There are many other similarities between Régnier's and Verlaine's nostalgic evenings: the heptasyllabic line of 'Terrasse'; the slow, measured rhythm, the verbal harmonies, and the refrains of 'Le Mauvais Soir':

La nuit se fait sereine et douce,
La lune luit sur le chemin,
Mes larmes tombent sur la main,
La main chère qui me repousse.   [p. 95]

There are a typically Verlainean handling of landscape description in the second stanza of 'Frisson du soir' and an evocation of blurred vagueness in the same poem: 'Les contours indécis des choses incertaines' (p. 48). Like Verlaine ('Le vent profond / Pleure, on veut croire', 'Charleroi', p. 197; 'Ils n'ont pas l'air de croire à leur bonheur', 'Clair

de lune', p. 83), who is loth to recognise emotion in his own breast, for
Régnier emotions happen in an impersonal mode: 'Il neige dans mon
coeur des souffrances cachées' ('Nocturne', p. 44); 'Au coeur les
souvenirs pleurent confusément' (*ibid.*, p. 45). A chief point of comparison is easily the simultaneity of natural phenomena with the poet's
emotional state: 'L'heure est si douce que l'eau semble / S'arrêter . . .'
('Insouciance', p. 97). In 'Le Mauvais Soir', above, the advancing night
parallels the poet's amorous despair. The wind rustles the trees or
wrinkles the water, the moon rises or a leaf falls, the fountains emit
their lament or wings rustle overhead, in each case the movements of
nature coincide exactly in time with the poet's melancholy nostalgia
for the past, for the love he once knew, for the love which is just beyond
attainment. Few of the many impressionist poets of the '80's thought
to imitate Verlaine's use of natural phenomena to indicate the passage
of time: '. . . et l'épais linceul / Des ténèbres vint noyer les suprêmes /
Rayons du couchant . . .' ('Promenade sentimentale', p. 71); Régnier
does so in a few poems: 'Le crépuscule lent monte jusqu'au plafond /
Où les rayons perdus caressent les moulures' ('Frisson du soir', p.
49);

> Et l'on va, s'accoudant aux rampes, et, bientôt
> La lune bienveillante aux endroits solitaires
> Eclaire vaguement les bois et les parterres.   ['Solitude', p. 93]

Kahn and Régnier are the only poets, to our knowledge, who adopt
a consistently Verlainean attitude; the others do so only intermittently,
or else they merely echo his phraseology. In a typical instance Albert
Samain professes the same tastes as those of 'Art poétique':

> J'adore l'indécis, les sons, les couleurs frêles,
> Tout ce qui tremble, ondule, et frissonne, et chatoie:
> Les cheveux et les yeux, l'eau, les feuilles, la soie,
> Et la spiritualité des formes grêles;[14]

'Musique sur l'eau' establishes the mood of languor, of passive semi-
existence, in which sounds from afar reach the poet in weakened
intensity:

> Oh! écoute la symphonie;
> Rien n'est doux comme une agonie
> Dans la musique indéfinie
> Qu'exhale un lointain vaporeux;

D'une langueur la nuit s'enivre,
Et notre coeur qu'elle délivre
Du monotone effort de vivre
Se meurt d'un trépas langoureux.   [p. 27]

Like Verlaine, Samain questions what goes on around him, and the
rhythm of the line is interrupted by a dash, or by an interjection; the
soft, open sonority of *chère* made it a favourite epithet of Verlaine, too:

L'amour est lourd—Mon âme est lasse . . .
Quelle est donc, Chère, sur nous deux,
Cette aile en silence qui passe?   [p. 26]

In 'Invitation' the first stanza ('Mon coeur est un beau lac solitaire qui
tremble', p. 87) recalls the Baudelairian trope of 'Clair de lune' as well
as, more generally, Verlaine's practice of equating a landscape with his
mood. In the second stanza we have his pale moonlight ('La lune y
fait rêver ses pâleurs infinies') and, farther on, an implication of the
passage of time by noting the change in colours as the light shifts (cf.
Verlaine's 'D'une lune rose et grise', in 'Mandoline', p. 116):

Le lac est vert, le lac est bleu;
Voici tinter le couvre-feu.

Sonnez l'heure aux ondins, petites campanules.

Dame aux yeux verts, Dame aux yeux bleus,
Dame d'autrefois au coeur frileux.   ['Invitation', p. 88]

A horn sounding in the fog, a perfume losing its scent as it dissipates—
Verlaine often expressed such evanescent modes of being, and he also
used the tight stanza form, with its rich rhymes and *vers impairs*:

Dans la brume un cor sonna;
Ton âme alors frissonna,
    Et, sans crise,
Ton coeur défaillit, mourant,
Comme un flacon odorant
    Qui se brise.   ['Chanson violette', p. 194]

Another stanza appears to have come straight from *Romances sans
paroles*:

Cette chanson—là-bas—écoute,
Cette chanson au fond du bois . . .
C'est l'adieu du dernier hautbois,
C'est comme si tout l'autrefois
Tombait dans l'âme goutte à goutte.   ['Hiver', p. 92]

These quotations, and there could be many more, represent the ubiquity of Verlaine's presence in *Le Jardin de l'infante*; although Samain does not maintain these states of sensibility for long, the frequency with which they do occur indicates the extent of his debt to Verlaine.

Such brief, musical stanzas are common to Banville, Gautier, Baudelaire, and Verlaine, among the Parnassians, as well as to most poets of the 1880's. So they are not uniquely Verlainean, although we correctly recall having seen them in his verse. If a few more of his mannerisms which became common poetic usage—an interjection set off by dashes, a series of *c'est* clauses, a nominal style, identical rhymes—are added, the illusion of his style seems indisputable. Echoes of Verlaine are thus easily created and may well be misleading as a measure of his influence. Perhaps, on the other hand, in our caution we underestimate Verlaine's influence. It has been pointed out that even if *Romances sans Paroles* had no other effect, with its sixteen different stanza forms it served as a display of metric combinations and as a sample book for beginning poets.[15] The diffusion of Verlaine's diction throughout minor decadent poetry may well indicate not random stylistic embellishments but the profound appeal of his *sensibilité* to those poets and their deliberate effort to copy the most effective means of expressing it.

Echoes of Verlaine are sparser and fainter in the poetry of Francis Vielé-Griffin. In a section of 'Un Poème de la mer' called 'Mare salax' his renouncement of carnal pleasure in favour of his unfinished master-piece reminds us somewhat of Verlaine's religious poems, although the first stanza recalls also the treatment of amorous exhaustion in the first 'Ariette oubliée':

> Ecoute dans la nuit d'août lascive, écoute;
> C'est comme un long sanglot d'amants exténués;
> L'atmosphère palpite . . . Allons, vieux coeur, en route
> Vers l'assouvissement de tes instincts rués;
>
> . . .
>
> Et, comme Parsifal au jardin érotique
> Parmi les fleurs du mal et leurs tentations,
> Je n'ai songé, ce soir, qu'au Chef-d'oeuvre authentique
> Où doivent converger toutes nos passions.[16]

A sonnet in the series called 'Euphonies' is somewhat like 'Kaléidoscope' or the sonnets of 'L'Almanach pour l'année passée' on account of its vague, nonsequitur dream atmosphere:

Dormir et rire d'aise, un sommeil: je divague;
Dormons: le mal d'aimer, ô coeur, t'a ravagé;
Et je me sens, ce soir, si follement âgé
Que je me crois le survivant d'un monde vague.

La nuit est formidable et triste à tout jamais,
Un souvenir qui hante emplit l'ombre déserte;
Mon regret est futile et mon désir inerte
N'appelle plus l'espoir des rêves abîmés;

Dormons: il n'est plus rien sous le crêpe d'azur
Où s'est drapée à tout jamais la vieille voie;
Tes ailes, que le saint désir ouvre et déploie,

Retombent, ton espoir d'aimer est presque impur . . .
Je divague au retour des vaines lassitudes,
N'avions-nous pas rêvé d'autres béatitudes?　　　['Euphonies, vii', p. 26]

Vielé-Griffin, too, has the short, song-like stanzas, the refrains, the pure music of Verlaine (see 'Euphonies, vii', p. 27). His 'L'Enervante Langueur' (p. 50) employs the Verlainean paraphernalia of verbal music, mention of musical instruments, melancholy, and conversational interjection of *n'est-ce pas* in the middle of a line. Again, Verlaine's favourite image of the cradle, his motifs of dream and passivity, and his treatment of sound as coming from afar are all present in a single passage:

Mais ce rêve idyllique est comme l'accalmie;
Ta voix chaude me berce ainsi qu'un océan;
Et ta parole arrive à mon âme endormie
Comme un chant vague avec l'oubli de ce néant
Du rêve, et de l'amour, et de son accalmie;
Laisse voguer mon âme au loin sur l'océan
Et berce de ta voix son rêve d'endormie;
Puisque demain devra pleurer tout ce néant.　　　['Euphonies, ix', p. 29]

We now turn from those three poets to consider treatments of the eighteenth-century theme, which, while naturally recalling Verlaine's *Fêtes galantes*, are in fact the continuation of a Romantic tradition which antedated Verlaine by thirty years.[17] Poets like Théophile Gautier, who turned away from Victor Hugo's conception of social art to pursue that of art for art's sake, found in the gracious manner of the eighteenth century, in the paintings of Watteau, Lancret, and Boucher, a refuge from the social concerns of their time.[18] In 1834 Gautier rented an apartment in the former Rue du Doyenné, a neighbourhood of dilapidated houses near the Pont du Carrousel and the Louvre, beside an apartment occupied by Gérard de Nerval and the painter Camille

Rogier. Not only did this neighbourhood recall the ghosts of Mme de Pompadour and du Barry, Nerval's apartment had an authentic Louis XV salon, and Nerval himself owned two Fragonards. Thus was born the *Bohême du Doyenné*, where Gautier, Nerval, Arsène Houssaye, and others indulged their taste for eighteenth-century art. Meanwhile, in spite of the severely Greco-Roman taste of the Empire, and Romanticism's disdain for everything classical or *ancien régime*, Watteau paintings and those of Boucher, Fragonard, and Lancret were purchased by private collectors, who formed significant collections at a time when the Louvre possessed only *L'Embarquement pour Cythére*.[19] In the magazine *L'Artiste* critical articles began to publicise the painting of the period: in 1835, twenty-five years before the Goncourts, an article discussed the improving fortunes of Watteau.[20] Thus, after an earlier enthusiasm for the Middle Ages, one branch at least of Romanticism turned to the eighteenth century and to the practice of transposing the themes and techniques of its painting into poetry; and this long before the Goncourts or Verlaine. The decadent poets of the 1880's, therefore, probably derived this theme from Gautier, Banville, and perhaps Baudelaire,[21] as Verlaine had done, without necessarily reading the latter's *Fêtes galantes*.

In this area, too, we meet the ubiquitous Huysmans, who, as the Goncourts before him, emphasised erotic aspects of the period. In *A Rebours* he wrote, '. . . seul, en effet, le XVIIIe siècle a su envelopper la femme d'une atmosphère vicieuse, contournant les meubles selon la forme de ses charmes, imitant les contractions de ses plaisirs, les volutes de ses spasmes . . .'[22] In his art criticism he observed, 'Cette époque érotisa le meuble d'une façon charmante, aphrodisia l'industrie des tapissiers et des ébènistes.'[23]

Hence we find poems on this theme which clearly are not derived from Verlaine. Jean Lorrain dedicates the five poems of his 'Fête galante' to Edmond de Goncourt;[24] he mentions *Pompadour*, and Victor Margueritte, *Louis*[25]—names which do not appear in Verlaine. Unlike Verlaine, some poets mingle this theme with that of autumn, as Victor Margueritte does in 'Vers d'automne'[26] or Stuart Merrill in 'Bergerie sentimentale'.[27] Many poets, like Merrill and Albert Samain, must have discovered the beauties of this theme directly in Watteau's paintings, or in Lenôtre's garden at Versailles, as well as in *Fêtes galantes*.[28]

Still, there are poems which are directly imitated from Verlaine, such as this one by Edouard Dubus:

La Nuit perdue

Sous les tilleuls irradiées de girandoles,
Un orchestre envolait de frivoles motifs,
Vers l'ombre des taillis fuyaient à pas furtifs
Des couples enjolés au gré des farandoles.

Dans tout le parc c'était un scherzo de baisers;
Du rose épanoui des lèvres, ces corolles,
S'exhalait un parfum magique de paroles,
Ouvrant un ciel menteur aux coeurs inapaisés.

D'un geste impérieux, notre menotte pâle
Vers un bosquets de blancs lilas m'avait conduit,
Une lueur de lune envahissait leur nuit,
Et vos cheveux fleuris s'auréolaient d'opale.

Nous frissonnions des violons si langoureux,
Dont la brise apportait les conseils par bouffées,
Et des coups d'éventail, et des voix étouffées
Qui ripostaient aux propos fous des amoureux.

Mais un éclat de rire ironique fit trêve
Au concert éperdu soupiré jusqu'à nous,
J'eus peur de vous conter fleurettes à genoux,
—Et vos regards interrogeaient mes yeux sans rêve.[29]

The *frivoles motifs* of the orchestra, the *parfums magiques de paroles* |
Ouvrant un ciel menteur aux coeurs inapaisés, the *propos fous des amoureux*,
the *éclat de rire ironique* suggest the contrasting gaiety and sombreness,
and the ironic use of humour to refute love, which distinguish *Fêtes
galantes*, and whose psychological subtlety is Verlaine's own contribution to the genre. Comparing lips to roses in the second stanza is like
Verlaine's comparing the lady's person to seashells in 'Les Coquillages';
the *geste impérieux* of the girl (line 9) and the kneeling lover's fear as he
counts flower petals (line 19) remind us of the timidity of Verlaine's
lovers; the handling of the moonlight in the third stanza is typical of
Verlaine. The *mentotte pâle* in line 9 echoes his decadent vocabulary,
and the last line iterates the same incomplete, equivocal endings that
Henri de Régnier found typical of Verlaine.

Such echoes of Verlaine in poems dealing with Sylvanie, Tircis, and
Lindor in parks by Lenôtre can be found throughout reviews and
collections of verse. Stuart Merrill's 'Fête au parc' (p. 11), 'Bergerie
sentimentale' (p. 14), and 'Fin de fête' (p. 17) are very reminiscent of
Verlaine, especially the last two in *vers impairs*. Albert Samain's 'L'Ile

fortunée' (p. 75), 'Nocturne' (p. 81), 'Arpège' (p. 83), and 'Indifférent'
(p. 85) are full of echoes from *Fêtes galantes*. Does not the note of
disillusionment, of inaccessible happiness, in Jean Lorrain's 'Fête
galante' recall that of Verlaine? 'Les yeux couleur de lune et surtout
l'air si peu / convaincu du réel de ces fêtes galantes! / . . . / Sylvanire
poudrée, en grand habit, fardée / sait trop qu'Amour, hélas! est un
songe lointain.'[30]

There is a curious problem in the treatment of this theme by poets of
the '80's. Since the paintings of Watteau have very few fountains or
moonlit scenes, their prevalence in *Fêtes galantes* represents an original
interpretation by Verlaine.[31] Yet many, perhaps a majority, of these
poems do refer to moonlight and to fountains. Were all these references
borrowed from Verlaine, or during the 1880's did enough Parisian
poets make the short trip to Versailles to admire the park by moonlight and to be inspired directly by the impressive water displays before
the north-west facade of the palace?

The echoes of Verlaine's poetry which we have discussed coalesce
into a recognisable portrait of Verlaine the decadent. Particularly
decadent are the themes of the stagnant pond and of the eighteenth-
century park *à la* Watteau; the constant emphasis on physical sensation
as the image of emotions, and the stylistic devices for rendering images
of sensation; the evanescence of a scene or mood, especially the impressionist practice of fixing nature in a moment of flux; and the
attitude of *langueur*, of passivity, in which the poet submits to his
emotions and sense-impressions, rather than actively apprehending
them.

What the classical gardens and rustic ponds, the rising moon and
distant music all have in common is the manner in which they are
perceived: '. . . un coin de la nature vu à travers un tempérament', as
Zola phrased it.[32] In his languor and passivity, so well reproduced in
the preceding poems, Verlaine passively waits for sense-impressions to
reach him; hence the ubiquity of *distant* music or of *dying* sounds and
odours. Hence also the tendency for only certain kinds of sense data to
get through: muted colours, mingling of unlike sensations, a single
sharp impression amid a blur of vague ones. Verlaine is not vague as
Lamartine was, in the sense of being general and unspecific; rather, he
is imprecise, as the message of the senses is filtered through an impressionistic lens, eroded by distance, or distorted by dream, drunken-
ness, or memory. The same is true of his emotional perceptions. The
paean of joy that is *La Bonne Chanson*, or the pain of a few poems from

Sagesse or *Amour*, are as inappropriate to Verlaine as the Parnassian etchings of *Poèmes saturniens*, in that all are direct, simple, and un-mitigated. The typically Verlainean emotion, like his sensations, is muffled, mingled with others, detached from its source; so complex, so subtle, that the mere act of undergoing it requires more attention than the emotion itself. Thus Verlaine's personal attitudes create a particular-ised mode of perception. Without his specifying that he is fatigued from long centuries of civilisation or jaded from over-indulgence, his langour, like des Esseintes' world-weariness, creates its own way of life. Hence his choice of the languid, nonchalant poet to epitomise the decadence.

Although it was this sensibility which attracted his younger con-temporaries to Verlaine, the duration of its appeal was brief. For a few years the apprehension of reality through sensation, and the expression of sensation as a version of reality, seemed to be what literature was all about. But as we saw in the previous chapter, this somewhat narrow view of literature did not endure. Just as serious writers quickly tired of the antics of the *farceurs*, so, as the ideas of Mallarmé and of Rimbaud gained currency, or indeed, as poets re-read Baudelaire's 'Correspond-ances' as carefully as they had read Gautier's 'Notice', the conception of sensory experience as the subject of literature lost ground. Was not nature a *forêt de symboles* rather than merely an impressionist experience? As writers began to seek a deeper meaning in their sensory experience the limited nature of Verlaine's *poétique* became apparent. It is significant that, with a few exceptions, all the poems we have studied were published, either in magazines or in book form, between 1885 and 1887.[33] Or, to put it another way, poets seldom looked to Verlaine after their first volume of verse. In spite of its ubiquity, Verlaine's influence failed to outlive the purely decadent phase of the new poetry.

Notes

1 'Nevermore', *Oeuvres poétiques complètes*, Y.-G. Le Dantec and Jacques Borel, eds. (Gallimard, 1962), p. 81. Hereafter quotations from poems by Verlaine will be identified in the text by title and page reference to this edition.

2 'Chroniques', *Ermitage*, III, 5 (15 May 1892), 313.

3 *La Contribution d'un Américain au symbolisme français; Stuart Merrill* (Champion 1927), p. 47.

4 Stuart Merrill, 'Oubli, II', *Les Gammes* (Vanier, 1887), p. 36.

5 'Le Voyage' and 'Parfum exotique', *Oeuvres complètes*, Y.-G. Le Dantec

and Claude Pichois, eds. (Gallimard, 1961), pp. 123 and 24, respectively. Jacques-Henry Bornecque lists four more examples of the *âme-paysage* trope in *Les Fleurs du mal*. See his *Lumières sur les Fêtes galantes de Paul Verlaine* (Nizet, 1969), p. 147.

6 'La Fête chez Thérèse', *Les Contemplations* (Garnier, n.d.) p. 43.

7 See Ernest Raynaud's remarks in 'Chronique littéraire', *Décadent*, 1–15 January 1888, and 'Résultats du congrès des poètes,' *Plume*, VIII, 163 (1 February 1896), 67.

8 E.g. '. . . les genres bas; / . . . sans bas', 'Réponse à un acte d'accusation', *Les Contemplations*, pp. 13–14.

9 E.g. 'La poésie est une musique, usant de moyens spéciaux à faire vivre, dans la vie de l'art, des sentiments spéciaux. La signification essentiellement musicale de la poésie, seule désormais donnant à cette forme littéraire une raison d'exister, fut déjà . . . aperçue clairement par les poètes des générations passées.' 'L'Apres-midi d'un faune', *Revue Indépendante*, n.s., II, 5, March 1887, p. 336.

10 For a complete study of Kahn's verse, see J. C. Ireson, *L'Oeuvre poétique de Gustave Kahn, 1859–1936* (Nizet, 1962), especially pp. 43–4 for the influence of Verlaine's sensibility on *Les Palais nomades* and pp. 93–4 for Verlaine's influence on Kahn's use of *vers impairs*. Wyzewa says of Kahn, 'La forme musicale de Kahn rappelle la méldodie fluide et comme tranquille de M. Verlaine . . .' 'Poésie', *Revue Indépendante*, n.s., III, 7 (May 1887), 197.

11 *Premiers Poèmes*, second edition (Mercure de France, 1897), p. 91. Hereafter quotations from poems by Kahn will be identified in the text by title and page reference to this edition.

12 See Jean-Pierre Richard, *Poésie et profondeur* (Seuil, 1955), pp. 168–9.

13 'Sites, IV', *Premiers Poèmes*, tenth edition (Mercure de France, n.d.), p. 123. Hereafter quotations from poems by Henri de Régnier will be identified in the text by title and page reference to this edition.

14 'Dilection', *Oeuvres*, I (Mercure de France, 1924), p. 59. Hereafter quotations from poems by Samain will be identified by title and page reference to this edition.

15 See Henry, *Stuart Merrill*, p. 54.

16 *Oeuvres*, I (Mercure de France, 1924), pp. 13–14. Hereafter quotations from poems by Viélé-Griffin will be identified in the text by title and page reference to this edition.

17 For a thorough discussion of the theme of eighteenth-century art in poetry, see Seymour O. Simches, *Le Romantisme et le goût esthétique du XVIIIe siècle* (Presses universitaires, 1964), especially chapter IV, 'Le Goût pour le XVIIIe siècle dans la poésie', pp. 65–101, and Georges Zayed, 'La Tradition des 'Fêtes galantes' et le lyrisme verlainien', *Aquila* (Boston College, Mass.). I (1969), 213–46. I am grateful to Professor Zayed for having called this matter to my attention.

18 See Simches, pp. 65–75.

19 See Simches, pp. 10-93, and Jacques-Henry Bornecque, *Lumières sur les Fêtes galantes de Verlaine*, pp. 20-25. There is some discrepancy between the two, Simches emphasising the circulation of Watteau canvases through auctions, Bornecque underlining the collapse of prices during the period 1783-1826.

20 See Simches, pp. 14-15.

21 See Simches, pp. 89-92. Baudelaire furnished his apartment in the Hôtel Pimodan almost completely in eighteenth century style. Besides the stanza on Watteau in 'Les Phrases', Simches discusses two uncollected poems ('A Mme du Barry', *Oeuvres complètes*, p. 222, and 'A une belle dévote', p. 223) and his *Salons* of 1845 and 1846. While Banville (b. 1823) was too young for the original Doyenné group, his poetry exhibits their painterly manner, p. 83. Simches places Hugo and his 'Fête chez Thérèse' 'en dehors de la tradition du Doyenné et de 'l'Ecole de l'art pour l'art',' p. 93.

22 (Fasquelle, 1955), p. 97.

23 Quoted by A. E. Carter, *The Idea of Decadence in French Literature, 1830-1900* (Toronto University Press, 1958), p. 83, n. 69.

24 *Basoche*, I, 12 (October 1885), 400-402.

25 See Lorrain, 'Fanerie', *Basoche*, II, 2 (February 1886), 75-7, and Margueritte, 'Vers d'automne', *Scapin*, 19 December 1886, p. 255. As a possible source, Gautier comes closer than Verlaine to the history of the court in a title like 'Versailles.' *Poésies complètes*, René Jasinski, editor (Firmin-Didot, n.d.), II, p. 144.

26 *Scapin*, 19 December 1886, p. 245.

27 *Poèmes, 1887-97* (Mercure de France, 1897), p. 16. This poem and 'Fin de fête' (p. 17) were added to this edition of *Les Gammes*. Further page references will be to this edition.

28 For the suggestion that Merrill and Samain derived their treatment of the eighteenth century directly from Watteau and from the gardens at Versailles, see Henry, p. 52, and Léon Bocquet, *Albert Samain, sa vie, son oeuvre* (Mercure de France, 1921), pp. 117-18.

29 *Scapin*, 19 December 1886, p. 247.

30 *Basoche*, I, 12 (October 1886), 400.

31 For a thorough discussion of the genesis of Verlaine's *Fêtes galantes*, see Jacques-Henry Bornecque, 'Le Problème des *Fêtes galantes*', *Mélanges d'histoire littéraire offerts à Daniel Mornet* (Nizet, 1951), pp. 209-20. For the relative prevalence of fountains and moonlight in Watteau and Verlaine, see p. 214.

32 Quoted by Elliott M. Grant, *Emile Zola* (New York: Twayne, 1966), p. 27. Originally appeared in *Le Salut Public*, 1865.

33 The publication dates of the collections from which we have quoted bear out this generalisation: Kahn, *Les Palais nomades*, 1887; de Régnier, *Les Lendemains*, 1885, *Apaisement*, 1886, *Sites*, 1887; Samain, *Au Jardin de l'infante*, 1893 (although at least two poems, 'Larmes' et 'Vers vagues',

appeared in *Le Scapin* for December 1886). In Merrill's *Les Gammes* the two poems in *vers impairs* were only added to the edition of 1897. Thus Merrill, and perhaps some poems by Samain, seem to be the only exceptions.

Kahn further illustrates Verlaine's appeal to young poets. In March 1885, during his military service in North Africa, Kahn copied in a notebook nineteen poems, apparently his very earliest compositions. The only two of these preserved in *Les Palais nomades* are the Verlainean' Mélopées, II and IV' ('Chantonne lentement et très bas . . .'). See Ireson, *Gustave Kahn*, p. 41.'

Chapter X
After decadence

The wavering persistence of the decadent current in symbolism can be seen in the four magazines born in 1889-91—another period fertile in new magazines—which Kenneth Cornell has characterised as 'the four important magazines of the symbolist movement during the eighteenth-nineties':[1] *Mercure de France* (January 1890), *L'Ermitage* (April 1890), *La Plume* (August 1889), and *La Revue Blanche* (October 1891). Only in *L'Ermitage* and *La Plume* do we find poems which can be called decadent. *L'Ermitage* had Tailhade's 'Prospero's Island' and 'Senescent Moon';[2] Georges Fourest's 'Quatorzain gris' and 'Ballade en l'honneur de la famille Trouloyaux',[3] which are decadent because of their diction and the comic irony of their social commentary; G. Bernard-Kahler's 'La Clinique' describes the cadaver of a girl in a public hospital;[4] Antoine Sabatier has two sonnets, a naturalist description in 'Le Ghetto', and a piece in pseudo-Middle French, 'Jehanne'.[5] This handful of poems is merely a reminiscence of the decadent sensibility at a time when, by and large, poets had abandoned naturalist description and experiments with exotic languages.

In *La Plume*, on the contrary, echoes of decadence are stronger and more frequent. Edmond Porcher's 'Circenses, sonnet byzantin', relates how a Roman gladiator slays a lion before the imperial court, and how afterward the empress continues to dream of the handsome gladiator.[6] The diction of Stuart Merrill's 'Airs ailés' is decadent.[7] In several poems the Baudelairean handling of voluptuousness recalls decadent verse of 1882-84.[8] More important, in an effort to 'mieux faire connaître, et plus impartialement, les nouvelles écoles littéraires', *La Plume* published special numbers on the various schools; those on *Les Modernes*, *Les Décadents* and *Le Chat Noir* revived the spirit of the mid-'80's. Léon Vanier was guest editor of the one on *Les Modernes*, the issue on *Les Décadents* contained a portrait of Ernest Raynaud and a special study by Baju, and Willette's black cat graced the *Chat noir* issue. Moreover, early poems by Verlaine, Moréas, Laforgue, and Rimbaud were republished, along with the parodies of Jean Nymphéas and Mitrophane Crapoussin. Thus, *La Plume* kept alive the memory of decadence when other magazines had let it drop. Although Verlaine published copiously in *La Revue Blanche* (he had very few poems in *L'Ermitage* or *Mercure de France*), *La Plume* treated him with particular esteem, publishing many of his poems, taking up a subscription for the publication costs of *Dédicaces*, and, alone among these four magazines, running a special Verlaine issue after his death.

Otherwise, some random references in the early 1890's show to what extent even the idea of a decadent school of poetry had died out. In an article on 'Notre Byzantinisme' Paul Radiot discusses the current taste for Byzantine art and history without even mentioning decadent poetry.[9] Conversely, for Louis Desprez in 1884 and Vittorio Pica in 1885 'byzantine' had been synonymous with 'decadent' as applied to poetry. In an article on symbolism in 1892 Rémy de Gourmont does not even mention decadence; the two classes of writers he observes are those who have talent, the symbolists, and—the others![10] Both the initial editorial of *Mercure de France*[11] and an article in *La Plume* complain that the public and the popular press call any new and original work decadent:

> Du moment où l'on ne suit plus les sentiers battus, où l'on explore les arcanes de l'Idéal, on passe pour être 'décadent'. Le pédantisme bourgeois englobe sous cette étiquette les personnalités les plus diverses. Les romans de J.-H. Rosny, les poèmes mystiques de Stéphane Mallarmé, les rêveries macabres ou religieuses de Verlaine, tout cela est décadentisme.[12]

As Alfred Vallette points out, though, this use of the term includes the connotation of 'charabia, pathos, incohérence' and suggests the work of immature 'Charlots de lettres vite exténués', who are to be contrasted with the hard-working symbolists, 'les jeunes laborieux en quête d'une vierge du beau et du vrai tels qu'ils les conçoivent en ces temps complexes'.[13] So the memory of *Les Déliquescences* survives and provokes opposite reactions: a favourable one which sees it as worthy artistic experimentation, and a pejorative one which deplores the antics described in the biography of Marius Tapora. The repudiation of the lunatic fringe, of course, is neither symbolist nor even new—in 1885 Léo Trézenik was already complaining of the *farceurs* and *agités*, and in 1886 Paul Adam affirmed that decadence was exploited by publishers who recognised its sales potential.[14] Only the use of decadence as a generic label for experimental writing recalls the spirit of those who first used the term in 1884 and 1885.

A similar change of perspective took place in Verlaine criticism. In 1885 Jules Lemaitre did not even mention Verlaine in his article on pessimism and the young generation, but now, in 1888, he devotes an article to 'M. Paul Verlaine et les poètes symbolistes et décadents'.[15]

After making fun of the decadents' and symbolists' obscurity for two and a half pages, Lemaitre finally gets to his point of departure, that perhaps there is room for innovation in French poetry, since it has always resembled fine prose. He asks the reader to imagine a poetry as spontaneous, charmingly incoherent, and casual as children's rounds or certain popular songs, a series of impressions jotted down as if in a dream:

> Mais supposez en même temps que ces impressions soient très fines, très délicates et très poignantes, qu'elles soient celles d'un poète un peu malade, qui a beaucoup exercé ses sens et qui vit à l'ordinaire dans un état d'excitation nerveuse. Bref, une poésie sans pensée, à la fois primitive et subtile, qui n'exprime point des suites d'idées liées entre elles (comme fait la poésie classique) ni le monde physique dans la rigueur de ses contours (comme fait la poésie parnassienne), mais des états d'esprit où nous ne nous distinguons pas bien des choses, où les sensations sont si étroitement unies aux sentiments, où ceux-ci naissent si rapidement et si naturellement de celles-là qu'il nous suffit de noter nos sensations au hasard et comme elles se présentent pour exprimer par là même les émotions qu'elles éveillent successivement dans notre âme . . .   [p. 5]

The poet who created such poetry would have to be an exceptional person: bizarre, morally and socially apart, almost illiterate, ignorant of the meaning of words. These suppositions need not refer to Verlaine and his verse, although it is true that Lemaitre visualises his hypothetical poetic primitive thus: 'Il a une tête étrange, le profil de Socrate, un front démesuré, un crâne bossué comme un bassin de cuivre mince!' (p. 5). Naming Verlaine for the first time, Lemaitre admits that he can barely understand his poetry ('La poésie de M. Verlaine représente pour moi le dernier degré soit d'inconscience, soit de raffinement, que mon esprit puisse admettre. Au delà, tout m'échappe: c'est le bégayement de la folie; c'est la nuit noire; c'est, comme dit Baudelaire, le vent de l'imbécillité qui passe sur nos fronts.' p. 6), but since 'les ahuris du symbolisme' consider him their master, perhaps by listening to those of Verlaine's songs which do have meaning we can understand what the symbolists are trying to do.

Lemaitre then proceeds to examine Verlaine's poetry, volume by volume, from *Poèmes saturniens* to *Jadis et naguère*. He complains that in

Poèmes saturniens the vowels of 'Chanson d'automne' are those which René Ghil, in his *Traité du verbe*, identifies with the brasses, not with violins: whom, then, should one believe among these symbolists? This was a common complaint on the part of hostile critics. *Fêtes galantes* is dismissed as atypical of the eighteenth century, *Romances sans paroles* is omitted altogether (too subliminal for the reviewer to understand, perhaps?), and *Sagesse* receives the lion's share of attention. Verlaine is naively sincere in his faith, unlike the other writers since Baudelaire, who, despite the decline of Catholicism in French life, practice it as a form of protest against their era. Lemaitre sees two kinds of obscurity in Verlaine's poems, that which comes by accident, and the deliberate obscurity which he prefers, as in 'L'espoir luit comme un brin de paille dans l'étable', to which he devotes several paragraphs of exegesis.

We may smile at Lemaitre's difficulty in 'understanding' Verlaine, and decadent critics took umbrage at his disdain for their verse and his patronising attitudes toward Verlaine; nevertheless his appreciation of Verlaine's poetry is generally accurate. He seems to acquire a taste for Verlaine as he goes along ('A force de l'étudier et même de le condamner sa douce démence me gagne', p. 14) so that by the end of his rather lengthy article he becomes distinctly charitable. Although disapproving of Verlaine's metrical innovations, he makes an authentic effort to explain how a poem is derived from the poet's experience (apropos of 'Kaléidoscope': 'Le poète veut rendre ici un phénomène mental très bizarre et très pénible, celui qui consiste à reconnaître ce qu'on n'a jamais vu. Cela vous est-il arrivé quelquefois?' p. 13). He is fair enough to recognise that while Verlaine's highly personalised techniques are often beyond the average reader's understanding, when he is simple enough for comprehension his poetry is a joy to read.

The significance of Lemaitre's article does not lie only in its official coronation of Verlaine's poetry. Although he correctly recognises that the essence of Verlaine's art is his equating sensation with emotions, in other respects Lemaitre rejects the decadent interpretation of Verlaine's verse and introduces a different one which has prevailed in our own century. First of all, he caricatures Verlaine as a sort of irrational, instinctive primitive: 'M. Paul Verlaine a des sens de malade, mais une âme d'enfant; il a un charme naïf dans la langueur maladive: c'est un décadent qui est surtout un primitif' (p. 14). We cannot imagine a Trézenik, Barrès, Desprez, or Huysmans agreeing to this characterisation, since conscious artistry is synonymous with the aestheticism of decadence. Verlaine himself was responsible for encouraging the naive poet legend in his *Poètes maudits* essay on 'Pauvre Lélian', yet Lemaitre's article is the first time, to our knowledge, that a serious critic has called Verlaine naive. Lemaitre anticipates the grotesque views Max Nordau expressed in *Dégénérescence* (1894). Moreover, by neglecting *Fêtes galantes*, Verlaine's most popular *recueil* during the 1880's, and by omitting *Romances sans paroles*, the best example of his impressionism, Lemaitre resolutely passes over that portion of his work which was most decadent. His emphasis on *Sagesse* foreshadows the choice of that volume by the poets who were asked by *La Plume* in 1896 to name their favourite among Verlaine's works. Catholicism, to be sure, is a decadent theme, and earlier critics, like Lemaitre, had contrasted Verlaine's sincerity with those poets for whom the religious theme was merely a literary affectation. Lemaitre's references to Verlaine's personal experience, however, have the effect of directing his article toward the man and his biography and away from the poet and his art. Thus he seems to have laid the way for the biographical approach, with its reliance on colourful anecdotes and the Catholicism of *Sagesse*, which has characterised too much Verlaine criticism during the first half of our own century.

In reply, both Gustave Kahn and Ernest Raynaud tax Lemaitre with incompetence as a critic (Raynaud devotes the entire second part of his article to this accusation), with having read decadent poetry poorly or not at all, and with having been misled by René Ghil's *Traité du verbe* and 'ses aspects de pythonisse'.[16] Kahn continues with several pages of defence for the alleged obscurity of the decadents; like Wyzewa before him, he deprecates the use of the terms *décadent* and *symbole*, since, misnomers at best, they are misleading as to the intentions of the new group of poets; such discussions, in any case, do not concern Verlaine, who is, before all else, simply himself, a spontaneous, elegaic poet in the tradition of Villon and Heine. Kahn's reply is somewhat general, in that it deals with the whole range of Verlaine's production and with Kahn's own goals of music and of poems turning around a single set of images. Ernest Raynaud, on the contrary, argues more on the basis of decadent orthodoxy.[17] For him, Lemaitre should have looked for the *raison d'être* of decadent theories in the works of Paul Verlaine; instead, he has read Verlaine incorrectly, without looking for 'l'explication des enthousiasmes qu'ils [les écrits de Verlaine] ont suscité chez une généra-tion neuve, érudite et subtile'. To Lemaitre's assertion that the deca-dents have done nothing new Raynaud replies that they have renewed the mould of poetry by shifting the medial caesura of the alexandrine;

that they have invented the *phrase mélodique* and continued Rimbaud's work of recreating a poetic *verbe* accessible to all the senses. Instead of expressing the general ideas of the Romantics and Parnassians, the decadents 'se sont ingéniés à rendre des sensations confuses, à écrire des silences, des nuits, à fixer le vertige, à noter jusqu'à l'inexprimable'. Lemaitre should have emphasised Verlaine's skill at rendering the phenomena of nature, and he might have deduced his Catholicism, if he had paid more attention to 'l'homme des champs qu'est Verlaine'.

Rebuttals of Lemaitre's article represent practically the last occasion on which we have found Verlaine associated with decadence, for he was regarded more and more as a sort of grand old man of French poetry: an honour he surely deserved, if only for the tact, courtesy, and quiet dignity with which he responded to all who approached him in the name of poetry. Accounts of being introduced to Verlaine and hearing him read his poems in cafés abound, and they all emphasise the same admirable qualities in his manner.[18] Critically, as the interests of comtemporary poetry moved away from what we have called decadence to idealism and to Catholicism—one of the special issues of *La Plume* in 1890 was devoted to the 'Catholiques-mystiques'—there was a tendency to seek these qualities in Verlaine's work. A few book reviews are revealing as to the changing perspective in which his contemporaries viewed Verlaine. When Gabriel Sarrazin reviewed *Jadis et naguère* in 1885 he did so in the light of *A Rebours* and of *Les Déliquescences*, and in a hostile tone he singles out individual poems which exceed '. . . les limites permises de l'énervement et de la déliquescence de la pensée . . .' and which are '. . . de vrais modèles du genre [décadent]. . .'[19] Three years later Gustave Kahn uses a review of *Amour* as a point of departure for an essay on human modes of perception, thus linking Verlaine's poetry with the more mature conception of decadence as an aesthetic of sensory impressions. Already in this 1888 article appear indications of later critical attitudes towards Verlaine, such as the epithet 'le primitif de *Sagesse*', and a tendency for Kahn to distinguish between his religious verse and his earlier work.[20] A year later appears the first tactful reference to the decline of Verlaine's creative powers. Reviewing *Parallèlement* in 1889, Kahn states that he does not think it is one of Verlaine's best books: '. . .comme si, avec l'abandon de ses thèmes les plus particuliers et de ses idées les plus essentielles, Verlaine perdait une partie de sa netteté et de sa décision de rythmes, aussi de sa valeur exceptionnelle de producteurs [*sic*] de vers frappés et générateurs d'une marge de rêve . . .'[21] Finally we read reviews which either resolutely ignore the declining quality of Verlaine's verse or else gloss over it: '*Les Chansons [pour elle]* d'aujour-d'hui sont loin des *Fêtes galantes*; ce sont des fêtes paillardes . . . ce n'est plus la griserie, c'est la morte-ivresse. . . . Mais ivresse et paillardise encore de Verlaine.'[22] While Verlaine is proclaimed the greatest poet of the end of the century and *Liturgies intimes* are called 'égaux en beauté aux plus parfaits de M. Verlaine', the very brief analysis of the poems has to do with his childlike simplicity and the sincerity of his faith: 'Les uns d'une simplicité quasi enfantine et que l'on dirait écrits pour des âmes primitives et violemment croyantes. . . . Les autres, c'est une âme qui se penche sur elle-meme, qui se mire au pur lac conquis de la Foi triomphante. . . .'[23] By 1892 reviewers have abandoned discussing Verlaine's decadence and his aesthetics in order to emphasise the now legendary simplicity and sincerity of the naive poet. Who would quibble with their interpretation, when there is little left to be praised in his later work?

The summing up of Verlaine's work and of his influence came on 1 February 1896, a few weeks after his death, when *La Plume* dedicated a memorial issue to him. In a 'Congrès des poètes' two hundred poets and other writers were asked, 'Quelles sont les meilleures parties de l'oeuvre de Paul Verlaine et quel a été son rôle dans l'évolution lit-téraire?'[24] Out of 169 persons who replied with letters for publication, ninety-three voted for *Sagesse* as his best work, forty-eight for *Fêtes galantes*, and thirty-one each for *Amour* and *Romances sans paroles*, thus crowning that portion of his work which had been characterised as Catholic, childlike, and primitive. Henceforth too much Verlaine 'criticism' would panegyrise his ingenuousness and his religious sincerity.[25] It is significant that *Fêtes galantes*, whose theme was at one time so popular, was placed a poor second, while *Romances sans paroles*, which most critics today would call his best work, was placed only third beside *Amour*, which today is not highly regarded. In twelve years, then, a second transformation in Verlaine's reputation had taken place: his popularity remained, but he was esteemed for quite different reasons from those of the period 1882–85. This changed evaluation of Verlaine's art is apparent in replies to the second part of the question. Charles Morice called his role 'celui d'un initiateur et d'un libérateur',[26] and Rachilde replied, 'Il ouvrit la fenêtre!'[27] Most respondents spelled out how they saw Verlaine as the innovator who had brought music into French poetry and prepared the way for free verse. Typical are replies such as 'Verlaine, qui sut s'affranchir de toute norme devant l'absolue nécessité du poète, fut le promoteur de la poésie lyrique libre' (respondent's italics),[28] 'Il a poursuivi . . . l'émancipation totale du vers français entreprise par l'Ecole romantique et suspendue par l'Ecole parnassienne,'[29] and 'Il prépara le vers libre en assouplissant à l'infini le rythme des siens. . . .'[30] Most writers, therefore, saw Verlaine as the musician who had made free verse possible, rather than as a decadent poet whose delicate and finely nuanced sensibility had been admired by des Esseintes. A few, however, had longer memories. Ernest Raynaud replied, 'Il survivra pour apporté en art, une sorte de sensualité triste; il a introduit en poésie, le clair-obscur. Ses vers ont du vague, de l'indécis, de lointains flottants, et valent en opposition avec le bloc, le marbre parnassien et le bronze de Hugo.'[31] Another reminds us even more of the critical mood of 1883–85 when he replied, 'La première [*Romances sans paroles*] de ces oeuvres prépara des voies nouvelles; la seconde [*Fêtes galantes*] nous apprit à balbutier ces mots spécieux que tous nous sentons affluer à nos lèvres, à telles heures où les inquiétudes que Baudelaire a si bien formulées et qui sont toujours nôtres s'orientent verse une sensibilité plus délicate.'[32] In contrast with the common emphasis on Verlaine's liberation of metrics, these statements could have been made by readers who first saw his verse in the pages of *La Nouvelle Rive Gauche* and *Le Chat Noir*.

Notes

1 *The Symbolist Movement* (New Haven: Yale University Press, 1951) p. 203.
2 I, 1 (April 1890), 41–3, and 5 (August 1890), 214, respectively.
3 I, 4 (July 1890), 154–6.
4 I, 7 (October 1890), 373.
5 II, 3 (March 1891), 138–40.
6 *Plume*, I, 9 (15 August 1889), 82.
7 I, 17 (15 December 1889), 166–7.
8 E.g. Théodore Hannon, 'Fleur des fièvres', I, 16 (1 December 1889), 155; Georges Proteau, 'Symphonie nocturne', I, 17 (15 December 1889), 171; Emile Foubert, 'Pâmoison', *ibid.*, 172.
9 *Revue Blanche*, VI, 28 (February 1894), 110–25.
10 'Le Symbolisme', *Revue Blanche*, II, 9 (June 1892), 321.
11 Alfred Vallette, 'Mercure de France', I, 1 (January 1890), 1–4.
12 Louis d'Eristal, 'La Décadence littéraire,' *Plume*, IV, 83 (1 October 1892), 419.
13 Vallette, *Mercure de France*, I, 1, pp. 1–2.
14 Plowert (Paul Adam), 'Les Marchands de la décadence,' *Symboliste*, I, 1 (7–14 October 1886), 1.

15 *Revue Politique et Littéraire* (*Revue Bleue*), XLI, 1 (7 January 1888), 2–14. Further quotations from this article will be identified in the text by page reference.

16 ' "Paul Verlaine", par Jules Lemaitre', *Revue Indépendante*, n.s., VI, 16 (February 1888), 287; the whole article, 287–93.

17 'M. Jules Lemaitre et les poètes décadents,' *Décadent*, 15–29 February and 1–15 March 1888.

18 E.g. see 'L.B.'s' account of an evening with Verlaine in a Montmartre cabaret in *Revue Blanche*, IV, 18 (April 1893), 268.

19 'Poésie', *Revue Contemporaine*, I, 1 (25 January 1885), 131–2.

20 'Chronique de la littérature et de l'art', *Revue Indépendante*, n.s., VII, 19 (May 1888), 344–5.

21 *Vogue*, IV, 1 (July 1889), 94.

22 'Chronique de la littérature', *Revue Blanche*, I, 3 (December 1891), 215.

23 Adolphe Retté, 'Chroniques', *Ermitage*, III, 5 (15 May 1892), 308–9. The same issue (p. 278) had a poem from *Odes en son honneur*.

24 'Résultats du congrès des poètes', *Plume*, VIII, 163 (1 February 1896), 67.

25 An example of this style of literary analysis is the reply of Edouard Beaufils: 'Ce qui est adorable en Verlaine, ce par quoi il est unique dans notre littérature, trop souvent de convention et d'artifice, c'est son ingénuité. Ah! qu'elles furent ingénues, ses fautes et qu'ils furent ingénus, ses repentirs! A l'heure de sa mort, c'est une âme de premier communiant, toute blanche, qui s'est envolée vers Madame Marie, et quand il l'a reçu dans son Paradis—car il y a un Paradis, n'est-ce pas?—le Seigneur a dû dire: Laissez venir à moi ce petit enfant!' *Ibid.*, p. 72.

26 *Ibid.*, p. 102.

27 *Ibid.*, p. 106

28 Michel Abadie, *ibid.*, p. 68.

29 Emile Blémont, *ibid.*, p. 72.

30 Louis Raymond, *ibid.*, p. 107.

31 *Ibid.*, p. 107.

32 Albert Arnay, *ibid.*, p. 69.

A selected bibliography[1]

Works by Verlaine

Verlaine, Paul. *Oeuvres poétiques complètes.* Y.-G. Le Dantec, editor. Gallimard, 1954.
— *Oeuvres poétiques complètes.* Y.-G. Le Dantec and Jacques Borel, editors. Gallimard, 1962.
— *Oeuvres complètes.* Preface by Octave Nadal; Jacques Borel and Henry de Bouillane de Lacoste, eds. Two volumes. Club du meilleur livre, 1959 and 1960.
— *Correspondance.* Adolphe Van Bever, editor. Three volumes. Messein, 1923.
— *Lettres inédites de Verlaine à Cazals.* Georges Zayed, editor. Geneva: Droz, 1957.
— *Lettres inédites à Charles Morice.* Georges Zayed, editor. Minard, 1964, and Geneva: Droz, 1964.

Works by other poets

Ajalbert, Jean. *Sur Les Talus.* Tresse and Stock, 1886.
Baudelaire, Charles. *Les Fleurs du mal.* Preface by Théophile Gautier. Lemerre, n.d.
— *Oeuvres complètes.* Y.-G. Le Dantec and Claude Pichois, eds. Gallimard, 1961.
Beauclair, Henri, and Vicaire, Gabriel. *Les Déliquescences d'Adoré Floupette.* Byzance: Lion Vanné, 1885, and Paris: Crès, 1911.
Corbière, Tristan. *Les Amours jaunes.* Y.-G. Le Dantec, editior. Third edition. Gallimard, 1953.
Cros, Charles. *Oeuvres complètes.* Louis Forestier and Pascal Pia, eds. Pauvert, 1964.
Hugo, Victor. *Oeuvres complètes; poésies,* II. Ollendorff, 1909.
— *Oeuvres complètes; théâtre,* I. Ollendorff, 1912.
— *Les Contemplations.* Garnier, n.d.
— *La Légende des siècles,* Two volumes. Garnier, n.d.
Kahn, Gustave. *Premiers Poèmes.* Second edition. Mercure de France, 1897.
Laforgue, Jules. *Oeuvres complètes,* I and II. Mercure de France, 1962 and 1951.
Lorrain, Jean (Paul Duval). *Modernités.* Giraud, 1885.
Mallarmé, Stéphane. *Oeuvres complètes.* Jean-Aubry and Henri Mondor, eds. Gallimard, 1956.

[1] The place of publication of all books is Paris, unless otherwise indicated.

Merrill, Stuart. *Les Gammes*. Vanier, 1887.
— *Poèmes, 1887–1897*. Mercure de France, 1897.
Moréas, Jean. *Oeuvres*. Two volumes. Mercure de France, 1923 and 1926.
Régnier, Henri de. *Premiers Poèmes*. Mercure de France, 1899.
Rollinat, Maurice. *Les Névroses*. Charpentier, 1910.
— *Choix de poésies*. Charpentier, 1926.
Samain, Albert. *Oeuvres*, Three volumes. Mercure de France, 1924.
Tailhade, Laurent. *Poèmes élégiaques*. Mercure de France, 1907.
— *Poèmes aristophanesques*. Third edition. Mercure de France, 1910.
Vielé-Griffin, Francis. *Ouevres*. Three volumes. Mercure de France, 1924, 1926, and 1927.

Articles published 1882–1889

The articles below have been selected either because they represent important moments in the decadent movement or because they are unusually informative.

Adam, Paul. 'La Presse et le symbolisme.' *Le Symboliste*, I, 1 (7–14 October 1886), 1–2.
Barrès, Maurice. 'La Sensation en littérature: la folie de Charles Baudelaire.' *Les Taches d'Encre*, I, 1 (5 November 1884), 3–26, and 2 (5 December 1884), 21–43.
Berrichon, Paterne. 'Paul Verlaine.' *Le Décadent*, I, 18 (7 August 1886).
Bloy, Léon. 'Maurice Rollinat.' *Le Chat Noir*, 2, 9, and 16 September 1882.
— 'On demande des malédictions.' *Le Chat Noir*, 3 May 1884.
Bourde, Paul. 'Les Poètes décadents.' *Le Temps*, 6 August 1885.
Desprez, Louis. 'Les Derniers Romantiques: 1, Paul Verlaine.' *La Revue Indépendante*, I, 3 (July 1884), 218–34.
France, Anatole. 'La Vie à Paris: le symbolisme—décadents et déliquescents— simples observations sur un manifeste de M. Jean Moréas.' *Le Temps*, 26 September 1886.
Ghil, René. 'Notre Ecole.' *La Décadence*, I, 1 (1 October 1886), 1–2.
Hennequin, Emile. 'Les Romans de M. Edmond de Goncourt.' *La Revue Indépendante*, I, 1 (May 1884), 28–34.
— 'J.-K. Huysmans.' *La Revue Indépendante*, I, 3 (July 1884), 199–216.
Laumann, Sutter. '*Les Déliquescences*.' *La Justice*, 19 July 1885.
Lemaitre, Jules. 'J.-K. Huysmans.' *La Revue Contemporaine*, I, 4 (25 April 1885), 544–59.
— 'La Jeunesse sous le Second Empire et sous la Troisième République.' *La Revue Politique et Littéraire* (*La Revue Bleue*), XXXV, 24 (3 June 1885), 738–44.
— 'M. Paul Verlaine et les poètes symbolistes et décadents.' *La Revue Politique et Littéraire* (*La Revue Bleue*), XLI, 1 (7 January 1888), 2–14.
'Mario, Jean.' 'Les Vivants et les morts: Paul Verlaine.' *La Nouvelle Rive Gauche*, II, 54 (9–15 February 1883).

Moréas, Jean. 'Les Décadents.' *Le XIXe Siècle*, 11 August 1885.
— 'Le Symbolisme.' *Supplément Littéraire du Figaro*, 18 September 1886.
Morice, Charles. 'Boileau–Verlaine.' *La Nouvelle Rive Gauche*, I, 4 (1–8 December 1882).
Ordinaire, Dionys. 'La Jeune Génération.' *La Revue Politique et Littéraire* (*La Revue Bleue*), XXXV, 23 (6 June 1885), 706–10.
Pica, Vittorio. 'I moderni bizantini.' *Gazetta Letteraria, Artistica e Scientifica* (Turin), IX, 18, 30, 46, 47, and 48 (2 May, 25 July, 14, 21, and 28 November 1885), 137–9, 233–5, 361–2, 369–71, 378–9.
Raynaud, Ernest. 'Chronique littéraire.' *Le Décadent*, III, 2 (1–15 January 1888).
— 'Chronique littéraire.' *Le Décadent*, III, 3 (15–31 January 1888).
— 'M. J. Lemaitre et les poètes décadents.' *Le Décadent*, III, 5 (15–29 February 1888), and 6 (1–15 March 1888).
— 'Du symbolisme.' *Le Décadent*, III, 7 (15–31 March 1888).
— 'Les Origines du mouvement décadent: les frères de Goncourt.' *Le Décadent*, IV, 26 (1–15 January 1889), and 27 (15–30 January 1889).
— 'Un Point de doctrine.' *Le Décadent*, IV, 29 (15–28 February 1889).
Vallette, Alfred. 'Les Symbolistes.' *Le Scapin*, second series, 3 (16 October 1886), 73–81.
Verlaine, Paul. 'A Karl Mohr.' *La Nouvelle Rive Gauche*, I, 6 (15–22 December 1882).
— 'Un Mot sur la rime.' *Le Décadent*, III, 6 (1–15 March 1888), and 7 (15–31, March 1888).

Books

Adam, Antoine, *Le Vrai Verlaine*. Droz, 1936.
Ajalbert, Jean. *Mémoires en vrac. au temps du symbolisme, 1880–1890*. Michel, 1938.
Balakian, Anna. *The Symbolist Movement: a Critical Appraisal*. New York: Random House, 1967.
Barre, André. *Le Symbolisme*, Jouve. 1912.
Bauche, Henri. *Le Language populaire*. Payot, 1929.
Beuchat, Charles. *La Revue Contemporaine (1885–1886)*. Jouve, 1930, and Champion, 1931.
— *Histoire du naturalisme français*. Two volumes. Correa, 1949.
Billy, André. *L'Epoque 1900: 1885–1900*. Tallandier, 1951.
Bocquet, Léon. *Albert Samain, sa vie, son oeuvre*. Mercure de France, 1921.
Bornecque, Jacques-Henry. *Etudes verlainiennes: Les Poèmes saturinens*. Nizet, 1952.
— *Etudes verlainiennes; Lumières sur les Fêtes galantes de Paul Verlaine*. Nizet, 1959.
Bourget, Paul. *Essais de psychologie contemporaine*. Lemerre, 1883.
— *Nouveaux Essais de pyschologie contemporaine*. Lemerre, 1886.
Brady, Patrick. *'L'Oeuvre' de Emile Zola, roman sur les arts*. Geneva: Droz, 1968.

Brunner, Henriette, and Cornick, L. L. de: *En Marge d'A Rebours*. Dorin, 1932.

Butler, John Davis. *Jean Moréas*. Paris and The Hague: Mouton, 1967.

Carter, A. E. *The Idea of Decadence in French Literature, 1830–1900*. Toronto University Press, 1958.

— *Baudelaire et la critique française, 1868–1917*. Columbia: University of South Carolina, 1963.

— *Verlaine, A Study in Parallels*. Toronto University Press, 1969.

Cazals, F.-A., and Le Rouge, Gustave. *Les Derniers Jours de Paul Verlaine*. Mercure de France, 1911.

Charlesworth, Barbara. *Dark Passages; the Decadent Consciousness in Victorian Literature*. Madison and Milwaukee: University of Wisconsin, 1965.

Clouard, Henri. *Histoire de la littérature française du symbolisme à nos jours*. Two volumes. Michel, 1947.

Cornell, Kenneth. *The Symbolist Movement*. New Haven: Yale University Press, 1951.

Cuénot, Claude. *Etat présent des études verlainiennes*. Belles Lettres, 1938.

Delsemme, Paul. *Un Théoricien du symbolisme: Charles Morice*. Nizet, 1958.

Donos, Charles. *Verlaine intime*. Vanier, 1898.

Fontaine, André. *Verlaine, homme de lettres*. Delagrave, 1937.

Ghil, René. *Les Dates et les oeuvres*. Crès, 1923.

Gourmont, Rémy de. *Le Livre des masques*. Mercure de France, 1896.

Grammont, Maurice. *Petit Traité de versification française*. Colin, 1958.

Grant, Elliott M. *Emile Zola*. New York: Twayne, 1966.

Guiraud, Pierre. *Le Français populaire*. Presses universitaires, 1965.

Hatzfeld, Helmut A. *Literature through Art; a New Approach to French Literature*. New York: Oxford University Press, 1952.

Hennequin, Emile. *Quelques Ecrivains français*. Perrin, 1890.

Henry, Marjorie Louise. *La Contribution d'un Américain au symbolisme français: Stuart Merrill*. Champion, 1927.

Huret, Jules. *Enquête sur l'évolution littéraire*. Charpentier, 1891.

Huysmans, Joris-Karl. *Croquis parisiens. A Vau l'eau. Un Dilemne*. Plon, 1908.

— *La Bièvre et Saint-Séverin*. Stock, 1908.

— *A Rebours*. Fasquelle, 1955.

Ireson, J. C. *L'Oeuvre poétique de Gustave Kahn, 1859–1936*. Nizet, 1962.

Jackson, A. B. *La Revue Blanche, 1889–1903*. Minard, 1960.

Jullian, Philippe. *Robert de Montesquiou; un prince 1900*. Perrin, 1965.

Kahn, Gustave. *Symbolistes et décadents*. Vanier, 1902.

Lehmann, Andrew G. *The Symbolist Esthetic in France, 1885–1895*. Oxford: Blackwell, 1950.

Lemaitre, Jules. *Les Contemporains: études et portraits littéraires*. Eight volumes. Twenty-third edition. Société française d'imprimerie et de librairie, n.d.

Le Rouge, Gustave. *Verlainiens et décadents*. Seheur, 1928.

Lethève, Jacques. *Impressionnistes et symbolistes devant la presse*. Colin, 1959.

Martino, Pierre. *Parnasse et symbolisme*. Eleventh edition. Colin, 1964.

Michaud, Guy. *Le Message poétique du symbolisme.* Three volumes. Nizet, 1947.

— *La Doctrine symboliste.* Nizet, 1947.

— *Mallarmé, l'homme et l'oeuvre.* Hâtier-Boivin, 1953.

Mitchell, Bonner. *Les Manifestes littéraires de la belle époque; 1886–1914: anthologie critique.* Séghers, 1966.

Mondor, Henri. *L'Amitié de Verlaine et Mallarmé.* Gallimard, 1939.

— *Vie de Mallarmé.* Galimard. 1941.

(Moréas, Jean). *Les Premières Armes du symbolisme.* Vanier, 1889.

Morice, Charles. *Paul Verlaine.* Vanier, 1888.

— *La Littérature de tout à l'heure.* Perrin, 1889.

Morrissette, Bruce. *The Great Rimbaud Forgery: the Affair of La Chasse spirituelle.* St Louis: Washington University, 1956.

Moser, Ruth. *L'Impressionnisme français: peinture, littérature, musique.* Geneva: Studer, 1951, and Droz, 1952.

Nadal, Octave. *Paul Verlaine.* Mercure de France, 1961.

Niess, Robert J. *Zola, Cézanne, and Manet: a Study of L'Oeuvre.* Ann Arbor: University of Michigan, 1968.

Niklaus, Robert. *Jean Moréas, poète lyrique.* Presses universitaires, 1936.

Plowert, Jacques (Adam, Paul). *Petit Glossaire pour servir à l'intelligence des auteurs décadents et symbolistes.* Vanier, 1888.

Porché, François. *Verlaine tel qu'il fut.* Flammarion, 1933.

Praz, Mario. *The Romantic Agony.* Angus Davidson, trans. Second edition. London: Oxford University Press, 1951.

Raitt, Alan W. *Villiers de l'Isle-Adam et le mouvement symboliste.* Cortie, 1965.

Raynaud, Ernest. *La Mêlée symboliste.* Three volumes. Renaissance du livre, 1920.

— *En Marge de la mêlée symboliste.* Mercure de France, 1936.

Richard, Jean-Pierre. *Poésie et profondeur.* Seuil, 1955.

Richard, Noël. *A L'Aube du symbolisme; hydropathes, fumistes et décadents.* Nizet, 1961.

— *Le Mouvement décadent; dandys, esthètes et quintessents.* Nizet, 1968.

Richardson, Joanna. *Verlaine.* New York: Viking, 1971.

Ridge, George R. *The Hero in French Decadent Literature.* Athens, Ga: University of Georgia, 1961.

Schmidt, Albert-Marie. *La Littérature symboliste.* Presses universitaires, 1963.

Simches, Seymour. *Le Romantisme et le goût esthétique du 18e siècle.* Presses universitaires, 1964.

Swart, Koenraad W. *The Sense of Decadence in Nineteenth-century France.* The Hague: Nijhoff, 1964.

Temple, Ruth Z. *The Critic's Alchemy: a Study of the Introduction of French Symbolism into England.* New York: Twayne, 1953, rpr. New Haven: College and University Press, n.d.

Trudgian, Helen. *L'Evolution des idées esthétiques de J.-K. Huysmans.* Conard, 1934.

Turnell, Martin. *The Art of French Fiction*. London: Hamilton, 1959.

Ullmann, Stephen. *Style in the French Novel*. New York: Barnes and Noble, 1964.

Zimmermann, Eléanor. *Magies de Verlaine*. Corti, 1967.

Zola, Emile. *Les Rougon-Macquart; histoire naturelle et sociale d'une famille sous le Second Empire*. Intr. Armand Lanou; Henri Mitterand, editor. II and IV. Pléiade, 1961 and 1966.

Articles

Arène, Paul. 'Le Décadent.' *Gil Blas*, 17 May 1885.

Bart, Paul de. 'L'Ecole décadente.' *L'Evénement*, 3 October 1886.

Bornecque, Jacques-Henry. 'Le Problème des *Fêtes galantes*.' *Mélanges d'histoire littéraire offerts à Daniel Mornet*. Nizet, 1951, pp. 209–20.

Brunetière, Ferdinand. 'Revue littéraire: les petits naturalistes.' *La Revue des Deux Mondes*, 64 (1 August 1884), 693–704.

— 'Charles Baudelaire.' *La Revue des Deux Mondes*, 189 (1 May 1887), 695–706.

— 'Symbolistes et décadents.' *La Revue des Deux Mondes*, 90 (1 November 1888), 213–26.

Chainaye, Hector. '*Germinal*.' *La Basoche* (Brussels), I, 6 (April 1885), 205–10.

Champsaur, Félicien. 'Poètes décadenticulets.' *Supplément Littéraire du Figaro*, 3 October 1885.

France, Anatole. 'La Vie littéraire—demain.' *Le Temps*, 5 August 1888.

— 'La Vie littéraire—la langue décadente.' *Le Temps*, 28 October 1888.

Hennequin, Emile. 'Le Pessimisme des écrivains.' *La Revue Indépendante*, I, 6 (September 1884), 445–55.

Kahn, Gustave. ' "Paul Verlaine," par Jules Lemaitre.' *La Revue Indépendante*, n.s., VI, 16 (February 1888), 287–93.

— '*Amour*.' *La Revue Indépendante*, n.s., VII, 19 (May 1888), 344–51.

— 'A M. Brunetière.' *La Revue Indépendante*, n.s., IX, 26 (December 1888), 481–6.

Laumann, Sutter. 'Les Décadents.' *La Justice*, 13 and 20 September 1886.

Lemaitre, Jules. 'Georges Ohnet.' *Les Contemporains: études et portraits littéraires*, IV. Twenty-third edition. Société française d'imprimerie et de librairie, n.d., pp. 337–55.

Lethève, Jacques. 'Quand Verlaine, Huysmans et Moréas partaient en guerre au nom des "poètes maudits".' *Le Figaro Littéraire*, 11 April 1959, pp. 6 and 11.

— 'Le Thème de la décadence dans les lettres françaises à la fin du XIXe siècle.' *La Revue d'Histoire Littéraire de la France*, LXIII, 1 (January–March 1963), 46–61.

Poggioli, Renato. 'The autumn of ideas.' *The Massachusetts Review*, II, 4 (summer 1961), 655–81.

Pouilliart, R. 'Paul Bourget et l'esprit de la décadence.' *Lettres Romanes*, V, 3 (August 1951), 199–229.

Raynaud, Ernest. 'Le Symbolisme et les cafés littéraires.' *Mercure de France*, CCLXVIII, 911 (1 June 1936), 282–93.

Sainte-Beuve, Charles-Augustin. 'Salambô.' *Nouveaux Lundis*, IV. Lévy, 1872, pp. 31–95.

Sonnenfeld, Albert. 'The forgotten Verlaine.' *The Bucknell Review*, XI (December 1962), 73–80.

Stephan, Philip. 'Paul Verlaine and Guy-Valvor.' *Romance Notes*, XI, 1 (autumn 1969), 41–5.

— Decadent poetry in *Le Chat Noir* before Verlaine's "Langueur".' *Modern Language Quarterly*, XXX, 4 (December 1969), 535–44.

— 'Naturalist influences on symbolist poetry, 1882–86.' *The French Review*, XLVI, 2 (December 1972), 299–311.

Sutton, Howard. 'Some literary cafés of the late nineteenth century.' *Kentucky Foreign Language Quarterly*, X, 2 (1963), 114–22.

Wyzewa, Téodor de. 'M. Mallarmé.' *La Vogue*, I, 11 (5–12 July 1886), 361–75, and 12 (12–19 July 1886), 414–24.

— 'Une Critique.' *La Revue Indépendante*, I, 1 (November 1886), 49–79.

A list of decadent and symbolist magazines

Le Chat Noir. Rodolphe Salis. Weekly from 14 January 1882, to 30 March 1895.

La Nouvelle Rive Gauche. Léo Trézenik, Georges Rall, and Charles Morice. Weekly from 9 November 1882, to 30 March–6 April 1883; then, *as Lutèce*, from 30 March–6 April 1883 (*sic*), to 3–10 October 1886.

La Revue Indépendante. Editors between 1886 and 1889 were Edouard Dujardin, Téodor de Wyzewa, Gustave Kahn, and Félix Fénéon. Monthly from May 1884 to April 1885; new series monthly from November 1886 to 1893.

Les Taches d'Encre. Maurice Barrès. Four issues from 5 November 1884, to 5 February 1885.

La Basoche (Brussels). Monthly from November 1884 to April 1886.

Le Scapin. E.-G. Raymond and André Bucquet. Bi-weekly from 1 December 1885 to 16 August 1886; second series, 1 September 1886 to 31 December 1886.

Le Décadent. Anatole Baju. Weekly from 10 April to 4 December 1886; one issue in December 1887; then bi-weekly from 1–15 January 1888 to 1–15 April 1889.

La Vogue. Léo d'Orfer and Gustave Kahn. Usually weekly from 11 April 1886, to 3 January 1887; three issues in 1889 by Kahn and Adolphe Retté.

La Décadence. René Ghil, E.-G. Raymond, and André Bucquet. Three issues only, 1, 8 and 15 October 1886.

Le Symboliste. Gustave Kahn, Jean Moréas, and Paul Adam. Four issues from 7–14 October to 39 October–6 November 1886.

La Jeune Belgique (Brussels). 1881–97.

La Plume. Léon Deschamps. Bi-weekly from 15 April 1889 to 15 December 1896.

Mercure de France. Alfred Vallette. Monthly from January 1890.

L'Ermitage. Henri Mazal. Monthly from April 1890 to 1906.

La Revue Blanche (Liège and Paris). Alfred Natanson, Paul Leclercq, and Joë Hogge. Monthly from October 1891 to April 1903.

Index